# The
# Secondary School
# Mathematics Curriculum

## 1985 Yearbook

**Christian R. Hirsch**
1985 Yearbook Editor
Western Michigan University

**Marilyn J. Zweng**
General Yearbook Editor
University of Iowa

## National Council of
## Teachers of Mathematics

*Copyright © 1985 by*
THE NATIONAL COUNCIL OF TEACHERS OF MATHEMATICS, INC.
*1906 Association Drive, Reston, Virginia 22091*

*Library of Congress Cataloging in Publication Data:*

Main entry under title:

The Secondary school mathematics curriculum.

    (Yearbook ; 1985)
    Bibliography: p.
    1. Mathematics—Study and teaching (Secondary)—
Addresses, essays, lectures. I.  Hirsch, Christian R.
II.  Zweng, Marilyn, 1932–    . III.  Series: Yearbook
(National Council of Teachers of Mathematics) ; 1985.
QA1.N3  1985  [QA12]    510 s [510′.7′12]    84-29622
ISBN 0-87353-217-1

*Printed in the United States of America*

# Contents

iii

## PART 4: COURSES AND PROGRAMS FOR TALENTED STUDENTS

## PART 5: INNOVATIVE THREE- AND FOUR-YEAR PROGRAMS

# Preface

The suggestion that this 1985 Yearbook be devoted to secondary school mathematics was advanced by the NCTM Educational Materials Committee in the fall of 1981. The theme was further delimited by the editors to the topic of curriculum. This seemed particularly appropriate in light of the fact that with the exception of the Council's *An Agenda for Action,* no major statements about the secondary school mathematics curriculum had been made by the profession since the late 1960s. In contrast, the period between the inception of this yearbook and its publication has been characterized by a plethora of reports by national and state commissions and task forces calling for an upgrading of requirements and student performance in mathematics and an updating of the curriculum. These reports, like the *Agenda for Action,* underscored the necessity for restructuring the curriculum to better meet the mathematical needs of a diverse student population in a society increasingly dominated by technology. However, the reports in general provided little substantive detail about curriculum content and its organization.

Within the space limitations imposed, this yearbook attempts to chart new curricular directions for high school mathematics in terms of content, organization, and priorities and also provides descriptions of promising curricular practices worthy of study and emulation.

This volume is organized into five parts as indicated in the Table of Contents. Chapters 1 and 2, which constitute Part 1, establish both a historical perspective and a rationale for needed curricular reform and provide a general framework for viewing the secondary school mathematics curriculum within the broader social and educational context.

Part 2 consists of chapters 3 through 9. Several of these chapters focus on new mathematics content and modes of mathematical thought that are supportive of the shifts in the uses of mathematics in society. Particular attention is given to reshaping the curriculum in response to computer technology, especially mathematical software such as symbolic manipulation packages and graphics utilities. Noted across this section are proposals and blueprints for (*a*) an increased emphasis on algorithmic approaches to mathematical topics with a focus on the utility of recursive thinking; (*b*) a more thematic problem-oriented approach to geometry; (*c*) greater stress on computer-enhanced mathematical modeling; (*d*) the introduction of discrete mathematics; and (*e*) the elevation of statistics to a more central position in the curriculum for all students.

Part 3, which consists of chapters 10 through 12, provides descriptions of an exemplary course in geometry that effectively integrates several approaches to the subject; an evolutionary course in advanced algebra with a focus on problem solving; and a unique alternative course for college-bound seniors who have had only marginal success in previous college preparatory courses. In Part 4, chapters 13 through 15, three alternative structures for meeting the particular needs of the mathematically gifted are presented: advanced placement courses, a complete six-year school/university cooperative program, and a special state two-year residential school.

Part 5, chapters 16 through 21, features descriptions of innovative three- and four-year programs that exemplify many of the general recommendations of the educational reports of the early 1980s. The first four chapters in this section provide a compelling rationale for, and outlines of, integrated mathematics programs, one of which is specifically designed for non-college-bound students. Another chapter describes a model three-year curriculum in which computers are integrated as a tool of instruction into all mathematics courses. The final chapter elaborates further on the theme of curricular flexibility embedded in the preceding chapters and provides the details of another school's successful attempt at providing flexible course offerings.

The task of developing guidelines for the direction and contents of the yearbook, reviewing submitted proposals and manuscripts, selecting those for inclusion, and making suggestions for revision of those selected was carried out by the editor and a review committee consisting of the general editor and four individuals, each with extraordinary insight into school curriculum issues. My sincere thanks and appreciation is extended to each of these review committee members:

| Arthur F. Coxford | University of Michigan, Ann Arbor, Michigan |
| F. Joe Crosswhite | Ohio State University, Columbus, Ohio |
| Charles D. Friesen | Lincoln Public Schools, Lincoln, Nebraska |
| Rheta N. Rubenstein | Renaissance High School, Detroit, Michigan |
| Marilyn J. Zweng | University of Iowa, Iowa City, Iowa |

A special note of gratitude is owed to Marilyn Zweng, who was always there to lean on for advice.

The editor also wishes to gratefully acknowledge the assistance of Charles R. Hucka and the able production staff of the NCTM for their help in making this yearbook a reality. Finally, deepest thanks is expressed to each chapter author and all those who submitted proposals or manuscripts for consideration.

The material in this yearbook suggests an exciting and important period of curricular innovation ahead. The ultimate reward to all who have contributed to this volume will be the extent to which the ideas contained herein help shape improved secondary school mathematics programs for all students.

CHRISTIAN R. HIRSCH
*1985 Yearbook Editor*

# We Need Another Revolution in Secondary School Mathematics

## Zalman Usiskin

THERE have been, in the past thirty years, a revolution (the new math) and a rebellion (back-to-basics) in school mathematics. Recent reports from inside and outside mathematics education suggest that today we either are in the midst of, or should be embarking on, a second revolution.

Many characteristics of the present situation were with us or were paralleled thirty years ago. Then as now there was dissatisfaction with student performance. Then as now there had been significant changes in both pure and applied mathematics that were not reflected in the curriculum. Then as now there was a shortage of people in the work force with training strong enough to enable them to understand and keep up with the latest in technology. Then as now we perceived the challenges of space and military competition with the Soviet Union; today, in addition, we have the challenge of computers and the economic competition with Japan and Western Europe.

To help understand and deal with the current situation, we follow the advice of Polya and study the similar situation of three decades ago. Lessons were learned in the last revolution and subsequent rebellion that can help guide us in making decisions today. There is also a more chilling reason for drawing on this experience:

> Those who cannot remember the past are condemned to repeat it.
> —George Santayana, *The Life of Reason*, Vol. 1

### THE REVOLUTION

The name *new math* that is commonly applied to this revolution sticks despite efforts to remove it (NACOME 1975). The new math was sparked by by the launch of *Sputnik* in October 1957 and fueled by federal money and public desire to beat the Russians, but like all revolutions it relied on work already in progress. Its passwords—discovery, rigorous logic, number-numeral distinctions, and structure—were hallmarks of the work of the University of Illinois Committee on School Mathematics (UICSM), begun in

1951 under Max Beberman (Hale 1961). The most widely used of the new math curricula, the materials of the School Mathematics Study Group (SMSG), were influenced in algebra by curricula developed at the University of Chicago in the 1940s and in geometry by the work of Hilbert and Birkhoff (Wooten 1965).

The condition of school mathematics before this revolution was not healthy; those who believe that there was a successful "old math" in the 1940s and 1950s should examine contemporary articles (e.g., Reeve 1955). Students' lack of mathematical skill was decried even though the curriculum at that time was virtually all skills. (We have never been satisfied with the skills of our students.) Today it is generally forgotten that the major reason for including theory in the new math was to increase skills as well as understanding. That is why new math was so easy to sell.

> **Lesson 1:  There are always those who wish to return
> to good old days that never were.**

Other reasons were given for this revolution. The College Entrance Examination Board Commission on Mathematics report (1959) noted that the curriculum had lagged far behind mathematical theory and applications. A major theme of the SMSG materials reflected the logical developments in mathematics at the beginning of this century, namely, that all of mathematics could be considered as a unified whole, as one system. Sets, functions, mathematical systems, and logic were consequently given strong play. Inequalities came to be taught alongside equalities. Solid geometry was merged with plane geometry. Trigonometry became taught with second-year algebra rather than as a separate subject, and the approach to it changed from geometric to algebraic. Analytic geometry almost disappeared as a separate course. Some of its topics were strewn among earlier courses (e.g., slope in first-year algebra, conics in second-year algebra); others were deleted altogether (e.g., the study of the cardioid, rose curves, and other special curves).

Discovery teaching is not in wide use today. The number-numeral distinction has vanished. Except for a bit of attention in geometry, treatments of sets and mathematical systems are seldom found in today's texts. Yet the larger changes in course structure remain with us. Few schools offer separate courses in solid geometry and analytic geometry. Slope is still taught in first-year algebra, conics in second-year algebra. Inequalities are given attention at many levels. For good students, trigonometry is taught alongside algebra. Thus the current secondary school curricula in the vast majority of schools in the United States and Canada reflect the new math revolution.

> **Lesson 2:  Changes in course structure and content are more likely
> to last than changes in mathematical approach or teach-
> ing style.**

The new math appeared at a time when there was a national need for people trained in up-to-date science and mathematics. Consequently, honors classes were established in many schools, and the Advanced Placement program became quite popular for better students. The new math was (and in some places still is) the curriculum for these students. By the early 1970s a shortage of scientists had turned into a surplus. Though economists would probably argue that supply and demand in the job market played the largest role in turning the shortage into a surplus, the effect of the new math was to ensure that those who got jobs were of higher quality than would have otherwise been the case.

Thus in some ways the new math was quite successful. Yet the public view is that this revolution was a failure. The public perception cannot be dismissed lightly, for it has made governmental agencies wary of putting money into curriculum projects, and this caution seems to have extended to the mathematics education profession as a whole. From 1972 until the time of writing this paper, not one large-scale curriculum project in secondary school mathematics has existed in North America.

---

**Lesson 3:  Public perceptions more than professional concerns determine whether money will be available for large curriculum projects.**

---

## THE DECLINE

New math is generally perceived as being the cause of a decline in test scores in the late 1960s and through the 1970s. The decline, as measured by performance on certain tests, is indisputable; it's the cause that is not so clear. Direct studies employing problem-solving tests like the SAT-M, skill tests like the Iowa Tests of Basic Skills (ITBS), individual items like those of the National Assessment of Educational Progress (NAEP), and comparison studies like the National Longitudinal Study of Mathematical Abilities (NLSMA) demonstrate that the public perception is wrong.

The Scholastic Aptitude Tests of mathematics (SAT-M) are designed to assess (1) how well students understand elementary and junior high mathematics, (2) how well they can apply what they already know to new situations, and (3) how well they can use what they know in insightful or nonroutine ways of thinking (Braswell 1978). The recall of factual knowledge and performance of mathematical manipulations are not emphasized on the SAT-M and are used only to discriminate at the low end of the ability scale. Thus *the SAT-M is not a test of computational skills but of problem solving, and the SAT-M is very clearly not a test of high school mathematics.* Despite these characteristics, the SAT-M is the most commonly cited barometer of the quality of the curriculum, of teaching, and of learning in high school mathematics.

Table 1.1 presents mean SAT-M and SAT-V (verbal) scores for all students taking the test for each year since 1951–52. On the SAT-M, the peak year is 1962–63, but the decline is so slow that not until 1969–70 is the mean below that of 1953–54. There is a continuous decline from 1967–68 through 1978–79; since then, the mean scores have been rather constant.[1] The declines in the SAT-V from the peak of 1962–63 were quicker and deeper; the difference between peak and valley scores on the SAT-V is 56 points, whereas on the SAT-M the difference is 36 points.

TABLE 1.1

| Scholastic Aptitude Test Score Means, All Students* | | | | | |
|---|---|---|---|---|---|
| Academic Year | SAT Verbal | SAT Mathematical | Academic Year | SAT Verbal | SAT Mathematical |
| 1951–52 | 476 | 494 | 1966–67 | 467 | 495 |
| 1952–53 | 476 | 495 | 1967–68 | 466 | 494 |
| 1953–54 | 472 | 490 | 1968–69 | 462 | 491 |
| 1954–55 | 475 | 496 | 1969–70 | 460 | 488 |
| 1955–56 | 479 | 501 | 1970–71 | 454 | 487 |
| 1956–57 | 473 | 496 | 1971–72 | 450 | 482 |
| 1957–58 | 472 | 496 | 1972–73 | 443 | 481 |
| 1958–59 | 475 | 498 | 1973–74 | 440 | 478 |
| 1959–60 | 477 | 498 | 1974–75 | 437 | 473 |
| 1960–61 | 474 | 495 | 1975–76 | 429 | 470 |
| 1961–62 | 473 | 498 | 1976–77 | 429 | 471 |
| 1962–63 | 478 | 502 | 1977–78 | 429 | 469 |
| 1963–64 | 475 | 498 | 1978–79 | 426 | 466 |
| 1964–65 | 473 | 496 | 1979–80 | 423 | 467 |
| 1965–66 | 471 | 496 | 1980–81 | 425 | 468 |
| | | | 1981–82 | 424 | 468 |
| | | | 1982–83 | 423 | 467 |

*Updated from Wirtz et al. (1977).

A distinguished panel that examined the decline (Wirtz et al. 1977) was able to blame the decline from 1962–63 to 1969–70 on changes in the population of students taking the test. That is, in these years the number of students taking the test was increasing, and the larger samples of students were not as select. However, from 1970 to 1976 the decline was felt to be

---

1. The population of students who take the SAT exams is more complex than suggested by either table 1.1 or media reports. For instance, the mean score of 467 for 1982–83 is the weighted mean of 748 360 seniors (mean 455), 596 760 juniors (mean 491), and 142 609 others (mean 430). In contrast, the mean score of 495 for 1965–66 is the weighted mean of 808 751 seniors (mean 490), 459 624 juniors (mean 505), and 77 313 others (mean 488). In recent years a significant portion of these "others" have been bright junior high school students who take the SATs in attempts to enter programs for the gifted. Although some of these students score quite well, many do not. Whereas in 1965–66 the scores of these students had no effect on the overall mean, the scores of those who were neither seniors nor juniors in 1982–83 lowered the overall mean by 4 points. Not including "others," the mean SAT-M score was lowest at 467 in 1978–79 and has been 471 since 1980. (I wish to thank Willie May of the College Board's Mathematical Sciences Advisory Committee for supplying the data from which this analysis was made.)

true and not due to changes in population. Although the SAT "is perhaps the most widely researched test ever developed," the panel was able to come up with only circumstantial evidence for the decline in student scores in those later years. All who have followed these data over the years probably have opinions regarding the causes of the decline. Due to the quite verbal nature of the problems on the SAT-M, I wonder why the panel did not study the effects of the decline on the SAT-V on the decline on the SAT-M.

---

**Lesson 4:   Results of research, when picked up by the news media, can have great impact on mathematics education.**

---

Roderick (1973) compared Iowa students' performance on the ITBS for the years 1936, 1951–55, 1965, and 1973. He reported that students in 1936 were superior to those in 1973 at both grades 6 and 8 in every area tested. He suggested that "this study presents evidence toward concluding that the modern mathematics curriculum and/or its implementation is seriously deficient and ineffective to most of the long-term and still-held curricular goals identified."

Max Bell and I looked at Roderick's data, giving particular attention to the intervening years and to the items tested. Comparison is difficult because different sets of items were originally given in 1936, 1951–55, and 1965. Furthermore, Roderick was forced to use items from the earlier tests to compare students even though comparable questions do not appear in today's textbooks. Similarly, items taught today, such as equations or open sentences, were not tested with grade 6 students in earlier years. In general, standardized tests from one era are almost always biased against students from a different era who take them. In this case, the bias was clearly against the 1973 students. Still, when we compared the years 1951–55 and 1973, we found that at grade 6, neither era was clearly superior and even at grade 8 there were intriguingly disparate results. Thus Bell and I concluded that most of the differences observed between 1936 and 1973 would have shown up between 1936 and 1951–55, with quite mixed results from then on (Usiskin and Bell 1976).

Our conclusion is supported by two other large studies. Beckmann (1970), in a study involving 1296 students from 42 Nebraska high schools taking the same 109-item arithmetic and geometry tests, found means of 45.7 in 1951 and 54.9 in 1965, a dramatic improvement. An extensive study in Ontario (OISE 1975) came to the following conclusion: "In contrast to the widely publicized opinions of critics, this study clearly indicates that elementary school students in 1974 are just as capable of arithmetic computation as their age mates of 10 years ago."

The first NAEP in mathematics in 1973–74 compared the performance of adults aged 26 to 35 (who presumably would have had "old math") with that of 13-year-olds and 17-year-olds (most of whom would have had new math) and found few differences in ability, despite the adults being given unlimited time to do the same problems that were carefully timed for the students (NAEP 1977). A summary article (Carpenter et al.1975) asked

> What do these NAEP data say about the effect of "new mathematics" programs? After all, the 13-year-olds and 17-year-olds could have been taught throughout their school experience in new mathematics classrooms. If the critics of the "new mathematics" were correct, the computational skills of these age groups would be very low. In fact the data show that 13-year-olds can do about as well as adults on most computational tasks, and 17-year-olds can do better.[2]

SMSG undertook NLSMA in the period 1962–66 during which orthodox models of both new and old curricula existed and true comparisons could be made. NLSMA involved 110 000 students, and its extensive analyses are reported in thirty-three volumes. However, the results are summarized in only three places (Begle and Wilson 1970; Wilson 1971; Begle 1973), which may account for the lack of attention given them. Although SMSG students in the study had slightly lower computational skills, they performed better in comprehension, analysis, and application. Thus SMSG may have given a little in arithmetic skill but got back in other areas more than enough to compensate.

---

**Lesson 5:   Results of even the best research have little effect unless announced and defended.**

---

## THE REBELLION

The revolution was successful in bringing about change, but even when it is looked at most positively, the result was not utopia. NLSMA found that some of the modern textbooks produced lower performance in skills *and* understanding (Begle and Wilson 1970). The logical approach was, for many students, not the correct psychological or pedagogical approach (Willoughby 1967). Despite a goal of keeping up with mathematical theory *and* applications, very few applications were taught (Kline 1966).

It was apparent rather quickly that the students who benefited most from the new math curricula were the better students. As a result, many of the same mathematics educators who had been involved in implementing the original revolution undertook corrective efforts. They established mathe-

---

2. The extent to which new math served as a scapegoat for the decline is illustrated by what happened at the 24 July 1975 press conference at which the first NAEP data in mathematics were publicized. A carefully drafted written statement, presented orally, indicated that students had scored poorly on certain skills but contained no reference to causes or curriculum. When the press probed why students had scored poorly, a spokesman who had no hand in drafting the statement or in any of the data analyses blamed the poor scores on the new math. The next day the *Wall Street Journal,* basing its article on the response to the question, used the headline "Study Says Students of New Math Flunk Consumer Problems." A week later *Science News,* basing its article on the written statement, used the headline "Johnny's dad can't add either." Thus is the ease with which preconceived notions reach the public consciousness.

matics laboratories to counter formalism. They encouraged behavioral objectives to offset the vagueness of discovery lessons. They instituted consumer mathematics courses to provide applications. All these corrections were aimed at slower students, and all first appeared before 1970.

> **Lesson 6: Materials written for the top students must be significantly altered for slower students.**

That the profession was rather content with the revolution and these corrections is evidenced by the fact that from 1964 through 1974 no report of national scope dealing with the secondary school mathematics curriculum appeared. But the general public was not satisfied. Test scores were declining, and the decline was blamed on the curriculum.

Rebellion appeared, with a calling card, *Why Johnny Can't Add* (Kline 1973; see also Begle 1974), and a seductive name, *back-to-basics*. The rebellion, existing still today in many locales, has emphasized paper-and-pencil manipulative skills. At the high school level, the rebellion has never been as strong as at the elementary school level; whereas a rebellion textbook series was the most-used elementary school text in the nation in 1977, the most-used high school texts were the same as those that dominated the market in the 1960s (Weiss 1978).

Like new math, back-to-basics has had some successes. One manifestation of this movement has been the establishment of minimal competence test performance requirements for promotion or graduation. Such tests are usually dominated by paper-and-pencil computation skills. Generally the percentage of students who fail these tests the first year they are given is quite large but decreases the next year, and almost all students who have failed can be brought up, with remediation, to the minimum standards necessary for passing. The most recent NAEP results (from the 1981–82 testing) show an increase in performance among black and Hispanic youth at all ages tested, among all 13-year-olds (Carpenter et al. 1983), and among the bottom 25% of students (NAEP 1983).

However, these successes have been gained at great cost. The performance of the top 25% of students on the NAEP declined from 1977–78 to 1981–82. Overall performance on applications and problem-solving items dropped from 1972–73 to 1977–78 and did not improve in 1981–82 (NAEP 1983; Carpenter et al. 1983). Roy Forbes, the director of NAEP, noted the irony (NAEP 1979):

> During a period when the public has placed great emphasis on the "basics", assessment data show that mathematics achievement has declined, especially in problem-solving and understanding of concepts.

For better students, the SAT-M data independently confirm these trends. Mean scores on this test of problem solving continued to decline until 1978–79 and have never significantly rebounded (table 1.1).

As an example of the emphasis on skill and not understanding, 57% of

13-year-olds and 72% of 17-year-olds in 1981–82 correctly calculated the exact answer to a multiplication problem similar to that found in the following multiple-choice item:

> ESTIMATE the answer to $3.04 \times 5.3$.
> (a)  1.6          (d)  1600
> (b)  16           (e)  I don't know
> (c)  160

However, this very estimation item was correctly answered by only 20.7% of 13-year-olds (about what would be expected from random guessing!) and only 36.6% of 17-year-olds.

Without some change, the future does not look bright. As Brownell (1935) noted: "It is not simple to build meaningful learning upon a foundation of mechanical learning." Many students today enter secondary schools from an elementary school experience that has given them little appreciation for the underlying concepts and meanings that enable effective use of mathematics. Even the best secondary school teachers find it difficult to change student learning styles built up over many years.

> **Lesson 7:  Materials written for the poorest students must be significantly altered for better students.**

Lessons 6 and 7 may seem too obvious to be worth emphasizing. But, just as mathematicians look for powerful algorithms that work in all problems of a given type, educators tend to adopt a single curriculum and then attempt to adapt it to all situations. For example, Houston, Detroit, and a number of other large cities adopt only one book for each secondary school course for all their schools. And there are still many secondary schools that do not ability group in mathematics. As a result, in many schools in the 1960s all students were subjected to a curriculum that was more appropriate for the better students. In the 1970s this was turned around and all students were subjected to a curriculum more appropriate for the poorer students.

## TODAY'S MASSIVE PROBLEM

The biggest problem in secondary school mathematics today is recognized by all, regardless of feelings toward new math or back-to-basics. It is that a large number—perhaps a majority—of high school graduates lack the mathematical know-how to cope effectively in society, qualify for the jobs they would like, or qualify for the training programs (including those in college) leading to the jobs they would like.

Lack of mathematical know-how among the populace is not unique to the United States or Canada. Similar concerns led to a lengthy report on mathematical education in England and Wales (Cockcroft 1982).

A problem as widely perceived as this one obviously has many aspects. We consider seven aspects here.

1. *Very simple questions involving secondary school mathematics topics are not answered correctly by many students.* For example, only 53% of all high school seniors report having taken a year of geometry (Peng, Fetters, and Kolstad 1981). Yet, in a representative sample of geometry takers, only 52% could answer the following item before studying geometry (Usiskin 1982):

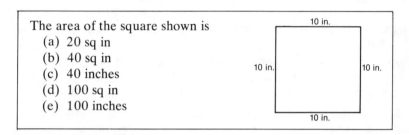

The area of the square shown is
   (a)  20 sq in
   (b)  40 sq in
   (c)  40 inches
   (d)  100 sq in
   (e)  100 inches

What does this imply about the knowledge of the 47% of seniors who never study high school geometry?

2. *Many students currently begin mathematics courses with knowledge so sparse that they are more than likely not to have success.* Performance on the item above suggests that many geometry students might have trouble with the course. This is exactly the case. In a study of 84 geometry classes in which there was an expectation of competence on proof, Senk (1983) found that 29% of students could not complete even a trivial triangle congruence proof in May of the school year. Over half (51%) could complete only such trivial proofs. Furthermore, this performance was highly correlated (mean correlation .56) with entering factual knowledge of the type in the area-of-square item.

The failure rate in first-year algebra may be higher than in geometry. So it seems that many students *wisely* choose not to take algebra or geometry, for they know that their knowledge is insufficient to afford a high probability of success in that course. Consequently, simply raising mathematics course requirements for high school graduation without changing the courses or the knowledge of entering students is likely only to increase mathematics failure and the accompanying avoidance, fear, and anxiety. Yet something must be done.

3. *In general, students are not taking enough mathematics in high school.* Of 17-year-olds in the spring of 1982, 71% reported having taken a semester of algebra, 52% a semester of geometry, and 38% a semester of second-year algebra (NAEP 1983; Carpenter et al. 1983). Thus about a quarter of all students take no algebra course in junior or senior high school. Since most vocational or technical training programs require an ability to work with formulas and since computers constantly deal with variables, these students

are not well prepared even for training programs. About half the population goes to a two-year or four-year college. Thus many students go to college never having taken a second year of algebra, and they find few college majors open to them.

4. *Even those students who have had one year of algebra and one year of geometry may not know much.* In a study of 68 average first-year algebra classes, 4 in each of 17 schools, Swafford and Kepner (1978) found some schools in which the *mean* school score on the Cooperative Algebra Test, Form A (ETS 1962) at the *end* of the school year was *lower* than the *mean* score in other schools at the *beginning* of that school year. Similar results for mean school scores were found in the geometry study mentioned earlier (Usiskin 1982). It is not surprising, then, that even students who have taken algebra and geometry in some schools are not at all ready to take a high school or college course in second-year algebra; they are not necessarily ready to begin the courses for which they have already received credit!

5. *The number of remedial courses taken by students in senior high schools and colleges is alarming.* Approximately 40% of entering high school freshmen are enrolled in general mathematics or prealgebra, indicating a lack of readiness for algebra, the standard ninth-grade mathematics course. Two-year colleges reported that 42% of mathematics enrollments in 1980–81 were in remedial courses (arithmetic, general mathematics, elementary or intermediate high school algebra, or high school geometry) and 17% additional were in precalculus mathematics (trigonometry, college algebra, or elementary functions) (Fey, Albers, and Fleming 1981). Universities and four-year colleges reported 18% and 24% in courses of these types, respectively.

At the high school level, the cause of this problem is almost always insufficient mastery of what was taught in elementary and junior high school. At the college level insufficient mastery is compounded with insufficient course-taking (aspect 2 above) and increases in the mathematical sophistication required of college majors in such areas as the social sciences, business, and psychology.

Although the causes of high enrollments in remedial courses may be different at the high school and college levels, the situations have much in common. Students in remedial courses are taught by teachers who, in the main, would prefer to teach more advanced content. There is less time to learn the material than there was at the grade level where it was originally taught. The classroom is filled with an aura of failure and frustration. The students are often taking the class unwillingly, only because it is required or is a prerequisite for another course they would like to take. There may be large numbers of students who drop out before the course ends.

For these reasons, efforts that reduce the potential numbers of students requiring remediation are likely to be of great benefit. In chapter 12 of this yearbook, Leitzel and Osborne describe a successful program with high school juniors and seniors to reduce numbers of remedial students at the college level, but the problem of remediation is one we must begin to attack at the elementary school level. Matthews (1983), in a discussion of intervention programs for minority students, puts it aptly: "It is as though we do not begin to look for ways to fill the cup until the cup is half empty."

6. *Even students who currently do take three years of college preparatory mathematics do not learn the uses of that mathematics.* Here is another 1977–78 NAEP item (Carpenter et al. 1982):

---

Some people suggest the following formula be used to determine the average weight for boys between the ages of 1 and 7:

$$W = 17 + 5A$$

where $W$ is the average weight in pounds and $A$ is the boy's age in years. According to this formula, for each year older a boy gets, how much more should he weigh?

---

This item was correctly answered by 53% of those who had no algebra, 58% of those who had one year of algebra, and 64% of those who had two years of algebra. Thus in two years of algebra study, only 11% more students learned what is a rather simple application idea and a basic property of linear relationships.

In a study of second-year algebra classes in 13 schools (Usiskin 1973), more students in the fall than in the spring agreed with the statement "Mathematics has many uses in the real world." More students in the spring than the fall agreed with the statement "Most of the mathematics known today was known to the ancient Greeks." Thus a population of the brighter mathematics students in schools at that time, studying a course virtually all of whose content was unknown to the Greeks (the concept of variable dating only from about A.D. 1560), a course whose content is undeniably applicable in a wide variety of areas, learned the opposite.

7. *Important mathematics other than algebra, geometry, and analysis is systematically avoided.* Consider the following two questions about probability that require only arithmetic, given on the 1972–73 NAEP (NAEP 1977):

---

In three tosses of a fair coin, heads turned up twice and tails turned up once. What is the probability that heads will turn up on the fourth toss?

---

The correct response (1/2 or any equivalent) was given by only 15% of 13-year-olds, 27% of 17-year-olds, 36% of adults, and only 46% of adults who went to college.

---

At the start of a party game, eight red, six green, four blue and two white slips of paper were thoroughly mixed in a bowl. The chances that the first slip drawn at random will be the WHITE one are given by which one of the expressions below?

| | |
|---|---|
| a) 2 divided by (8 + 6 + 4) | d) 2 divided by (8 + 6 + 4 + 2) |
| b) 1 divided by (8 + 6 + 4 + 1) | e) I don't know |
| c) 1 divided by (8 + 6 + 4 + 2) | |

The correct response (d) was given by only 31 % of 17-year-olds and 28% of all adults. Even including choice (a), whose numbers reflect thinking in terms of odds rather than probabilities, the corresponding totals correct are only 52% and 45%.

An increase in the mathematics requirements of students that brings more students into the standard college-preparatory curriculum is not likely to increase these percentages because this content is not in that curriculum. Students in consumer mathematics courses do not find probability, because consumer mathematics texts are almost exclusively devoted to money matters. After an extensive analysis of applications of arithmetic, Max Bell and I have concluded (Usiskin and Bell 1984) that many types of applications that are rather common in the real world are taught nowhere in the curriculum, so that students are forced to proceed by feel when they encounter them. Some choose to proceed, but others avoid the applications entirely.

## QUELLING THE REBELLION

The similarities between the situations of the 1950s and 1970s were well known to the leaders of mathematics education. In back-to-basics, these leaders saw a return, not to an era in which students were mathematically capable, but to an era where neither skills nor understanding was achieved. As the back-to-basics rebellion gained momentum, there emerged response from within the professional community to quell it.

In 1975, the National Advisory Committee on Mathematical Education (NACOME), a group appointed by the Conference Board of the Mathematical Sciences (CBMS), called for a repudiation of a curriculum dominated by manipulative skills and presaged coming reports by recommending more work with calculators, computers, statistics, and applications. The content recommendations of NACOME (1975) read rather well ten years later:

  a) That logical structure be maintained as a framework for the study of mathematics

  b) That concrete experiences be an integral part of the acquisition of abstract ideas

  c) That the opportunity be provided for students to apply mathematics in as wide a realm as possible—in the social and natural sciences, in consumer and career related areas, as well as in any real life problems that can be subjected to mathematical analysis

  d) That familiarity with symbols, their uses, their formalities, their limitations be developed and fostered in an appropriately proportioned manner

  e) That beginning no later than the end of the eighth grade, a calculator should be available for each mathematics student during each mathematics class.

Each student should be permitted to use the calculator during all of his or her mathematical work including tests.

*f)* That the recommendations of the Conference Board of the Mathematical Sciences 1972 committee regarding computers in secondary school curricula be implemented

NACOME especially underlines recommendations:

- that *all* students, not only able students, be afforded the opportunity to participate in computer science courses
- that school use of computers be exploited beyond the role of computer assisted instruction or computer management systems
- that "computer literacy" courses involve student "hands-on" experiences using computers

*g)* That all school systems give serious attention to implementation of the metric system in measurement instruction and that they re-examine the current instruction sequences in fractions and decimals to fit the new priorities

*h)* That instructional units dealing with statistical ideas be fitted throughout the elementary and secondary school curriculum

To implement these ideas, NACOME called for curriculum development and revisions in specific areas.

At almost the same time, the National Institute of Education (1975) sponsored a conference in Euclid, Ohio, at which ten basic goals for mathematics education were identified:

1. Appropriate computational skills
2. Links between mathematical ideas and physical situations
3. Estimation and approximation
4. Organization and interpretation of numerical data, including using graphs
5. Measurement, including selection of relevant attributes, selection of degree of precision, selection of appropriate instrument, techniques of using measuring instruments, and techniques of conversion among units within a system
6. Alertness to reasonableness of results
7. Qualitative understanding of and drawing inferences from functions and rates of change
8. Notions of probability
9. Computer uses: Capabilities and limitations (gained through direct experience)
10. Problem solving

Problem solving was identified as the unifying goal interrelating the other nine.

The next year, the National Council of Supervisors of Mathematics widely circulated a position paper in which the Euclid goals were termed "basic skills" (a natural move, since the Euclid conference was called a conference on basic skills, but just as much a political ploy to take advantage of the popularity of back-to-basics rhetoric). Problem solving was elevated to be the first basic skill and the "principal reason for studying mathematics." The other Euclid goals were reordered (appropriate computational skills being placed fifth) and only the seventh goal was deleted, replaced by geometry (NCSM 1977, 1978). (It is rather ironic that a mathematics education conference in a place called Euclid ignored geometry.)

Not long afterward, the National Council of Teachers of Mathematics (1980) widely distributed *An Agenda for Action,* a document combining many of the recommendations of its predecessors. Four of the *Agenda*'s eight recommendations deal directly with curriculum content:

1. That problem solving be the focus of school mathematics in the 1980s
2. That basic skills in mathematics be defined to encompass more than computational facility
3. That mathematics programs take full advantage of the power of calculators and computers at all grade levels

   . . .

6. That more mathematics study be required for all students and a flexible curriculum with a greater range of options be designed to accommodate the diverse needs of the student population

All these documents carry the same message: back-to-basics is a dangerous movement that should be reversed. But they all go one step further, for if the recommendations in any one of these documents were to be adopted *in toto,* the result would be a major revolution in school mathematics.

## PICKING UP THE GAUNTLET

This massive problem with its many aspects could not long exist without attracting the attention of those outside the mathematics education community. Thus, whereas the documents referred to in the preceding section were all written in the period 1975–80 by committees dominated by mathematics educators, in more recent years groups with broader representation have picked up the gauntlet.

Government reports have related mathematical know-how to economic well-being, to the country's future strength, and to the ability of citizens to participate in and make intelligent decisions in an increasingly technological age (NSF-DE 1980; NAS-NAE 1982). In *A Nation at Risk,* the most widely cited of recent government reports, the National Commission on Excellence in Education (1984) recommends three years of mathematics for high school graduation (echoing a recommendation in *An Agenda for Action*), with the following elaboration:

> The teaching of mathematics in high school should equip graduates to: (*a*) understand geometric and algebraic concepts; (*b*) understand elementary probability and statistics; (*c*) apply mathematics in everyday situations; and (*d*) estimate, approximate, measure, and test the accuracy of their calculations. In addition to the traditional sequence of studies available for college-bound

students, new, equally demanding mathematics curricula need to be developed for those who do not plan to continue their formal education immediately.

For Project EQuality (College Board 1983), mathematics is one of six basic areas without which subject-matter competence in all other areas is unattainable. The basic mathematical proficiency needed by all college entrants is described as follows:

> The ability to apply mathematical techniques in the solution of real-life problems and to recognize when to apply those techniques
>
> Familiarity with the language, notation, and deductive nature of mathematics and the ability to express quantitative ideas with precision
>
> The ability to use computers and calculators
>
> Familiarity with the basic concepts of statistics and statistical reasoning
>
> Knowledge in considerable depth and detail of algebra, geometry, and functions

These general statements are followed by content specifications for the entire college-bound population and for those expecting to major in science or engineering or to take advanced courses in mathematics or computer science.

Taken as a body, the reports from inside and outside mathematics education agree almost unanimously that two concurrent changes must take place in secondary school mathematics. First, that the performance of students be upgraded: requirements for graduation should be increased, emphasis should be shifted from rote manipulation to problem solving, and students need to be better at both of these. Second, that the curriculum be updated: estimation, applications, computers, and statistics and probability all should play important roles in secondary school mathematics study.

## REVOLUTION, NOT EVOLUTION

With current expectations, it takes a full three years—two years of algebra and a year of precalculus mathematics, with trigonometry integrated in both—for even very good students to gain the concepts and skills that constitute adequate preparation for calculus. (A position paper of a joint committee of the NCTM and the Mathematical Association of America [1978] underscores this point.) Unless the school year is lengthened as recommended in *A Nation at Risk,* or unless time is taken from geometry, or unless we start algebra earlier, there is no time to upgrade student performance as the reports have recommended. But no report has recommended less geometry, and none of these reports has suggested that algebra start earlier. (In fact, in the NCTM *Agenda for Action,* there is the suggestion that algebra start after ninth grade even for many students who now take it then.) Even if the school year is lengthened to give time to upgrade, there still would be no time to insert new content without lessening the importance of other content areas in the high school. So it would seem that despite the consensus recommendations of so many reports over the past decade, their goals constitute an impossible dream.

But there is a kicker—the ability of computers to perform symbolic manipulations and, indeed, virtually any task for which an algorithm can be constructed. Existing software can do almost all the manipulative skills now taught in algebra and precalculus classes (Pavelle, Rothstein, and Fitch 1981; muMath 1981). Chapters 3, 4, and 5 of this volume describe such software and discuss its potential curricular impact in detail.

Just as the omnipresence of calculators has made it unnecessary to teach certain paper-and-pencil skills that have dominated the arithmetic curriculum, this software makes it unnecessary to become proficient at certain paper-and-pencil skills in algebra. Deleting just a few topics could free up considerable time; on the average, at least 30% of first-year algebra is spent factoring trinomials and other polynomials and applying these skills to manipulations with rational expressions. Much of this content was useless for most students even before the computer (see Usiskin [1980] for an elaboration of this point); now we have even more reasons for its deletion.

The major argument raised against the use of calculators and computers to do traditional paper-and-pencil skills concerns the need to have skill to understand concepts. Yet it seems that skill and understanding are distinct notions; just as one can learn skills mechanically and not understand the underlying concepts. so mathematics is already filled with many examples of concepts we learn despite not knowing the underlying skills. Our understanding of cube root does not come from having calculated many cube roots by hand (as was required of algebra students a century ago). Few of us have ever used infinite series to calculate logarithms or trigonometric values to

---

The full implications of the [computer] technology force a more substantial reworking of the curriculum in which the primary goal (calculus) . . . lose[s] some of [its] preeminence.

---

three or four decimal places, and some of us may not even know how this is done, but we still make use of the values given in tables or presented by a calculator and feel that we understand what these values represent. The history of mathematics is filled with the development of techniques that take difficult problems and make them automatic. Usually these automatic procedures provide a benefit; with tedious calculation out of the way, understanding the ideas and purposes of the mathematics itself becomes easier.

The desire to teach students the skills ultimately needed in calculus continues to dominate all of high school mathematics except geometry. But in 1980, 24% of college freshmen planned to major in engineering or the natural sciences (including the mathematical sciences), areas in which calculus plays a key role, whereas 36% planned to major in computer science, business, or the social sciences, areas in which mathematical sophistication is needed but calculus does not dominate (data from Albers and associates, as reported in Fey, Albers, and Fleming [1981]). In fact, eight times as many college freshmen (4.9%) planned to major in computer science, data processing, or computer programming as planned to major in mathematics or statistics. Naturally, this has resulted in a movement to replace the one-year course in calculus by a curriculum that pays more attention to the mathematics needed by computer scientists and others not majoring in engineering or the natural sciences (Ralston 1981; Ralston and Young 1983; see also chapter 3 of this yearbook). A corresponding movement at the secondary level is reflected in a CBMS report (1983) in which discrete mathematics and algorithmics are seen as new elements of a high school curriculum:

> Careful study is needed of what is and what is not fundamental in the current curriculum. Our belief is that a number of topics should be introduced into the secondary school curriculum and that all of these are more important than, say, what is now taught in trigonometry beyond the definition of the trigonometric functions themselves. These topics include discrete mathematics (e.g., basic combinatorics, graph theory and discrete probability), elementary statistics (e.g., data analysis, interpretation of tables, graphs, surveys, sampling) and computer science (e.g., programming, introduction to algorithms, iteration).

Thus the full implications of this technology force a more substantial reworking of the curriculum in which the primary goal (calculus) and the primary time-consuming activities (manipulative skills done with paper and pencil) lose some of their preeminence.

In summary, the problem of lack of mathematical know-how is so massive, and the changes in the field of mathematics so pronounced, that current student needs in mathematics cannot be met without modifying the very goals and nature of secondary school mathematics. Recent reports confirm that the current curriculum needs overhauling rather than adjustment, revolution rather than evolution.

## PRINCIPLES FOR IMPLEMENTING THE REVOLUTION

History tells us that such a revolution can be implemented, but only if several principles are followed.

1. *The content of any new curriculum must be specified in as much detail as current content.* For instance, applications are presently taught when they are clearly specified. The formulas $A = lw$ and $I = prt$ are mainstays of the junior high school curriculum. The calculation of hidden distances using the law of sines is seldom omitted in trigonometry. Compound interest is almost always studied after logarithms. If more applications or some statistics or discrete mathematics is desired, it will have to be specified.

2. *The content of any new curriculum must be specified by intended grade level.* For perhaps twenty years there has been a significant amount of geometry in elementary school textbooks. Yet this geometry is often not

taught because there is no expectation by the next teacher that students should know some particulars about geometry. As a result, the experience from one year is not built on in the next year. The same holds today for problem solving; I know of no senior high school that has modified its curriculum in any way because its feeder schools have decided to emphasize problem solving.

3. *Materials must be available to implement recommendations.* It is not just that the easiest way to specify content is through materials. It is that change does not occur without such materials. As Begle (1973) noted:

> . . . the evidence indicates that most student learning is directed by the text rather than the teacher.
>
> This is an important finding, since the content of the text is a variable that we can manipulate. In fact, it seems at present to be the only variable that on the one hand we can manipulate and on the other hand does affect student learning.

It is not enough to have supplementary resource materials. Even good materials with reasonably wide distribution (e.g., *Statistics by Example* [Mosteller et al. 1973]; *Statistics: A Guide to the Unknown* [Tanur et al. 1972]; and the *Sourcebook of Applications of School Mathematics* [Bushaw et al. 1980] have had impact on few classrooms). Textbooks designed for particular student populations are needed. But even they do not suffice.

4. *Students must be held accountable for the new content.* Minimal competence examinations have taught us that standards for students can be raised (though, of course, we cannot be satisfied with minimums). The success in implementing the new New York State integrated mathematics curriculum (see chapter 17) has come about in large part because the Regents' Exams require that curriculum. The new admission requirements of California state

---

If our present curriculum were a new experimental curriculum that we were testing, we would be forced to pronounce it a failure.

---

colleges and universities will increase the amount of mathematics taken by students in that state and decrease the number of remedial courses offered at the college level. The fastest way to get changes implemented is to place pressure not on teachers but on students.

The speed with which dramatic change can be effected by following these principles is illustrated by the Advanced Placement examination in Computer Science. A detailed specification of content (assumed to be at the twelfth-grade level) was put forth by the College Board in 1982 together with the announcement that the exam would be first offered in 1984. Immediately written were texts, and immediately changed were the ways in which large numbers of secondary schools treated computer science. Computer literacy without programming is now viewed as a trivial exercise. The final goal is no longer BASIC; it is Pascal. A one-semester or one-year offering of computer science has become the minimum, not the maximum. The resulting number of students who took the exam in 1984 surpassed even the most optimistic predictions of the College Board.

## CONCLUSION

History shows that we can change the curriculum if we have the resolve. But we must know what to expect. Some will wish to return to good old days that never were. Public perceptions, not professional concerns, will determine whether money is available for development and implementation. Results of research will have little effect unless they are announced and defended outside the professional community. And, most important, if we want to affect average students, we will have to write materials specifically for these students.

But these difficulties must be considered worthy of the required amount of investment, work, and risk. We can no longer tolerate a situation in which the typical adult fears mathematics like no other subject, in which the typical student has little notion of how much he or she will need to understand and use mathematics as an adult worker or consumer. If our present curriculum were a new experimental curriculum that we were testing, we would be forced to pronounce it a failure for many of our students. Mathematics is too important today to the average citizen who must deal with numerical information and for the person who must use mathematical techniques on the job for us to allow them to lack sufficient mathematical know-how. For this alone, if for no other reason, we need another revolution in school mathematics.

### REFERENCES

Beckmann, Milton W. "Eighth-Grade Mathematical Competence—15 Years Ago and Now." *Arithmetic Teacher* 17 (April 1970): 334–35.

Begle, Edward G. "Some Lessons Learned by SMSG." *Mathematics Teacher* 66 (March 1973): 207–14.

_____. "Review of *Why Johnny Can't Add.*" *National Elementary Principal* 53 (January/February 1974): 26–31.

Begle, Edward G., and James W. Wilson. "Evaluation of Mathematics Programs." In *Mathematics Education,* Sixty-ninth Yearbook of the National Society for the Study of Education, pt. 1. Chicago: University of Chicago Press, 1970.

Braswell, James. "The College Board Scholastic Aptitude Test: An Overview of the Mathematical Portion." *Mathematics Teacher* 71 (March 1978): 168–80.

Brownell, William A. "Psychological Considerations in the Learning and Teaching of Arithmetic." In *The Teaching of Arithmetic,* Tenth Yearbook of the National Council of Teachers of Mathematics. New York: Bureau of Publications, Teachers College, Columbia University, 1935.

Bushaw, Donald, Max Bell, Henry Pollak, Maynard Thompson, and Zalman Usiskin. *A Sourcebook of Applications of School Mathematics.* Reston, Va.: National Council of Teachers of Mathematics, 1980.

Carpenter, Thomas P., Terrence G. Coburn, Robert E. Reys, and James W. Wilson. "Results and Implications of the NAEP Mathematics Assessment: Secondary School." *Mathematics Teacher* 68 (October 1975): 453–70.

Carpenter, Thomas P., Mary Kay Corbitt, Henry S. Kepner, Jr., Mary Montgomery Lindquist, and Robert E. Reys. "Results of the Second NAEP Mathematics Assessment: Secondary School." *Mathematics Teacher* 73 (May 1980): 329–38.

_____. "Student Performance in Algebra: Results from the National Assessment." *School Science and Mathematics* 82 (October 1982): 514–31.

Carpenter, Thomas P., Mary M. Lindquist, Westina Matthews, and Edward A. Silver. "Results of the Third NAEP Mathematics Assessment: Secondary School." *Mathematics Teacher* 76 (December 1983): 652–59.

Cockcroft, W. H. *Mathematics Counts.* Report of the Committee of Inquiry into the Teaching of Mathematics in Schools under the Chairmanship of Dr. W. H. Cockcroft. London: Her Majesty's Stationery Office, 1982.

College Board. *Academic Preparation for College: What Students Need To Know and Be Able to Do.* New York: College Board, 1983.

College Entrance Examination Board, Commission on Mathematics. *Program for College Preparatory Mathematics.* New York: CEEB, 1959.

Conference Board of the Mathematical Sciences, Committee on Computer Education. *Recommendations Regarding Computers in High School Education.* Washington, D.C.: CBMS, 1972.

Conference Board of the Mathematical Sciences. *The Mathematical Sciences Curriculum K–12: What Is Still Fundamental and What Is Not.* Report to NSB Commission on Precollege Education in Mathematics, Science, and Technology. Washington, D.C.: CBMS, 1983.

Educational Testing Service. *Cooperative Mathematics Tests.* Algebra I, Form A. Menlo Park, Calif.: Addison-Wesley Publishing Co., 1962.

Fey, James T., Donald J. Albers, and Wendell H. Fleming, assisted by Clarence B. Lindquist. *Undergraduate Mathematical Sciences in Universities, Four-Year Colleges, and Two-Year Colleges 1980–81.* Report of the Survey Committee, Conference Board of the Mathematical Sciences, Vol. 6. Washington, D.C.: CBMS, 1981.

Hale, William T. "UICSM's Decade of Experimentation." *Mathematics Teacher* 54 (December 1961): 613–19.

Kline, Morris. "A Proposal for the High School Mathematics Curriculum." *Mathematics Teacher* 59 (April 1966): 322–30.

_____. *Why Johnny Can't Add.* New York: St. Martin's Press, 1973.

Matthews, Westina. *Influences on the Learning and Participation of Minorities in Mathematics.* Program Report 83-5. Madison: Wisconsin Center for Educational Research, 1983.

Mosteller, Frederick, William H. Kruskal, Richard F. Link, Richard S. Pieters, and Gerald R. Rising. *Statistics by Example.* Reading, Mass.: Addison-Wesley Publishing Co., 1973.

*muMATH/muSIMP-80*℠ *Symbolic Mathematics System for the Apple II with SoftCard.* Honolulu: The Soft Warehouse, 1981.

National Academy of Sciences and National Academy of Engineering. *Science and Mathematics in the Schools: Report of a Convocation.* Washington, D.C.: NAS-NAE, 1982.

National Advisory Committee on Mathematical Education (NACOME). *Overview and Analysis of School Mathematics: Grades K–12.* Reston, Va.: National Council of Teachers of Mathematics, 1975.

National Assessment of Educational Progress. "Low Achievers Improve Reading Skills, but Top Students Lose Ground in Math, Science." *NAEP Newsletter* 16 (Winter 1983): 1.

_____. "Math Achievement Is Plus and Minus." *NAEP Newsletter* 12 (October 1979): 1.

_____. *Mathematics Technical Report: Exercise Volume.* Mathematics Report No. 04-MA-20. Washington, D.C.: U.S. Government Printing Office, 1977.

_____. *The Third National Mathematics Assessment: Results, Trends and Issues.* Report No. 13-MA-01. Denver: Education Commission of the States, 1983.

National Commission on Excellence in Education. *A Nation at Risk: The Imperative for Educational Reform.* Washington, D.C.: U.S. Department of Education, 1983.

National Council of Supervisors of Mathematics. Position Paper on Basic Mathematical Skills. Distributed to members January 1977. Reprinted in the *Mathematics Teacher* 71 (February 1978): 147–52.

National Council of Teachers of Mathematics. *An Agenda for Action*. Reston, Va.: NCTM, 1980.

National Council of Teachers of Mathematics and the Mathematical Association of America. *Recommendations for the Preparation of High School Students for College Mathematics Courses*. Reston, Va., and Washington, D.C.: NCTM and MAA, 1977.

National Institute of Education. *The NIE Conference on Basic Mathematical Skills and Learning*. Vols. 1 and 2, Euclid, Ohio. Washington, D.C.: NIE, 1975.

National Science Foundation and Department of Education. *Science and Engineering Education for the 1980s and Beyond*. Washington, D.C.: U.S. Government Printing Office, 1980.

Ontario Institute for Studies in Education. *Study of the Characteristics of Current Elementary School Mathematics Programs in Ontario*. Toronto: OISE, 1975.

Pavelle, Richard, Michael Rothstein, and John Fitch. "Computer Algebra." *Scientific American*, December 1981, pp. 136–52.

Peng, S., W. Fetters, and A. Kolstad. *High School and Beyond: A Capsule Description of High School Students*. Washington, D.C.: National Center for Educational Statistics, 1981.

Ralston, Anthony. "Computer Science, Mathematics, and the Undergraduate Curricula in Both." *American Mathematical Monthly* 88 (August-September 1981): 472–75.

Ralston, Anthony, and Gail S. Young, eds. *The Future of College Mathematics*. New York: Springer-Verlag, 1983.

Reeve, William David. "The Need for a New National Policy and Program in Secondary Mathematics." *Mathematics Teacher* 48 (January 1955): 2–9.

Roderick, Stephen. "A Comparative Study of Mathematics Achievement by Sixth Graders and Eighth Graders, 1936 to 1973, 1951–55 to 1973, and 1965 to 1973." Ph.D. diss., University of Iowa, 1973.

Senk, Sharon. "Proof-writing Achievement and van Hiele Levels among High School Geometry Students." Ph.D. diss., University of Chicago, 1983.

Swafford, Jane O., and Henry S. Kepner, Jr. *A Report of the Evaluation of "Algebra through Applications."* Marquette, Mich.: Department of Mathematics, Northern Michigan University, 1978.

Tanur, Judith, ed. *Statistics: A Guide to the Unknown*. San Francisco: Holden-Day, 1972.

Usiskin, Zalman. *Three Reports on a Study of Eleventh Grade Mathematics*. Chicago: Department of Education, University of Chicago, 1973. ERIC document no. SE 017 077.

_____. "What Should *Not* Be in the Algebra and Geometry Curricula of Average College-bound Students?" *Mathematics Teacher* 73 (September 1980): 413–24.

_____. *Van Hiele Levels and Achievement in Secondary School Geometry*. Chicago: Department of Education, University of Chicago, 1982.

Usiskin, Zalman, and Max Bell. *Applying Arithmetic*. Preliminary ed. Chicago: Department of Education, University of Chicago, 1984.

_____. "Calculators and School Arithmetic: Some Perspectives." Appendix D to *Electronic Hand Calculators: The Implications for Pre-College Education*, by Marilyn Suydam, Final Report for NSF Grant No. EPP 75-16157, 1976. ERIC document no. ED 127 205.

Weiss, Iris R. *Report of the 1977 National Survey of Science, Mathematics, and Social Studies Education*. Washington, D.C.: U.S. Government Printing Office, 1978.

Willoughby, Stephen S. "Revolution, Rigor, and Rigor Mortis." *Mathematics Teacher* 60 (February 1967): 105–8.

Wilson, James W. "Evaluation of Secondary School Mathematics." In *Handbook on Formative and Summative Evaluation of Student Learning*, edited by Benjamin S. Bloom, Thomas Hastings, and George Madaus. New York: McGraw-Hill Book Co., 1971.

Wirtz, Willard, et al. *On Further Examination. Report of the Advisory Panel on the Scholastic Aptitude Test Score Decline*. New York: College Entrance Examination Board, 1977.

Wooten, William. *SMSG: The Making of a Curriculum*. New Haven, Conn.: Yale University Press, 1965.

# 2

# Mathematics in Secondary Schools: Four Points of View

Ralph W. Cain
L. Ray Carry
Charles E. Lamb

**T**HIS chapter presents a model of secondary school mathematics consisting of four points of view and relates those points of view to the roles and goals of the school. The model describes high school mathematics in a manner intended to help mathematics educators clarify their own perspectives and to help them communicate with each other and with others about the nature of secondary school mathematics.

The four points of view included in this model may not all be represented within most secondary school mathematics programs. As with some programs within a high school mathematics department, certain specific courses may fall into one of the points of view while other courses are representative of another. It might even be that individual teachers may be identified with a particular point of view. Although the points of view may not be mutually exclusive, the intent of the model is that all facets of high school mathematics, including a wide variety of programs and approaches, can be categorized using the model. It is also hoped that commonalities and differences can be expressed in terms of levels of the model.

The application of the model to the mathematics program in a particular high school should be done in the context of two major, related factors: (1) the goals or purposes of the school system, its mathematics program, and even specific courses in the program; and (2) the population (with specific subgroups) of students being served. Although the model is a theoretical one, any attempt to analyze a given program without considering the practicalities of intent and student characteristics would lessen the usefulness of the model.

## THE MODEL

The four points of view are presented in figure 2.1. Each row of the figure represents one of the points of view and each column one of the characteris-

**Program Characteristics**

| Points of View | Implicit Values | Order of Priorities | Curriculum Organization | Primary Instructional Goals | Teacher Role/Preparation | Responsibility for Outcomes | Target Population |
|---|---|---|---|---|---|---|---|
| Basic Skills | Utility in future work<br><br>Citizenship | Computation<br>Comprehension<br>Application<br>Analysis | Structured sequential hierarchy | Mastery of skills | Diagnostician/Prescriptor<br><br>Minimum content knowledge required | Instructor | Total student population |
| "Conceptual" Mathematics | Transfer; generalization of concepts<br><br>Utility in future thinking | Comprehension<br>Application<br>Computation<br>Analysis | Spiral | Understanding of concepts and relationships | Communicator of concepts<br><br>Content knowledge sufficient to generate varied examples | Instructor, then student | Top 75% of student population |
| Applied Mathematics | Transfer to science, engineering, etc.<br><br>Success in those fields | Application<br>Computation<br>Comprehension<br>Analysis | Problem-centered<br><br>Dependent on fields of application | Facility in solving real-world problems | Source of example problems and models for solving them<br><br>Extensive content knowledge required | Student, then instructor | Top 25% of student population |
| "Pure" Mathematics | Mathematics for its own sake | Analysis<br>Comprehension<br>Application<br>Computation | Axiomatic | Independent production of solutions by students<br><br>Logical precision | Authority and role model<br><br>Intensive content knowledge required | Student | Top 10% of student population |

Fig. 2.1. Four points of view of secondary school mathematics

tics of a secondary school mathematics program. The labels given to the points of view (the row headings) are used for reference only. The intent of the figure is to describe for purposes of comparison, not to label. It is also not the intent to place greater or lesser value on any of the points of view; such judgments must be made in light of the intents and clientele of a particular mathematics program.

## The First Point of View

The top row of the figure describes the first point of view, "basic skills." Although some educators would say that computation with whole numbers, fractions, decimals, and the like should be mastered in grades K–8, most high schools do include basic skills as a part of their offerings, probably because the realities of the classroom suggest that many students are deficient in basic skills.

The major goal encompassed in this point of view is competence in basic mathematics skills, especially computational skills. The level of the mathematics content is low, as are the cognitive expectations of the students. The contribution of the instructor to the learning of the content is very high. The role of the instructor is to "show and tell" and to diagnose errors and prescribe remediation for them. The role of the student is to replicate that which they have been shown and told. It is assumed that all students enrolled in the mathematics program are capable of doing the work required at this level.

Although some students will have reached most, if not all, of the learning goals embodied in this point of view by the time they reach high school, many have not. Many of the textbooks being offered for use in secondary school now heavily reflect this point of view in their emphasis on basic skills.

## The Second Point of View

The second point of view is referred to as "conceptual mathematics." It emphasizes the understanding of quantitative and spatial relationships and concepts. Top priority goes to comprehension instead of computation. The teacher becomes a clarifier and explainer instead of simply a source of factual knowledge and basic techniques, and students are expected to assume more responsibility for their own learning. Although not all students are expected to be able to work at this level, most are.

The spiral curriculum organization is designed to give students several opportunities to encounter concepts at different levels. Intuition, graphic representations, and numerous examples from the experiences of students are used to establish, broaden, and reinforce concepts. The ability to generalize and transfer concepts to unfamiliar situations is a major goal of this point of view. Moise (1965, 28) spoke to the nature of the "modern math" movement when he said:

> If we view mathematics realistically, as a human activity, it is plain that there are degrees of mathematical understanding; imperfect understanding is the

kind that occurs most commonly, and it is the kind that occurs first in the development of an individual. For this reason, no teacher need feel ashamed of bringing students merely to the level of understanding that they are capable of achieving at a given stage of their education.

The point is that logical rigor is not necessary for conceptual understanding and that such understanding is a worthy goal itself and may be for a large segment of the student population in our high schools the best we can hope for.

### The Third Point of View

The third point of view is "applied mathematics." Its major goal is competence in understanding and describing real-world phenomena mathematically and in using mathematical skills to solve problems in science, engineering, economics, and other fields. The complexity of those problems often requires relatively sophisticated mathematical techniques and processes, so that the level of content knowledge required of instructors rises. Although the instructor acts as a source of sample problems and solutions and a motivator of student effort to solve problems, the primary responsibility for the learning has shifted to the student, who must be involved in much more cognitive processing activity, especially at the level of problem-solving strategies. The proportion of students in the target population is reduced to the top quarter.

The role of the high school with regard to this point of view may be reduced somewhat, since many of the more advanced techniques for solving complex problems are usually taught at the college level. However, many aspects of this point of view are included in mathematics courses for some vocational programs, and, of course, college or technical school preparatory courses prerequisite to advanced applied mathematics courses often reflect this viewpoint.

This point of view is problem centered, with the solution of real-world problems the ultimate goal. The emphasis on problem solving brings to mind the work of Polya (1957, 1962), and the emphasis on the real world, especially in the physical sciences, suggests the work of Kline (1973). The shift in priority to applications is consistent with movements in which support for mathematics in the curriculum has been based on its usefulness in solving real-world problems, especially politically related ones such as those involving national defense or national economic goals.

### The Fourth Point of View

The fourth point of view, "pure mathematics," is thought by some to represent the highest level of a mathematics program. Its goals are competence in analyzing mathematical structures and discovering and developing new mathematics. This point of view is for the few who, on the basis of both ability and interest, can or wish to pursue it. The responsibility has shifted almost entirely to the student; the independent production of solutions and proofs replaces any passive role for the student. The teacher becomes an example setter and an evaluator of student performance. Many may see this point of view as related primarily, or exclusively, to advanced college work. However, the secondary school has a role that *is* related to this point of view—the recognition and encouragement of those students who are capable of performing at this level. Thus it becomes a viable option for them as they go on to more advanced studies.

A well-known advocate of this point of view was R. L. Moore. His position was presented in the MAA film *Challenge in the Classroom* and is still advocated and practiced within the mathematics community. The nature of the "pure mathematics" of this point of view has been expressed in the following statement by one of Moore's colleagues (Wall 1963, 3):

> Mathematics is a creation of the mind. To begin with, there is a collection of things, which exist only in the mind, assumed to be distinguishable from one another; and then there is a collection of statements about these things, which are taken for granted. Starting with the assumed statements concerning these invented or imagined things, the mathematician discovers other statements, called theorems, and proves them as necessary consequences. This, in brief, is the pattern of mathematics. The mathematician is an artist whose medium is the mind and whose creations are ideas.

Such a conceptualization of mathematics as that described above is quite foreign to a large majority of students at any level and certainly to the general public. This fact in no way suggests that the search for the abstraction of quantitative and spatial phenomena is not a valuable and important endeavor, but it may be too far removed from the realities of most high school classrooms to be viewed as important by those who feel that basic skills, some understanding of mathematical concepts, and some application of mathematical skills and concepts to the solution of problems are the most realistically attainable goals for their students. However, if "pure mathematics" is important, then we should be on the lookout for students whose abilities and interests may lead them in that direction.

## IMPLICATIONS OF THE MODEL

Many possible implications can be derived from the model presented here. For example: (a) course selection; (b) textbook selection; (c) student selection; and (d) staff selection. Of course, one should not undertake an analysis of these activities as listed independently of the purpose of the school system and its mathematics program as well as the nature of the student population being served.

### Course Selection

Many high school mathematics programs offer a wide variety of courses designed to meet the needs of a broad range of students. What kinds of courses should be available for students in the high school? Certainly, part of that decision is related to the types of students involved. Do they have plans for a traditional college education or do they have certain vocational desires in mind? Is it possible to select a set of courses that take into account such student characteristics while at the same time not closing doors to alternative choices? For example, should some content at levels 1, 2, and 3 be included in all mathematics courses? Also, does the program ensure equal access to all groups of students and should it do so?

### Textbook Selection

Consider the selection of a textbook for a course in high school algebra. Some are "cookbook" in their approach; others may use an applications-problems approach; others may use a "rigorous" approach; still others may use a combination of approaches. How does one decide which textbook to choose? Certainly part of that decision is related to which point of view is held by the one making the selection. Is she or he a believer in accurate use of formulas with or without rationale or carefully understood concepts or the ability to solve a wide variety of problems or the proving of theorems? Similar questions could be asked regarding selections of textbooks for other courses.

### Student Selection

In a time of dwindling output of high school graduates with good mathematics backgrounds it may be foolish to speak of being selective in allowing students into programs or courses, but whether the emphasis is on basic skills or applications, concepts or axioms, it is important that there be some congruence between the point of view and the characteristics of the students. The placement of students in the "proper" mathematics course is a major problem at any level, and high schools are not exempt from this problem. How are decisions made regarding who takes what courses? Is some congruence between point of view and the student population a factor?

We hope it is obvious to the reader that the target population percentages given in figure 2.1 are not precise, but neither do we consider them arbitrary. Our own experience tells us they may be considered reasonable upper bounds.

### Staff Selection

How important is it for the point of view of a faculty member and the department in which he or she teaches to be reasonably compatible? Should faculty members alter their points of view, or should they try to find positions in school systems whose points of view are consistent with their own? These questions are important implications of the model, as are questions regarding the training and background of potential faculty members. Are those whose interest is "pure mathematics" able to work with remedial, basic-skills students in a high school and be happy?

## SUMMARY

A model of high school mathematics has been presented, and some of its implications have been explored. If this chapter stimulates thought about the nature of secondary school mathematics programs among those involved in them or provides some basis for discussion of those programs, then it has served its purpose.

### REFERENCES

Begle, Edward G., and James W. Wilson. "Evaluation of Mathematics Programs." In *Mathematics Education,* Sixty-ninth Yearbook of the National Society for the Study of Education, part 1. Chicago: The Society, 1970.

Kline, Morris. *Why Johnny Can't Add: The Failure of the New Math.* New York: St. Martin's Press, 1973.

Moise, Edwin. "The SMSG Geometry Program." In *Philosophies and Procedures of SMSG Writing Teams.* Stanford, Calif.: School Mathematics Study Group, 1965.

Polya, G. *How to Solve It.* 2d ed. New York: Doubleday, Anchor Books, 1957.

———. *Mathematical Discovery.* Vol. 1. New York: John Wiley & Sons, 1962.

Wall, H. S. *Creative Mathematics.* Austin, Tex.: The University of Texas Press, 1963.

# 3

# The Really New College Mathematics and Its Impact on the High School Curriculum

## Anthony Ralston

**W**ITHIN the next decade, the first two years of the college mathematics curriculum will gradually shift from the traditional calculus–linear algebra sequence to one that has a balance between the traditional material and discrete mathematics. What is discrete mathematics? This rubric covers those branches of mathematics—such as combinatorics—that deal with discrete, individual objects in contrast to the continuous functions that are generally the fodder of calculus and classical analysis. Whereas calculus focuses on the real number system, discrete mathematics deals mainly with integers.

Such changes will take place almost entirely because of the impact of computer technology *and* computer science both on what seems important in mathematics itself and on the disciplines in which mathematics is applied. Whereas applications of mathematics to the physical world overwhelmingly require the tools of calculus and related mathematics, solving problems on computers almost entirely requires the tools of discrete mathematics, since the *digital* computer is inherently a discrete device. Therefore, just as the first Industrial Revolution, which was concerned with the production of *material* goods, required the mathematics of analysis and thereby spurred the development of the necessary mathematics, the contemporary second industrial revolution, which deals with the *immaterial*—knowledge, communication, and the like—will be supported by, and will give, great impetus to the development of discrete mathematics. It is essential that students of mathematics in college and high school receive a balanced mathematics education that focuses not only on the still very important classical areas of mathematics but also on the newer areas of discrete mathematics, which will assume ever-growing importance in their working lives. See Ralston (1981a, 1984) for a more detailed version of this argument.

This chapter is about what changes should occur in the high school mathematics curriculum as a result of changes in the college curriculum and the direct impact of computer science and computers on the high school curriculum. We shall focus on three areas:

1. How the high school curriculum itself is going to be affected by the new discrete mathematics in the college curriculum. Such changes will be modest but not trivial.

2. How computer *technology* is going to affect the high school curriculum. These changes are going to be considerable but rather different from what most people suppose. They will not be the direct result of changes in the college curriculum, but they are related to it.

3. How computer *science* is going to change both the high school curriculum itself and how the subject matter of the mathematics curriculum is presented. Here, too, the changes will be major ones and will be closely related to similar changes in the college curriculum.

Although some of the changes will be challenging, they should not be frightening. Rather, they should increase your enjoyment of teaching and your sense of accomplishment. The subject matter of the new mathematics of the 1980s has almost nothing in common with that of the 1960s. It is based not on abstract notions of what students need to know but rather on concrete developments in the world of science and technology that are affecting what young people *must* know if they are to survive in the tough economics of the twenty-first century.

Let us begin by considering, as briefly as possible, the college mathematics curriculum—what it has been, what it is today, and particularly where it is going. Not only must a major purpose of the high school curriculum be to prepare students for the college curriculum, but also the same forces that are shaping changes in the college curriculum are also influencing the secondary school curriculum.

## THE COLLEGE MATHEMATICS CURRICULUM:
## SOME HISTORY AND PREDICTIONS

It was well into the 1950s before calculus became the standard freshman mathematics course. For the first half of this century the more common freshman course was college algebra. But the great impetus given to science (particularly physics) and technology by World War II markedly increased the importance of the physical sciences and engineering at universities. For students wishing to major in these areas or even take courses in them, it became important that they take calculus in their freshman year so that they could, for example, take college physics concurrently.

But even before calculus became the standard freshman course, it was the fulcrum of all college mathematics. This was not because all higher mathematics depended on calculus; a considerable amount did—and does—but an even greater amount did not. Rather it was because—

1. the astounding successes of applications of classical analysis meant that

calculus was that mathematical subject one had to know if one was interested at all in applied mathematics directly or in any of the disciplines where the applications of mathematics played a major role;

2. a belief, almost religious it sometimes seems, that, better than any other subject in mathematics, calculus develops mathematical sophistication and maturity (whatever they are!).

The second of these reasons, like most beliefs in education, had no factual evidence whatsoever to back it up. But the undeniable cogency of the first reason has allowed the second to stand unchallenged for a quarter century or more. But now the merits of the first reason are being challenged, and, thus, the whole calculus edifice is starting to crumble.

Calculus is no longer the obvious starting point for the study of applied mathematics itself or for the study of those disciplines where mathematics is heavily applied. This is because the advent of computers and computer science has meant two things:

1. The single largest source of problems for applied mathematicians today and the foreseeable future is directly related to applications of digital computers. These applications are overwhelmingly of discrete mathematics. This is not to say that the physical world is not still the source of many problems in applied mathematics and neither is it to say that classical applied mathematics does not have many triumphs ahead of it (it does); it is just to say that the "unnatural" world of computers is now and will continue to be a larger source of problems for applied mathematicians than the natural world. Current patterns of research in applied mathematics provide support for this contention (Ralston 1981b).

2. Computer science students are, with the possible exception of engineers, the largest group of American undergraduates who need considerable amounts of mathematics in their professional training (and the popularity of computer science is no passing fad—it is here to stay as a major academic discipline); calculus is not the place for computer science students to start their study of mathematics because it is generally unsupportive of the undergraduate curriculum in computer science. Discrete mathematics, however, provides such support and, in addition, supports the curricula in a variety of other disciplines such as the social and management sciences and including even the physical sciences and engineering.

Thus, in the future discrete mathematics will play a role equal to that of calculus in the first two undergraduate years of mathematics. Indeed, there is movement in that direction and some signs that it is accelerating:

1. At a conference at Williams College in the summer of 1982, a number of leading mathematicians and mathematics educators discussed the future of the first two years of the college mathematics curriculum from a variety of perspectives. The proceedings of that conference (Ralston and Young 1983) provide cogent support for this argument.

2. In the summer of 1983, the Alfred P. Sloan Foundation made grants to six colleges and universities—Colby College, University of Delaware, University of Denver, Florida State University, Montclair State College, and St. Olaf College—that submitted proposals (in a competition involving thirty institutions) to revamp the first two years of their college mathematics curriculum to provide a balance between the classical curriculum and discrete mathematics. It is too early to report results from this program, but if these six institutions appear to have successful new curricula (however defined or measured), then similar programs will no doubt be adopted by numerous other colleges and universities.

There is more evidence than this. Several surveys indicate that many other institutions in the United States and elsewhere are moving toward more discrete mathematics in their basic undergraduate mathematics curriculum.

## Discrete Mathematics

Before getting to the main subject of this chapter, it may be helpful to define discrete mathematics at some length. A considerable amount of discrete mathematics is already familiar to high school mathematics teachers, and, indeed, some is commonly taught now in the high school mathematics curriculum:

1. *Combinatorics.* Basic material on permutations, combinations, and the binomial theorem are part of secondary school mathematics now. In a freshman or sophomore discrete mathematics course more comprehensive material on these subjects would be covered (e.g., permutations and combinations with repetitions) as well as more advanced topics, such as the multinomial theorem, counting problems involving such things as partitions of sets or integers, the principle of inclusion and exclusion, and combinatorial algorithms for such tasks as generating all permutations of a particular kind.

2. *Discrete probability.* This is a very important topic in discrete mathematics. Building on simple notions of probability developed in high school mathematics, one would cover in a discrete mathematics course discrete probability distributions like the binomial or Poisson, the notion of expectation (including mean and variance), and applications such as simple queueing theory, random number generation, and the analysis of simple algorithms.

3. *Mathematical induction.* This is a topic of profound importance in discrete mathematics both because induction is *the* quintessential proof technique in discrete mathematics and because the development of inductive reasoning skills is very important in discrete mathematics. Mathematical induction is often discussed in secondary school mathematics now, but more emphasis on it is in order.

4. *Linear and abstract algebra.* Aspects of matrix algebra are often part of high school mathematics as are some aspects of linear algebra (e.g., solving

simultaneous equations and simple linear programming). These topics would be dealt with in more depth in a college course, where linear programming, for example, might get considerable attention. Subject matter from abstract algebra sometimes finds its way into high school mathematics now (e.g., groups), and such material is a common component of college discrete mathematics courses. Most, if not all, of this material is better left to the third and fourth years of college because, important and applicable though it is, most of the applications cannot be made relevant or meaningful until fairly advanced undergraduate courses have been taken.

This list is not comprehensive but should convince secondary teachers that much of the subject matter of discrete mathematics is familiar. Other important areas of discrete mathematics that should be taught to freshmen and sophomores is probably much less familiar:

1. *Graph theory*. This branch of mathematics, which deals with structures consisting of *nodes* and the *edges* joining them, has myriad applications, such as in all kinds of networking problems (e.g., traffic networks). A particular type of graph called a *tree* is ubiquitous in computer science applications. (See fig. 3.1.) Many problems not obviously couched in graph theoretic terms become much more tractable when they are. (A famous example is the four-color theorem.)

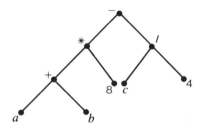

Fig. 3.1  Ordered tree representation of $(a + b) * 8 - c/4$

2. *Difference equations and recurrence relations*. These are most simply understood as the discrete analogs of differential equations. As recurrence relations they are probably familiar through such topics as Fibonacci numbers. Recursion and difference equations are discussed at length in chapter 8 of this volume.

Other areas of discrete mathematics are mathematical logic (including Boolean algebra) and sequences and series (including limits). A more extensive discussion of discrete mathematics can be found in Ralston and Young (1983). Be warned, however, that there is no monolithic agreement among mathematicians on exactly what is subsumed, and what is not, under the rubric of discrete mathematics.

## THE IMPACT OF COLLEGE CURRICULUM CHANGE
## ON THE HIGH SCHOOL CURRICULUM

Geometry, algebra, and trigonometry are the mainstays of high school mathematics, and the possible changes in the college curriculum alluded to above will not change this. They will still be the "basics." Nevertheless, some modest adjustments of the curriculum would be desirable to prepare students for a changed college curriculum:

1. Whatever the relevance of the subject matter itself, an important reason for studying Euclidean plane geometry in high school has always been to give students their first introduction to formal deductive reasoning. Since this is a valid reason for teaching geometry, changes in the college curriculum will not lessen this motivation for geometry as part of the secondary school mathematics curriculum. The only change in the geometry curriculum that might be suggested by the introduction of discrete mathematics into the college curriculum would be to introduce some basic graph theory (where "graph" is as used above). Such material could be nicely integrated into a geometry course and could be made to seem more relevant and interesting to students than much of the standard material.

2. Algebra is probably even more important as preparation for discrete mathematics than it is for calculus, since algebraic manipulation plays an important role in many areas of discrete mathematics. Probably little change is indicated in the syllabus of high school algebra courses.

3. Trigonometry plays a lesser role in discrete mathematics than in calculus, but a knowledge of basic trigonometry is still necessary in discrete mathematics. No significant curriculum changes in high school trigonometry are implied by a changed college curriculum.

The one place in the high school mathematics curriculum where a new college curriculum may necessitate real change is in Advanced Placement programs. For some years at least, a new college curriculum for the first two years will take the form of two separate one-year sequences, one in calculus and one in discrete mathematics. AP calculus will thus still be an alternative to the former, although the reduction of three or four terms of calculus to two will imply some changes in both the AB and the BC Advanced Placement calculus syllabi. It seems likely that before too many years have passed, Educational Testing Service (ETS) will develop an AP discrete mathematics course as an alternative to the one-year discrete mathematics sequence mentioned above. When that happens, high school mathematics departments will have to decide which of the three AP courses—calculus, discrete mathematics, and computer science—they are going to offer. Few will be able to offer all three. Since the discrete mathematics and computer science courses will be mutually supportive, it may be that the trend will be to stop offering the AP calculus. In the long run, the first two years of college mathematics will find calculus and discrete mathematics *integrated* into a single two-year sequence. Then, of course, it will be necessary to revamp the high school AP program accordingly.

## THE IMPACT OF COMPUTER SCIENCE AND TECHNOLOGY ON THE HIGH SCHOOL CURRICULUM

The purpose of the previous section was to lull you into a belief that my "really new mathematics" doesn't presage major change for the high school mathematics teacher. In this section I shall try to wake you up with a start.

Microcomputer technology is becoming so powerful and so inexpensive that it will soon be possible to have micros in every classroom for whatever purposes are deemed desirable. However, the classroom revolution, if there is to be one, will be caused, not by the hardware technology itself, but rather by—

- related *software* technology;
- the influence of the paradigms and methodology of computer science on mathematics education.

The results of these two effects will be ($a$) the rapid obsolescence of important parts of the current high school curriculum and ($b$) the introduction of significantly new approaches to much of the mathematics curriculum. No high school mathematics teacher will be able to escape these effects. Although the result will afford exciting new opportunities for teachers, it is necessary to note also that there will be challenges, too, which some high school teachers of mathematics will see, probably correctly, as threats.

### Symbolic Mathematical Systems and Their Impact on High School Mathematics

Elementary school mathematics is being profoundly affected by hand calculators. Since children *will* use them, how can they be harnessed? Must we resign ourselves to a decline, perhaps a rapid one, in the manipulative arithmetic skills of American children? Even if we must, does it matter? Challenging questions these, but answers to them would be the subject of another chapter. Still, they do illustrate the reasons for the current ferment among elementary school mathematics educators.

High school mathematics teachers may have been congratulating themselves for not having to deal with similar problems. At the high school level, calculators and computers, although they may be unfamiliar still to many teachers and therefore worrisome, are not threats to cause wholesale upheaval in the curriculum but rather are potential enhancers and broadeners of the curriculum. Any changes that may occur because of computers will be modest and gradual at most, as outlined in the previous section—or so high school teachers may think. If so, they are wrong. *Symbolic mathematical systems* will have as profound an effect on the high school curriculum (and, for that matter, the college curriculum) as hand calculators are having on the elementary school curriculum. And that effect is just around the corner.

Briefly, symbolic mathematical systems are computer programs with the capacity to perform symbolically the standard processes of algebra, trigonometry, and even calculus. The examples that follow have a somewhat more readable syntax than actual symbolic systems in order to make them easily understood. However, the capabilities shown are available on most such systems.

1. These systems can do polynomial algebra—addition, subtraction, multiplication, *and* division of polynomials. For example:

   **Input:** P1(X) = X*X + 4*X
         [where the * indicates multiplication]
         P2(X) = X↑3 + X*X − 2
         [where the ↑ indicates exponentiation]
   **Command:** P1*P2
   **Output:** X↑5 + 5*X↑4 + 4*X↑3 − 2*X↑2 − 8*X

   Another example, using the same input:

   **Command:** P1(X)↑3
   **Output:** X↑6 + 12*X↑5 + 48*X↑4 + 64*X↑3

   Such systems can do considerably more sophisticated operations on polynomials than what is shown in the examples above. For example:

   **Command:** PARTIAL FRACTION (P1(X)/P2(X))
   **Output:** 1/(X−1) + 2/(X↑2 + 2*X + 2)

2. Trigonometric manipulations are duck soup for such systems:

   **Input:** SIN(X+Y) + SIN(X−Y) = ?
   **Output:** 2*SIN(X)*COS(Y)
   **Input:** SIN(ARCCOS(X)) = ?
   **Output:** SQRT(1 − X↑2)

3. They can also do symbolic equation solving:

   **Input:** SOLVE (A*X + 4*B = 7 FOR X)
   **Output:** X = (7 − 4*B)/A

   Of course, if the equation contains just numbers, the numerical answer will be given:

   **Input:** SOLVE (5*X + 7 = 11 FOR X)
   **Output:** X = 4/5

   Note the answer of 4/5 rather than .8. Symbolic systems always try to give numerical answers that are exact rational numbers rather than decimals, which must sometimes be rounded.

4. Considerable calculus capabilities are available, too. For example:

   **Input:** F(X) = X*SIN(X)
   **Command:** DIF(F(X) WRT X)
   **Output:** X*COS(X) + SIN(X)

If instead the input had been DIF(X∗SIN(X) WRT X), the output would have been as shown. As another example using the same input:

**Command:** INTEGRATE (F(X) WRT X)

**Output:** SIN(X) − X∗COS(X)

Since analytic integration is not entirely algorithmic, symbolic systems will fail for some integrands (even on the one above for some simple systems). But the best symbolic systems (one called MACSYMA, developed at M.I.T., is perhaps the best known and most powerful) can do analytic integration better than most professors of mathematics, and this will soon be true of systems available on micros, the best known of which currently is called muMATH. For a very readable article on the facilities of muMATH, see Wilf (1982); for an article showing how muMATH can be used in calculus courses, see Heid (1983). The latter will suggest similar uses in high school mathematics.

Though the examples above give only a very rudimentary idea of the flavor of symbolic mathematical systems, they do illustrate that large chunks of the symbolic manipulations that are an important part of high school algebra and trigonometry are now available on microcomputers. Moreover, they will soon be available to students on hand-held computers, which in the near future will be as common as hand-held calculators are today. If this idea of symbolic mathematics by computer is surprising, it is probably because most people still think of computers as essentially numerical engines, whereas actually they are—and always have been—quite general *symbol manipulators*.

What are the implications of such systems for high school mathematics? The first one is that before very long students will be using these symbolic systems to do much of the algebraic and trigonometric manipulations that play such an important role today in high school mathematics. Now one could try to finesse this problem, as some elementary school teachers have, by forbidding their use or by requiring that students do these manipulations by hand on tests. Neither approach would succeed, nor should we wish it to succeed. No sound argument can be adduced to support a thesis that claims that high school students must be very skillful at polynomial algebra, trigonometric identities, the solution of linear or quadratic equations or systems of equations, or *any* of the myriad manipulative tasks that are part of the current high school mathematics curriculum.

Strong words. Does this mean that it doesn't matter whether students understand how to add two polynomials or solve two equations in two unknowns or why $\sin(x + y) = \sin x \cos y + \cos x \sin y$? Not at all; it means only that they don't have to be very good at *doing* the manipulations. Pure casuistry, you may say. How can students understand these things if they aren't good at doing them? And this is the crux of the matter. How much correlation is there between *understanding* mathematics and being a good *manipulator* of the mathematics one wants to understand? Although very little is known about this (very difficult) question, most mathematics educators believe that the correlation between good manipulative abilities and an understanding of the underlying mathematics is quite low. Considerably more research needs to be done on this question. But let me ask: How many students have learned to perform the manipulative tasks but had little perception of what was going on, little "feeling" for the mathematics itself? I suspect this is a quite common phenomenon. If so, then there is just no point in spending a lot of time trying to achieve a high level of manipulative skills when these can be performed by a hand-held computer.

## Significant portions of the . . . curriculum in which algebraic and trigonometric manipulations are stressed must be sharply curtailed.

Still, it may be argued that we teach manipulative skills in high school not just to try to promote better understanding of mathematics but to give students skills they will need to use at work or just in ordinary living. Certainly learning to do arithmetic once had this motivation even if the doer didn't really understand numbers or the processes involved in any depth. But just as the hand calculator has meant that being a good arithmetician has little or no societal value, the hand-held symbol manipulators of the (near) future will mean that the kinds of manipulations listed above will shortly have *almost no societal value.* So, if they have no societal value and if they do not facilitate mathematical understanding, why teach them at all?

This argument leads to the main curricular implication of symbolic mathematical systems. Significant portions of the high school mathematics curriculum in which algebraic and trigonometric manipulations are stressed must be sharply curtailed. (A similar conclusion holds about much of the calculus curriculum, too.) What should replace this material? One example will give the general flavor. High school students now routinely learn how to solve systems of two or even three linear equations in the same number of unknowns. Even if they are taught to do this by an elimination method, seldom does much understanding of the general problem result. (Sometimes determinants are still used in this context, but that is not defensible on any grounds.) There is no reason, however, why high school students cannot learn to solve $n$ linear equations in $n$ unknowns by Gaussian elimination. The calculations are easily carried out on hand computers, and the more general problem is much more interesting and its solution much more conducive to mathematical understanding. In fact, the general theorem on the solution of $n$ linear equations in $m$ unknowns, which is a staple of college linear algebra courses, is well within the grasp of high school juniors or seniors. This example illustrates a general proposition: The more that routine calculation and manipulation can be done by a machine, the more that real mathematics comes within the purview of the student at any level.

Indeed, it is often true that the generalizations of simple problems are easier to understand than the special cases, and such generalizations are almost always much more useful to the student mathematically than the special cases. Thus, software technology, in the form of symbolic mathematical systems, will allow the high school curriculum to include mathematics that was previously beyond its reach because the related manipulations and calculations could not reasonably be performed. Moreover, the focus of all mathematics teaching must soon become teaching students to understand mathematics rather than teaching them to manipulate symbols; that's what computers are for.

### The Impact of Computer Science on High School Mathematics

The emergence of computer science as an intellectual discipline requires that a substantial part of school mathematics be reconsidered from the perspective of computer science, particularly from an algorithmic standpoint. In an algorithmic approach to teaching, teachers must do more than just teach a procedure for doing some task. They must also—

- use a *language* to express the algorithm that has sufficient generality to be applied to a variety of problems;
- show students how to *develop* the algorithm and not just tell them what it is; that is, students must understand the "why" as well as the "how";
- consider how to *analyze* the algorithm to discover its salient properties (such as its efficiency), although, of course, this analysis will not be very sophisticated for most high school mathematics.

By these criteria, little of what is now done in primary or secondary school mathematics could be said to be taught algorithmically.

At the precollege level it is possible to start quite early with a simple but somewhat formal notation for algorithms (see, for example, Engle [1983]). For a concrete example, let me use the secondary school curriculum. The solution of quadratic equations is still a staple of the secondary school curriculum, and most high school—and college—mathematics instructors consider it a straightforward, cut-and-dried problem. But it is not. Assume that the quadratic formula has been derived and that we want to teach students how to use it. The right way is *not* to tell them to plug in the coefficients and calculate the square root together with the usual discussion of real and complex roots. Figure 3.2 displays an algorithm to solve quadratic equations. It contains two lessons that I think few high school mathematics students are taught:

1. The first you may think trivial—namely, that under the assumption that the three coefficients can be *any* real numbers (or even any integers), the special cases of $a = 0$, $b = 0$, or both must be considered. This aspect of algorithmic thinking—that *all* possible cases of the data must be handled—is a lesson that cannot be taught too often. It lies at the heart of all good problem solving and, of course, is a sine qua non for all good computer use.

The development of the algorithm in figure 3.2 is a good one to have students do themselves. Unless they have been introduced earlier to the importance of considering all cases, almost none will design the checks for $a$ and $b$ in their first version.

```
Input       a, b, c                              [Coefficients of ax² + bx + c]
Algorithm
  if a=0 then
                if b=0 then output
                        'degenerate equation'; stop
                      else output
                        'one root', −c/b; stop
                endif
        else
                disc ← b² − 4ac                          [Discriminant]
                if disc < 0 then
                        output 'complex roots'
                               'real part', −b/(2a)
                               'imaginary part', √−disc/(2a)
                           else
                        output 'real roots'
                        if b < 0 then
                            x1 ← (−b + √disc)/(2a)            [Larger root]
                               else
                            x1 ← (−b − √disc)/(2a)
                        endif
                        x2 ← c/(a∗x1)                        [Smaller root]
                        output x1, x2
                endif
  endif
  stop
```

Fig. 3.2. A quadratic equation algorithm

2.  The case of two real roots provides an important and much more subtle lesson. Why is the smaller (in magnitude) real root calculated not using the quadratic formula but rather using the result that the product of the two roots is $c/a$? Because this enables the smaller root to be calculated accurately in cases where the quadratic formula fails to do so when $b$ is much larger than $4ac$. This lesson is easily demonstrated using hand calculators and provides insight into the general rule that even the simplest problems often have hidden subtleties. This idea is well within the grasp of secondary school students but is unlikely to be taught unless the algorithmic approach is stressed.

Another lesson implicit in figure 3.2 is that a good notation for algorithms is understandable with little explanation even to someone who has not seen it before. Figure 3.2 by no means captures all the subtleties of the quadratic equation problem. See, for example, the excellent review of it in Forsythe (1967).

> Although clear and precise thinking is a hallmark of mathematics, a stress on algorithmic thinking brings a clarity and precision to mathematics teaching greater than what is normally present.

A distinguished mathematician said to me not long ago that he had never realized the subtlety inherent in so homely a problem as solving quadratic equations until he heard a computer scientist describe it. What he meant was that although clear and precise thinking is a hallmark of mathematics, a stress on algorithmic thinking brings a clarity and precision to mathematics teaching greater than what is normally present. Much more will be heard about the algorithmic approach to teaching high school mathematics in the next few years. All high school mathematics teachers will have to adapt to this approach if they wish to avoid shortchanging their students. For more on the algorithmic approach, see Maurer (1984, in press).

Computer science has considerably more to offer to the teaching of mathematics than just the stress on the algorithmic approach. Among the other paradigms stressed by computer science, the only one space allows to be mentioned here is the inductive approach to mathematics. Particularly in problems in discrete mathematics, the following paradigm is a very powerful approach to problem solving:

1. *Compute* some sample cases of the problem at hand. (A simple example: Compute the number of subsets of sets with one, two, three, and four elements.)
2. Conjecture some generalization based on these results (i.e., that the number of subsets of a set with $n$ elements is $2^n$).
3. Prove the correctness of the conjecture (if it is true) by some normal deductive process.

By itself, but even more so combined with the algorithmic approach to mathematics, this paradigm provides a powerful tool to teach high school students logical, structured thinking and the idea of a mathematical proof. Since these are exactly the values often claimed for geometry and since the relevance of the material amenable to the approach above is much greater than that of most of geometry, it will not be too many years before plane geometry is relegated to one semester in the high school mathematics curriculum.

## WHAT SHOULD HIGH SCHOOL MATHEMATICS TEACHERS DO?

The crisis in science and science teaching in primary and secondary schools is receiving wide publicity (see, for example, the reports of the Conference Board of the Mathematical Sciences [CBMS 1982] and the National Science Board Commission on Precollege Education in Science, Mathematics and Technology [NSB 1983]). While awaiting action to alleviate this crisis, it will, at least, be desirable to implement (gradually) the changes recommended in this chapter. At least three things need to be done:

1. Good, new textbooks must be written by knowledgeable high school and college mathematics educators.

2. The schools of education and mathematics departments throughout the United States must revamp their mathematics education programs to require discrete mathematics and some computer science in programs for mathematics teachers.

3. Teachers already in service need to learn to live with—and maybe love—the hardware, the software, and the ideas of computer science.

### REFERENCES

Conference Board of the Mathematical Sciences. *Report to National Science Board Commission on Precollege Education in Mathematics, Science and Technology.* Washington, D.C.: The Board, 1982.

Engel, Arthur. *The Impact of Algorithms on Mathematics Teaching.* Proceedings of the Fourth International Congress on Mathematics Education. Boston: Birkhauser, 1983.

Forsythe, George E. "What Is a Satisfactory Quadratic Equation Solver?" Technical Report No. CS 74. Stanford, Calif.: Computer Science Department, Stanford University, 1967.

Heid, M. Kathleen. "Calculus with muMath: Implications for Curriculum Reform." *Computing Teacher* 11 (November 1983): 46–49.

Maurer, Stephen B. "The Algorithmic Way of Life Is Best." *College Mathematics Journal,* in press.

————. "Two Meanings of Algorithmic Mathematics." *Mathematics Teacher* 77 (September 1984): 430–35.

Technology. *Educating Americans for the Twenty-first Century.* Washington, D.C.: National Science Foundation, 1983.

Ralston, Anthony. "Computer Science, Mathematics, and the Undergraduate Curricula in Both." *American Mathematical Monthly* 88 (1981a): 472–85.

————. "Computer Science, Mathematics, and the Undergraduate Curricula in Both." Technical Report No. 161 (an expanded version of the previous reference). Buffalo, N.Y.: State University of New York at Buffalo, Department of Computer Science, 1981b.

————. "Will Mathematics Surpass Calculus in Importance?" *College Mathematics Journal* 15 (November 1984): 371–82.

Ralston, Anthony, and Gail S. Young, eds. *The Future of College Mathematics: Proceedings of a Conference /Workshop on the First Two Years of College Mathematics.* New York: Springer-Verlag, 1983.

Wilf, Herbert S. "The Disc with the College Education." *American Mathematical Monthly* 89 (1982): 4–8.

# 4

# Rethinking the Sequence and Priorities of High School Mathematics Curricula

James T. Fey
Richard A. Good

IN THE past three years numerous local, state, and national advisory committees have produced policy analyses critical of education, particularly mathematics and science education. Each description of the crisis comes with its own view of the problems. The common ingredient in most proposals is a call for a return to presumably more successful practices of an earlier period. Colleges and universities in many states are working with secondary schools to establish detailed specifications of mathematics courses that could be adopted by all schools and monitored by uniform testing. Such recommendations, supported enthusiastically by representatives from both secondary schools and higher education, have generally prescribed a traditional agenda of algebra, geometry, trigonometry, and analytic geometry.

Our own position is a sharp dissent from such "more of the same" strategies. We are convinced that however comforting such conservatism and stability might be, they represent an inadequate response to the strong challenges we face. The world of mathematics, science, and technology has changed dramatically in the past twenty years. To assure that our students are prepared for the future, we must reexamine the content, organization, and emphases of our programs. We believe that such reexamination will justify new, strikingly different school curricula and, further, that these new curricula will attract students who find current offerings very unappealing.

The case for fundamental reform becomes apparent in any careful analysis that compares current school mathematics offerings to the technology-rich environment in which mathematical ideas and methods are now used. The new programs we envision are best characterized by selected illustrative examples.

Work on this paper was supported in part by the National Science Foundation under NSF Award No. SED80-24425 (DISE). Any opinions, findings, conclusions, or recommendations expressed herein are those of the authors and do not necessarily reflect the views of the National Science Foundation.

## CURRENT CONTENT AND PROCESS GOALS

The most common college preparatory mathematics program in U.S. high schools is probably some modest variation on the following basic scheme: algebra 1, Euclidean geometry, algebra 2, trigonometry, analytic geometry, elementary functions, and calculus. Depending on their aptitudes and interests, students drop out at various points along this path to calculus. Some encounter statistics as a post–algebra 2 option, and an increasing number choose "computer math" as an option to traditional core mathematics.

To describe fully the character of this traditional program, as it is delivered to most students, it is essential to look beneath the content labels to the cognitive processes that are stressed in each topic area. Although our view might be challenged, it seems fair to say that current curricula are dominated by computational algorithms in arithmetic and by transformation of symbolic expressions in algebra, trigonometry, analytic geometry, and calculus. The objectives of comprehension, problem solving, and analysis are not prominent, despite formal attention to such goals in our published statements of philosophy. Any doubt about this should be removed by a survey of the tests mathematics teachers use. For most students, the real message of a course is in the content of its examinations, and in most mathematics exams the dominant requirement is to recite facts or demonstrate skills that have been carefully modeled and practiced. Even teachers who admit the diminished importance of routine skills in the modern mathematical world commonly argue that higher level objectives cannot be taught effectively until a broad base of factual knowledge and skills has been established.

It seems clear to us that the demonstrated and promised capabilities of computers and related information technology change the assumptions on which this traditional program is based. Although the new situation does not require completely reshaping the topics and organization of current curricula, it does call for substantial change in what we offer. Technology opens effective ways to teach important new topics and new ways to approach traditional topics. It offers both a means and a reason for change. Consider the following possibilities and challenges.

## NEW TOPICS AND PRIORITIES

The impact of computing on mathematics can be seen in every major content strand of the subject. We suggest some major changes that seem advisable in two areas and give a more specific description of a new approach to another.

### Geometry and Computing

Geometry has been a troubled strand of the curriculum for many years. Despite bold proposals for new approaches, the standard experience of most students is still limited to a modest taste of informal geometry and measurement in middle school and the formal Euclidean style of deductive course in high school. Only students who pursue mathematics as a special subject will learn more than a little of coordinate, transformation, or vector methods; the treatment of geometry in three-space is generally neglected for all.

Computers, of course, use coordinate methods extensively, often to describe situations in which the transformation of objects is a central activity (e.g., CAD/CAM or space flight). Vectors are a fundamental tool also. Furthermore, computer-generated graphics make instruction in these alternative geometry tools and concepts attractive in special new ways. Computer assistance makes the basic ideas of trigonometry (both triangle and periodic function aspects) readily accessible. It seems highly desirable to put these intellectual tools in the hands of students far earlier.

What we propose is a new way to look at the content and organization of geometry. Instead of a linear progression through the traditional deductive sequence, we suggest an approach that places problems of shape and position in space at the center of the curriculum and seeks to give students an array of intellectual tools to address those problems. Given a geometry problem, students should be able to recognize and use effectively the geometric concepts and methods (synthetic, vector, coordinate, or transformation) most appropriate to the situation (fig. 4.1).

Providing such an alternative in geometry education will require a radical reorientation of the goals, methods, and materials that most teachers use. What is probably required is a collection of geometry modules, each developing the concepts, principles, and problem-solving or reasoning methods of a specific approach, such as those shown in figure 4.1. The formal logical organization of this knowledge can be effectively given through short local axiomatic sequences rather than the ponderous year-long trek of current courses. The implied change is striking, but it seems timely and feasible in the computer environment of the near future.

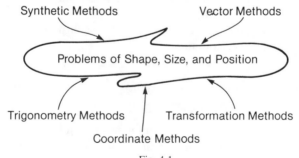

Fig. 4.1

## Statistics and Computing

One of the astonishing influences of computers on decision-making processes of government, business, and industry is the vastly increasing use of various management information systems. Because computers have the capacity to collect, organize, and manipulate very large and complex data sets, people are coming to expect that such information will be routinely available. This sharpens the need for *every* educated person to understand a variety of fundamental concepts of descriptive and inferential statistics. Some courses in high school mathematics curricula contain elements of descriptive statistics, and a mathematics elective (usually available to advanced students) will give a semester of statistics. Weighed against the usefulness of other traditional mathematics topics, statistics should rank far higher in curriculum priorities than it now does. Further, the power of computers makes such study very attractive to young students. Realistic data sets can be manipulated in a variety of numerical, logical, and graphic ways as students begin to acquire the critical understandings basic to random phenomena. We must find new curriculum structures that place such objectives in prominent positions.

## Algebra and Computing

As we mentioned earlier, there can be little doubt that the driving force behind curricular decisions in high school mathematics is the goal of preparing students for the study of calculus. A great deal of the manipulative skill in algebra, trigonometry, and analytic geometry is clearly prized because of its usefulness in calculus, or at least calculus as it has been traditionally conceived. But this entire interlocking directorate of mathematical concepts and skills has been shaken vigorously by intelligent symbolic mathematics systems that perform the routine manipulations that we currently spend long hours training students to execute with mechanical proficiency. If computers can do algebraic manipulations like factoring, solving equations (including those with literal coefficients), and operating on matrices, the importance of developing student skill in those areas is seriously questioned. If, further, the same type of program exists to do differentiation, integration, Taylor series expansion, or limit evaluations in calculus, traditional curricula seem to collapse like a house of cards.

The muMath package of programs provides such power in easy-to-use format. For instance, the command

$$\text{SOLVE}(X \wedge 2 + 5*X + 6 == 0, X)$$

yields solutions to the quadratic equation, $x^2 + 5x + 6 = 0$, and

$$\text{DIF}(X \wedge 2 + 5*X + 6, X)$$

gives the derivative of the function. Commands of equal simplicity perform the other operations of algebra and calculus and readily digest more complex functions. All this is available now on microcomputers at moderate cost, but soon we can expect the power in ubiquitous, inexpensive hand-held hardware.

A natural reaction is that we ought to be able to decrease the time we spend building students' manipulative skills. At the very least we should be able to identify a level of performance that is more efficiently done by humans and to consign the more complex cases to machine execution. The simple plausibility of this reasoning, however, disguises a quagmire of difficult curricular choices. One faces the almost impossible questions of "How much personal skill is enough?" and "How does proficiency in algorithmic skills influence the understanding of basic concepts?"

After wrestling with these difficult questions, we formulated an alternative proposal that we feel has tremendous promise. Questioning the future of manipulative skills in algebra, and their counterparts in trigonometry or calculus, led us to an analysis of the problem situations in which those subjects are commonly applied. We found that a small number of familiar and powerful mathematical ideas are at the heart of most common applications and, further, that a student assisted by the type of tool software available need not endure a long skill-building apprenticeship in order to become an effective problem solver—if the key organizing concepts are well understood.

## NEW CONTENT AND ORGANIZATION FOR ALGEBRA

The easiest way to describe the spirit and substance of our proposed new look in secondary school algebra is to begin with some specific illustrative examples. Consider a familiar and fundamental topic, the quadratic equation $ax^2 + bx + c = 0$. There can be no question that this quantitative model is enormously useful for describing relations among variables in a vast array of situations. Unfortunately, most secondary school students see few of those applications. If they are lucky, they will meet the classic projectile motion problem in a form like

$$-4.9t^2 + 14.7t + 19.6 = 0,$$

complete with parameters carefully chosen to give a solution to the equation by factoring and the answer to a single question: When will the projectile, with initial height 19.6 meters and initial velocity 14.7 meters per second, return to earth?

In reality, there are many other interesting questions, including the following, that might be asked about the projectile in this situation:

- When is the elevation of $m$ meters reached?
- What will be the maximum elevation and when?
- How fast will the projectile be falling at any time $t$?
- What is the average speed?

If a student approaches these questions with the computer tools now readily available, a whole new world opens up. By simply graphing or producing a table of values for the function $H(t) = -4.9t^2 + 14.7t + 19.6$, students can determine very good approximations for the desired quantities. Questions that are major issues in elementary calculus can be studied by students who have endured none of the laborious skill-building that is ordinary preparation for that subject.

What algebra students *do* need as preparation for the questions about projectile motion is a fundamental change in their view about the nature and uses of algebraic expressions. Traditional high school algebra deals almost exclusively with questions of the form "Find $x$ that makes a well-behaved expression equal to zero." This "find $x$" mentality misses a crucial point about the sources of mathematical questions—the study of relations among two or more quantitative variables, frequently functional relations. The expression $-4.9t^2 + 14.7t + 19.6$ is of interest not only for the single positive value of $t$ that makes it zero. It provides useful information for any value of $t$ within a reasonable domain. It expresses a dynamic relation between quantities that *vary*, not a static condition disguising a fixed but unknown number.

Computing [can] turn the mathematics curriculum on its head. . . . students can begin now with the most natural and motivating aspect of mathematics—its applications.

The questions that one would ask about the quadratic function have structural analogs in the other familiar classes of elementary functions. For instance, the tides in an ocean harbor are described roughly by functions like

$$W(t) = 3 \sin (0.5t) + 20.$$

In studying this function, we naturally ask for the value of $W$ at some specified time $t$, the value of $t$ that yields some specified water depth $W$, the time and value of maximum or minimum depth, the rate of change in water depth at a specified time $t$, and the average water depth. Again, a computer-generated graph or table of values for the function is an effective tool for answering the interesting range of questions.

The pattern underlying these two illustrations, and many others involving elementary functions, is as follows:

For a given function $f(x)$, find—

1. $f(x)$ for $x = a;$
2. $x$ so that $f(x) = a;$
3. $x$ so that maximum or minimum values of $f(x)$ occur;
4. the rate of change in $f$ near $x = a;$
5. the average value of $f$ over the interval $(a, b)$.

For nearly every function of interest, computer utilities make all five questions accessible in some intellectually honest and mathematically powerful form to students who have not followed the conventional regimen of skill development. They open a fast track to the polynomial, trigonometric, exponential, and algebraic functions that model interesting phenomena in the physical, biological, economic, and social worlds. Computing offers an opportunity to turn the secondary school mathematics curriculum on its head. Instead of meeting applications as a reward for years of preparation, students can begin now with the most natural and motivating aspect of mathematics—its applications.

The new curriculum structure that this environment makes possible replaces the manipulative skill program in algebra with a study of the major families of elementary functions. For each type of function, we envision a developmental sequence like the following:

### Stage 1. *Recognition and mathematization of relations*

Through an exploration of motivating situations in which quantitative relations are modeled well by rules of the type in focus (linear, quadratic, trigonometric, etc.), students can develop the ability to identify functional relations and to express those relations in suitable mathematical form. Their mathematization skills should include the translation of rules or physical principles into function expressions ($d = rt$, $V = IR$, etc.) but also the realistic and important strategy of fitting functions to experimental data (using a curve-fitting computer utility).

### Stage 2. *Answering questions about functions*

Strategies for studying function behavior can progress from informal mental approximation to the use of sophisticated computer utilities: first guess and test by hand, then computer-generated tables of values and graphs, then exact solution by computer programs like muMath or TK!Solver.

### Stage 3. *Formal organization and verification*

A structured summary of principles and methods discovered in exploratory work can highlight powerful generalizations that help students retain and expand their mathematical understanding. The important properties of each family of functions and of all functions taken together (number and location of zeros, extrema, operations of combination, etc.) can be formally stated and verified by methods of deductive mathematics. This phase of activity will also raise new questions and stimulate further investigations in the exploratory-to-confirmatory cycle.

Although such a curriculum would represent a radical departure from current school mathematics programs, it offers a number of powerful advantages. It begins with real-world situations and promises the best motivation: learning something obviously useful. It sidesteps the almost unsolvable question of "How much technique is enough?" by allowing students to progress as far as their needs and interests permit. It stresses informal, easy-to-remember, and powerful successive approximation and graphic methods that should do much to build the intuition our students so often miss in our haste to teach manipulative rules for the many algorithms required by formal methods. Finally, it places the function concept at the heart of the curriculum, preparing students for the dynamic, global quantitative thinking that typifies most models they will encounter in future mathematics and its applications.

The array of computer utilities available for mathematics also offers an invitation to include in the algebra curriculum many new topics that, because of their computational complexity, have usually been judged beyond all but the best high school and early college students. One of the most striking new possibilities is the fitting of function rules to scatter plots of realistic data by a least-squares procedure. For instance, in many business problems a relation of crucial importance is the demand curve relating price ($p$) and projected sales ($s$) of a product. The typical class procedure is to present such a rule with the familiar introduction, "Suppose $s = -1000p + 15\ 000$." Such equations routinely drop out of the mathematical sky on skeptical students. As a result, what was intended to be an illustration of mathematics at work becomes simply another exercise in symbol manipulation, since students need not confront the meaning of the variables or the complexities of discovering a good predictive demand curve. Genuine demand curves undoubtedly come from market research surveys that produce approximately linear scatter plots of (price, sales) pairs (fig. 4.2). Students can readily understand the principle of a least-squares fit to such data, and with computer assistance in the calculations, they can use the method to get a far more realistic and vivid applications experience.

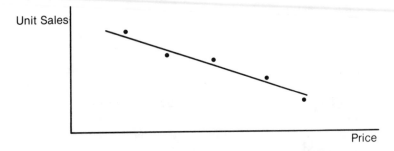

Fig. 4.2

The use of computer mathematical tools relieves the tedium of complex calculations, but it also presents new challenges that demand higher-level analytical thinking. For instance, the family of optimal assignment problems present situations of the following sort:

> Given a complex task with $m$ jobs and a pool of $n$ potential workers, what assignment of workers to jobs is "best"?

Commonly, each possible pairing of a worker and a job is given a rating (effectiveness or cost), expressible by an $m \times n$ array from which choices must be made. If each worker can be assigned at most one job, the problem is to select one entry in each job row and at most one in each worker column with the criterion that total effectiveness be maximized (or cost minimized).

The naive approach to this problem would be to evaluate the effectiveness or cost of each possible assignment. This strategy might be suitable for very small values of the parameters $m$ and $n$. For slightly larger $m$ and $n$, a computer will help in comparing the possibilities. However, for realistic parameter values, the number of combinations to be checked grows so large that such exhaustive searching is impractical, even by computer. Instead, thoughtful analysis is required to reduce the problem to manageable size. Algebraic concepts, principles, and methods play a crucial role in this process. An appreciation of the need for such analytic simplification and understanding of the effects can be enhanced by explorations on sample data at computer speed.

The optimal assignment problems are only one example of the multiple variable linear problems that are important throughout mathematics and its applications. For most secondary school students today the only experience that heads in this direction is the solution of two equations in two unknowns. Because students are commonly expected to master all the techniques for identifying roots, the curriculum scarcely gets past the case of a unique root. However, converting the time-consuming algorithms to computer programs removes the shackles that confine problems to simple arithmetic and "nice looking" answers. A far broader view is gained when students are able to analyze systems with many roots and discover the richness of interrelationships that occur for $n > 2$. Further discussion of linear systems and their utility may be found in chapter 8.

Opportunities in other directions are opened with computers sharing the load. For example, many mathematical models are faithful to reality only if integral values for the variables are admitted. In current elementary algebra courses such restricted answers are achieved by the application of "regular" methods to problems with equation parameters that have been carefully planned to yield only integral solutions. With computer assistance such artificial and misleading restrictions need not dictate the problem material. Similarly, the study of systems of inequalities can be approached in efficient and realistic problem settings because the complex algebra is no longer a barrier.

We believe that each of the indicated themes should become more prominent in the algebra experience of secondary school students. First encounters can be informal problem recognition and mathematization tasks, with the computer tools helping to find specific answers and to suggest patterns worthy of formalization into theory at a later stage. As each family of concepts and methods is explored and crystallized into an organized body of mathematical results, it will provide raw material for a cycle of deeper investigations later.

## WHERE TO BEGIN?

The curriculum changes outlined above cannot take place quickly. The selection of new content and its organization must be translated into curriculum materials of demonstrable effectiveness. Even with that task accomplished there will be a major job of selling the new type of program to teachers, the public supporters of mathematics education, and the publishers of influential textbooks and tests. Work on prototypes of radical new curricula of the future is beginning. However, for those who are convinced by the logic of arguments in support of this type of curriculum change, there are ways to move in the right direction immediately.

First, many of the recommended topics in geometry and statistics now appear in commercial text materials. The problem is that they are commonly considered peripheral in importance and skipped when instructional time is running short (as it inevitably does). Finding time for coordinate, vector, or transformation geometry will mean cutting back on other topics that are supported by long tradition. In geometry, however, the choice of topics to be diminished should not be too difficult.

In algebra the prospects for eliminating some particular skills from the usual list of that subject will not be easy. [See chapter 5.] A clean break and movement to something substantially different might be easier than evolution there. Nonetheless, there are things that can be done in algebra. First, it should be easy to introduce the function concept early in algebra and to use it as a unifying theme throughout the subject. Graphs of functions can be treated throughout the course. The value of successive approximation can be demonstrated at many stages with simple computer programs and graphic methods. The concepts and methods required to deal with situations of linear complexity can be motivated and illustrated by computer-based explorations extending current "small $n$" studies.

Finally, and perhaps most important, it should be possible for every teacher to place greater stress on situations in which mathematics is used to model the structure of real-life situations. There is a growing supply of resource material for this purpose (cf., chapter 7 of this volume), and its use will force attention to important themes in the curriculum of the future.

## BIBLIOGRAPHY

Conference Board of the Mathematical Sciences. *The Mathematical Sciences Curriculum K–12: What Is Still Fundamental and What Is Not?* Washington, D.C.: CBMS, 1983.

Fey, James T., ed. *Computing and Mathematics: The Impact on Secondary School Curricula.* Reston, Va.: National Council of Teachers of Mathematics, 1984.

Fey, James, and M. Kathleen Heid. "Imperatives and Possibilities for New Curricula in Secondary School Mathematics." In *Computers in Mathematics Education,* 1984 Yearbook of the National Council of Teachers of Mathematics, edited by Viggo P. Hansen, pp. 20–29. Reston, Va.: The Council, 1984.

Heid, M. Kathleen. "Calculus with muMath." *Computing Teacher* 11 (1983): 46–49.

Ralston, Anthony, and Gail S. Young, eds. *The Future of College Mathematics.* New York: Springer-Verlag, 1983.

Usiskin, Zalman. "What Should *Not* Be in the Algebra and Geometry Curricula of Average College-bound Students?" *Mathematics Teacher* 73 (September 1980): 413–24.

# 5

# School Algebra: What Is Still Fundamental and What Is Not?

## Arthur Coxford

IN THE 1960s and 1970s, when the major effort for school mathematics reform was undertaken, the impetus for change was *Sputnik* and the race it generated to catch up with the Russians scientifically and technologically. The public—you and I—viewed our school curriculum as deficient, since it did not emphasize the basic concepts and processes of mathematics appropriately. The reform was geared to bring concepts, logic, axiomatic method, and deduction into the school curriculum more fully. This it did to a great extent but sometimes at the expense of manipulative skills and, perhaps, at the expense of the weaker students.

Since *Sputnik,* we have improved our algebra curriculum rather regularly, except for one horrible side trip into no-read, skill-oriented basic algebra in the early 1970s. Topics have been moved around in the sequence and minor changes have been made, such as a de-emphasis of Cramer's rule. For the most part, however, the algebra curriculum has become relatively standard. It emphasizes concepts underlying the procedures used to solve linear, quadratic, polynomial, and rational equations as well as the skill in applying the procedures. It emphasizes the foundation of the real numbers. It emphasizes graphical representation to tie algebra to geometry. It emphasizes the function concept and a number of specific examples. It emphasizes the solving of "story" problems in relation to all appropriate topics. This course is substantial and well designed mathematically and pedagogically.

Pressure is now building to modify algebra again. This time the basic motivation is economic, though there are scientific and technological aspects also. The argument put forward is that we are losing our superiority in the marketplace to the western Europeans and the Japanese. To compete, our nation must become technologically literate so it can produce workers who can use technology to become more productive.

The concern came to a head in May 1982 when the National Academy of Sciences and the National Academy of Engineering called for a national convocation to express concern for the improvement of the mathematics and science curricula in the schools. More than six hundred people from government, industry, and education gathered to hear forty speakers discuss the issues and suggest possible solutions. The curricular implications of this meeting were that more young people should master mathematics and science and that the mathematics they study should be useful in a workaday world dominated by technology.

## THE PRESSURE OF COMPUTER TECHNOLOGY ON ALGEBRA

At the center of this technology is the computer—in particular, the microcomputer—which is now affordable to a large portion of our population. As recently as 1980, eight times as many high school graduates planned to study computer science (4.8 percent) as mathematics (0.6 percent). Ten years earlier, the order was reversed, with the number planning to study mathematics two to three times greater. The increasing sophistication of computer technology has put pressure on algebra and the rest of the school mathematics curriculum as well. This pressure takes three forms: (1) incorporating work related to computer programming into the ongoing curriculum, (2) introducing symbolic mathematical systems, and (3) meeting the needs of computer science itself.

### Programming in the Algebra Curriculum

Schools around the country are beginning to integrate computer programming into the mathematics curriculum. Every recent algebra text series has instruction and exercise material dealing with BASIC programming. The usual tactic is to introduce commands and syntax and give an example, then ask the student to find computer solutions to other similar problems. Thus the learner may be asked to prepare a program that will solve a pair of linear equations or to graph a quadratic or to invert a general $3 \times 3$ matrix. During two years of algebra, as much as twenty-five to thirty days of instruction might be devoted to instruction in BASIC. I am not critical of this but simply note that twenty-five to thirty teaching days in algebra are lost, or 8 percent of the two years.

As time goes on, this use of computers will become more and more feasible because students will be learning the fundamentals of BASIC in the junior high school. In Michigan a subcommittee of the Superintendent's Study Committee on Mathematics and Science Education recommended in 1984 that programming in BASIC become part of the junior high school mathematics curriculum for most students.

### Symbolic Mathematical Systems

The second form of pressure is symbolic mathematical systems—computer programs or systems designed to manipulate symbol systems other than our numerical system. The most common system for microcomputer use is called muMATH. According to the user manual (muMATH 1981, iii) muMATH is a fully interactive *Symbolic Math System* that efficiently and accurately performs true algebraic and analytic operations. These operations are utterly beyond the built-in facilities of traditional scientific programming languages such as APL, BASIC, FORTRAN, PASCAL or PL/1. Unlike those languages and unlike typical scientific subroutine libraries written for them, muMATH can evaluate and simplify expressions containing variables that have not been assigned numeric values.

For example, muMATH can automatically expand expressions over a common denominator, employ trigonometric identities to simplify expressions and symbolically integrate expressions exactly. Unassigned variables in the data are carried along algebraically just as is done in algebra, trig and calculus courses. Moreover, the arithmetic performed on numerical coefficients of such variables is exact rational arithmetic for numbers exceeding 600 decimal digits.

---

Although muMATH may reduce the amount of manipulative skill needed by students, it does not reduce the level of understanding of central concepts and the ability to recognize algebraic forms.

---

For example, if you wish to simplify the expression $2y(y^2 - z) + 2z(y + z)$ using muMATH, you enter the equivalent muMATH expression

$$2 * Y * (Y \wedge 2 - Z) + 2 * Z * (Y + Z),$$

and muMATH returns

$$2 * Y \wedge 3 + 2 * Z \wedge 2.$$

muMATH can also solve equations.

To solve $x(3 + x^2) = 4x(1 + c^2) - x$ for $x$ in terms of $c$, enter

$$\text{SOLVE } (X * (3 + X \wedge 2) == 4 * X * (1 + C \wedge 2) - X, X);$$

and muMATH displays

$$\{ == -2 * C,$$
$$X == 2 * C,$$
$$X == 0\}$$

In trigonometry, muMATH will simplify

$$\text{SIN}(2 * Y) * (4 * \text{COS}(X) \wedge 3 - \text{COS}(3 * X)) + (\text{COS}(X + Y + \#PI) - \text{COS}(X - Y)) * \text{SIN}(Y)$$

to

$$4 * \text{SIN}(Y) * \text{COS}(X) * \text{COS}(Y).$$

Such programs will have an effect only to the extent that the technology is available to all. Although muMATH may reduce the amount of manipulative skill needed by students, it does not reduce the level of understanding of central concepts and the ability to recognize algebraic forms. (Maurer [1983, 164] suggests that such systems are as good as a B student in algebra two.)

Under the assumption of the availability of such systems, what concerns should we investigate before adopting the technology? The first point to note is that no one has suggested completely eliminating the teaching of algebra skills and manipulations. Usiskin (1980) suggests, for example, deleting trinomial factoring and complicated rational expressions from the algebra 1 curriculum. Fey (1983, 21) suggests that "student ability to manipulate algebraic expressions . . . needs to cover only the simpler cases of useful operations . . . and those that are needed to give students an adequate understanding of the computer-generated results." Manipulative skill would not be developed for complex exponential expressions, radical simplification, factoring quadratics, or the more complicated manipulation of rational expressions. These positions leave open the definitions of *complicated, simpler cases,* and *adequate understanding.* Thus we need to determine the level of skill necessary to make algebra comprehensible and the output of symbol systems meaningful.

The second point relates directly to the first. The manipulation of algebraic expressions, sometimes quite complex (such as in deriving the quadratic formula, generating the equation of a hyperbola from the definition, and solving a general set of two linear equations) is used in mathematics and science to explain *new* ideas. For example, can a high school physics student understand the equation for final velocity

$$V_f = \sqrt{V_i^2 + 2a\Delta s}$$

if the needed simplification of

$$\Delta s = V_i \left( \frac{V_f - V_i}{a} \right) + \frac{a}{2} \left( \frac{V_f - V_i}{a} \right)^2$$

is not available to the student? The major areas of application for mathematics need to be reviewed regarding their prerequisite skills before major changes are made.

The third point is that we do not know the psychological relationships between *procedure learning* (manipulative skill) and *concept learning* (algebraic ideas). For example, many algebra students do not thoroughly understand the concept of *variable.* Would decreasing the skill associated with manipulating variables help, hinder, or have no effect on the comprehension and use of that idea? We need to investigate this question before large segments of manipulative skills are deleted.

### The Needs of Computer Science

The third force on algebra is based in the needs of the discipline of computer science itself. The question here is whether there are topics or modes of thought fundamental to computer science that may be appropriately included in school algebra. Certainly, if seven to eight times as many seniors plan to study computer science as mathematics, some modifications to help these young people need to be considered.

In order to study computer science at the university level, the study of calculus is required. Therefore changes in the algebra curriculum must leave in place the goal of algebra as preparation for calculus. (At the University of Michigan, three semesters of calculus with a minimum grade of B− in each course is required for computer science concentration.) Of course, if the calculus sequence changes, as suggested by Ralston and Young (1983) (also see chapter 3 in this yearbook), greater pressure to modify algebra will develop.

Is there other mathematical content, not presently found in the school mathematics curriculum, that would help the computer science concentrators? One source of information is the textbooks used in discrete mathematics—a course designed especially as an initial course for computer science concentrators. One in wide use is *Mathematical Structures for Computer Science* (Gersting 1982).

This textbook indicates that its first two chapters are vital to the text but are considered review. These chapters include logic, proof techniques, sets, combinatorics, relations, functions, and graphs:

1. *Logic* includes and, or, implication, antecedent, consequent, if and only if, not, truth tables, and tautologies.
2. *Proof techniques* includes inductive reasoning, deductive reasoning, counterexample, direct proof, contrapositive, proof by contradiction, math induction.
3. *Sets* includes notation, equality, subset, proper subset, power set, ordered pairs, binary operation, unary operation, union, intersection, complement, disjoint, set identities and Cartesian product of two sets.
4. *Combinatorics* includes fundamental counting principle, permutations, factorials, combinations.
5. *Relations* includes binary relations, reflexive, symmetric, transitive, antisymmetric, partial ordering, equivalence relation, congruence modules.
6. *Functions* includes domain, codomain, map, image, preimage, range, onto, one-to-one, one-to-one and onto, equivalent, composition, permutations, inverses.
7. *Graphs* includes graphs, nodes, arcs, endpoints, loop, adjacent, isolated node, complete, path, connected, tree, directed graph, simple, adjacency matrix, Euler path.

Since these seven areas are considered review in college, we need to find them in the high school mathematics curriculum. Clearly, the work on logic is found in school geometry; so are proof techniques, with the exception of mathematical induction, which is done in senior mathematics. The set work is scattered throughout the curriculum. Most of the combinatorics is found quite late in algebra two. More complete work is often found in the senior mathematics course. The work on relations is included except for partial ordering and equivalence. Much of the function work is included—the exception being permutations as functions. None of the work on graphs as described here appears consistently in the school curriculum.

If this textbook is a fair example of what mathematics is needed in schools to prepare students for computer-oriented mathematics, then what we presently do is not too far off. The additional topics could be included in two or three weeks of instruction. Additional time may also be needed to do the thorough teaching needed for the critical topic of mathematical induction.

For the latter topic to be useful, we must break the stereotypical idea of induction being useful only with sequences and series.

## NEW EMPHASES

For the most part, mathematical ideas that are needed for computer science are already in the curriculum. But what about new emphases and different ways to look at present content? Do they exist, and, if so, what are they?

Much of the work in computer science deals with the construction, trial, efficiency, and evaluation of algorithms. A tool used in this study is the flowchart, or flow diagram. In algebra, also, algorithms are a major topic of study.

This suggests that flow-diagram descriptions of common algebraic algorithms be included in algebra. The experience of organizing the algorithm into a step-by-step procedure that considers all cases and depicts its flow can be considered an initial experience with algorithmic thinking. In teaching flow diagrams, mathematics teachers should use representation techniques that are reasonably standard in computer science. For example, the right-hand branch of a decision point always represents *true* or *yes* whether it is labeled or not. In addition, three flow-diagram structures should be emphasized: *sequence* (one step follows another); *selection* (a choice of sequence of steps is made); and *looping* (a procedure is performed until a condition is met). Figure 5.1 illustrates the flow diagram for finding the greatest common divisor of two positive integers using Euclid's algorithm.

There are many areas in algebra where flow diagrams could be used to describe the thinking in an algorithmic procedure: solving linear equations, graphing points, solving linear systems, computing with polynomials. Even those topics leading to a formula that can be evaluated to solve similar problems can be approached algorithmically through flowcharts. In these cases the formula can be thought of as a summary of the algorithm. For example, the quadratic formula is a summary of the algorithm of completing the square. Maurer (1983, 167) suggests that "an algorithmic *frame of mind* should become pervasive" in algebra. Such thinking processes are clearly applicable to computer science.

The additional new topics of recursive definition and iteration can be introduced using the flow diagram representation of algorithms. Euclid's algorithm represented in figure 5.1 illustrates recursive definition. Initially $R_0 = 35$ and $R_1 = 21$ and $n = 1$. Then $R_{n+1}$ is defined to be the remainder when $R_{n-1}$ is divided by $R_n$. Mathematically, $R_{n+1} = R_n \cdot \{R_n / R_{n-1} - [R_n / R_{n-1}]\}$. Since $R_{n+1}$ is expressed in terms of previously known values of $R_n$, it is recursively defined.

Figure 5.1 also illustrates an iterative or repetitive procedure. Since the first division by $R_1$ (21) does not yield a zero remainder, the $n$ is incremented by 1 and the procedure is repeated for the new dividend (21) and divisor

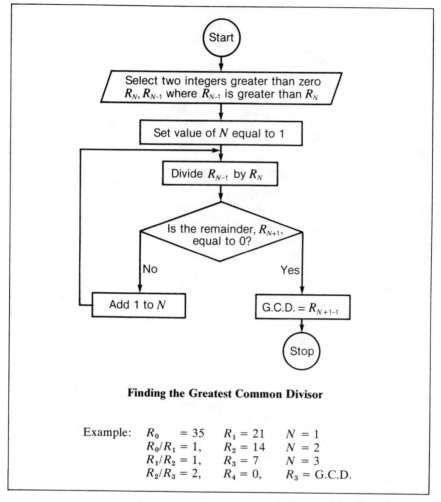

**Finding the Greatest Common Divisor**

Example: $R_0 = 35$   $R_1 = 21$   $N = 1$
$R_0/R_1 = 1,$   $R_2 = 14$   $N = 2$
$R_1/R_2 = 1,$   $R_3 = 7$   $N = 3$
$R_2/R_3 = 2,$   $R_4 = 0,$   $R_3 = $ G.C.D.

Fig. 5.1

(14). This loop is repeated until the remainder is zero. Another example of iteration will be given later.

Another area of use to computer science is the evaluation of expressions and the error introduced due to round-off or truncating procedures. Perhaps we should include in algebra alternative means of evaluating expressions that reduce the error. Consider the following tables that illustrate what round-off can do to computation in evaluating $6x^4 + 4x^3 - 5x^2 + 6x + 4$. Table 5.1 illustrates the effects of round-off error when evaluating $6x^4 + 4x^3 - 5x^2 + 6x + 4$ as we do in algebra. Table 5.2 illustrates the results when the polynomial is written

$$x(x[x\{x \cdot 6 + 4\} - 5] + 6) + 4.$$

TABLE 5.1
The Effects of Round-Off Error:  First Method

| Operation | For x = 2 No round-off | Round-off | For x = 2.05 No round-off | Round-off | For x = 2.01 No round-off |
|---|---|---|---|---|---|
| 1.  Select $x$ | 2 | 2.05 | 2.05 | 2.01 | 2.01 |
| 2. $x \cdot x = x^2$ | 4 | 4.20 | 4.2025 | 4.04 | 4.0401 |
| 3. $x^2 \cdot x = x^3$ | 8 | 8.61 | 8.615125 | 8.12 | 8.120601 |
| 4. $x^3 \cdot x = x^4$ | 16 | 17.65 | 17.66100625 | 16.32 | 16.32240801 |
| 5. $x \cdot 6 = 6x$ | 12 | 12.30 | 12.30 | 12.06 | 12.06 |
| 6. $x^2 \cdot 5 = 5x^2$ | 20 | 21.00 | 21.0125 | 20.20 | 20.2005 |
| 7. $x^3 \cdot 4 = 4x^3$ | 32 | 34.44 | 34.460500 | 32.48 | 32.482404 |
| 8. $x^4 \cdot 6 = 6x^4$ | 96 | 105.90 | 105.96603750 | 97.92 | 97.93444806 |
| 9. $6x^4$ | 96 | 105.90 | 105.96603750 | 97.92 | 97.93444806 |
| 10. $+4x^3$ | 128 | 140.34 | 140.42653750 | 130.40 | 130.41685206 |
| 11. $-5x^2$ | 108 | 119.34 | 119.41403750 | 110.20 | 110.21635206 |
| 12. $+6x$ | 120 | 131.64 | 131.71403750 | 122.26 | 122.27635206 |
| 13. $+4$ | 124 | 135.64 | 135.71403750 | 126.26 | 126.27635206 |

TABLE 5.2
The Effects of Round-Off Error:  Second Method

| Operation | For x = 2 No round-off | Round-off | For x = 2.05 No round-off | Round-off | For x = 2.01 No round-off |
|---|---|---|---|---|---|
| 1. Select $x$ | 2 | 2.05 | 2.05 | 2.01 | 2.01 |
| 2. $\cdot 6$ | 12 | 12.30 | 12.30 | 12.06 | 12.06 |
| 3. $+4$ | 16 | 16.30 | 16.30 | 16.06 | 16.06 |
| 4. $\cdot x$ | 32 | 33.42 | 33.4150 | 32.28 | 32.2806 |
| 5. $-5$ | 27 | 28.42 | 28.4150 | 27.28 | 27.2806 |
| 6. $\cdot x$ | 54 | 58.26 | 58.250750 | 54.83 | 54.834006 |
| 7. $+6$ | 60 | 64.26 | 64.250750 | 60.83 | 60.834006 |
| 8. $\cdot x$ | 120 | 131.73 | 131.71403750 | 122.27 | 122.27635206 |
| 9. $+4$ | 124 | 135.73 | 135.71403750 | 126.27 | 126.27635206 |

Algebra (the exact) and computer science (the approximate) are in con-
flict regarding solution methods. Algebra teachers tend to teach exact solution procedures when possible. This is as it should be, but we need to
introduce the learner to iterative procedures that provide answers within
specified tolerances also.

Consider the following system:

$$x^2 + xy = 10$$
$$2x + xy^2 = 22$$

Rearrange:

$$x = \frac{10}{x + y}$$
$$y = \frac{22 - 2x}{xy}$$

Now, rather than solve the equation exactly, choose a beginning value for $x$ and $y$ and then iterate several times to get a solution. To do this, we rewrite our expressions so that the repetitive process can proceed.

$$x_1 = \frac{10}{x_0 + y_0} \quad \text{or} \quad x_n = \frac{10}{x_{n-1} + y_{n-1}}$$

$$y_1 = \frac{22 - 2x_1}{x_1 \cdot y_0} \quad \text{or} \quad y_n = \frac{22 - 2x_n}{x_n \cdot y_{n-1}}$$

Now study the iterative procedure in figure 5.2. A computer implementation of this flow diagram yields $x = 1.99626492$ and $y = 3.00120833$ in twelve passes when $x_0 = 1$, $y_0 = 4$, and $\epsilon = .01$. The exact answer is $x = 2$, $y = 3$.

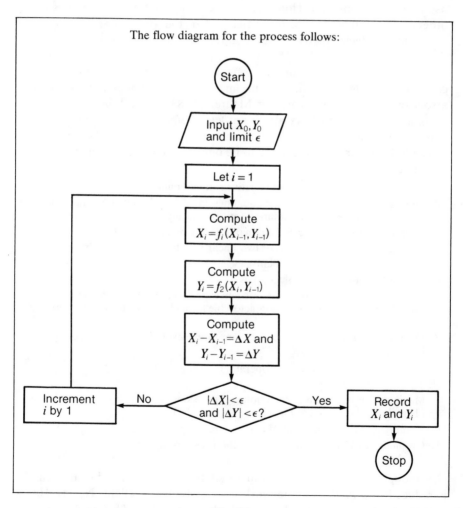

The flow diagram for the process follows:

Start

Input $X_0, Y_0$ and limit $\epsilon$

Let $i = 1$

Compute $X_i = f_i(X_{i-1}, Y_{i-1})$

Compute $Y_i = f_2(X_i, Y_{i-1})$

Compute $X_i - X_{i-1} = \Delta X$ and $Y_i - Y_{i-1} = \Delta Y$

Increment $i$ by 1

No

$|\Delta X| < \epsilon$ and $|\Delta Y| < \epsilon$?

Yes

Record $X_i$ and $Y_i$

Stop

Fig. 5.2

Thus we see a variety of appropriate and needed additions to the algebra curriculum. Presently, the goal in algebra 1 is to reach quadratics—a goal that a substantial number of classes do not attain—and algebra 2 is known for its crowded content. The question is: What will go to make room for new topics and new emphases?

The common content of algebra 1 includes work on integers and rational numbers, solving linear equations and inequalities, linear analytic geometry, linear systems, exponents and polynomials, rational expressions, radicals, and quadratics. Very little here can be reduced significantly or omitted. Perhaps the amount of time spent on operations with polynomials can be reduced but not the time on the concept of exponent.

The time spent on factoring quadratics has been criticized (Usiskin 1980, 416; Fey 1983, 21). Certainly the ability to factor $ax^2 + bx + c$ is not, in itself, an important skill, However, this work on factoring quadratics has other purposes. It tends to be the initial work on the concept of factoring and on the idea of factoring over a set, and it is the simplest situation in which these ideas can be taught. Additionally, the work in rational expressions depends on factors, if not on factoring. Finally, a certain amount of procedural knowledge (factoring) seems important for an understanding of the associated ideas. In the words of Maurer (1983, 162), "One still has to become facile at elementary algebra at least before one can do much else, and for most students absorbing even elementary algebra takes *lots* of time."

The following major skills need to be taught and mastered completely in algebra one:

1. Operating on the positive and negative rational numbers
2. Solving linear equations and inequalities involving the integers and rational numbers; representing the solution sets graphically
3. Graphing linear functions and inequalities with integral and rational coefficients
4. Solving and graphing systems of two linear equations in two variables
5. Operating with integral exponents
6. Adding and multiplying polynomials
7. Factoring $x^2 + bx + c$ over the integers (Special cases of $x^2 + bx$ and $x^2 - d^2$ should be noted as well as the nonfactorable form $x^2 + d_2$; factoring $ax^2 + bx + c$ should be optional.)
8. Operating on simple rational expressions to the level of complexity represented by

$$\frac{ax + b}{cx + d} \quad \text{(operator)} \quad \frac{ex + f}{gx + h}$$

9. Manipulating equations with rational expressions such as those in number 8 (This should be sufficient for science application.)
10. Simplifying square root radical expressions
11. Graphing and applying quadratic functions as is common now

Although the complexity of the manipulative skill demanded in algebra 1 is reduced, the *quality* of the work done must be excellent. Nearly 100 percent mastery of points 1–6 should be demanded. The fundamental conceptual bases for points 7–11 need to be carefully and completely taught or the later use of symbol-manipulating devices may not be meaningful.

## STREAMLINING ALGEBRA 2

In algebra 2 one finds the same topics as in algebra 1 as well as the additional topics of complex numbers, conic sections, exponential and logarithmic functions, sequences and series, trigonometry, and often probability. The purpose of algebra 2 is to prepare the student for senior mathematics and, ultimately, calculus. As such, algebra 2 seems to be accomplishing its goal.

However, the overlap with algebra 1 is substantial. The major differences between algebra 1 and algebra 2 in the first third of the course seem to be minor extensions of the algebra 1 topics and more complex manipulations. Time in algebra 2 could be gained if the extensive overlap were reduced.

The essential review could be established in the context of new and important topics such as flowcharting, iteration, and recursion. For example, if sequences and series became the initial topic, subscripted variables could be introduced; recursive definition of the $n$th term could be included using radical, rational, and polynomial expressions; and sequences of approximate solutions for linear systems would be possible as would approximate solution procedures for quadratics. Series would also provide a nice vehicle for approximation and iteration. Such a beginning could save considerable time in reviewing algebra 1 fundamentals.

Another topic that could be reduced or eliminated is conic sections. Many newer calculus texts have reduced their reliance on conics. Also the topic tends to be well done in senior mathematics courses that emphasize functions and analytic geometry. The corresponding work on systems involving quadratics could also be cut or reduced.

Whether the work on series and sequences is done early or late in algebra 2, it should be expanded moderately to include more work on recursion, convergence, and divergence. The material on three or more linear systems should be revised to focus on general computer-compatible methods of solution. Finally, if these changes do not produce the time desired, then the work on trigonometry should be postponed until the beginning of the senior year. Since most algebra 2 texts have four to six weeks of work on trigonometry, this postponement would yield substantial time.

## CONCLUSIONS

The basic conclusion of this analysis of the forces and changes needed in school algebra is that a major overhaul is not needed. Algebra 1, in particular, is a tightly sequenced course with little opportunity or need for major modification. Although skill work may be reduced, the quality of the skill developed should be improved. Algebra 2, however, has built-in repetitions that deserve attention, and if savings cannot be met by attending to such repetitions, trigonometry should be postponed until the senior year.

The second conclusion is that technology, particularly the microcomputer, is forcing educators to consider additional changes in the algebra curriculum. Some we have suggested here are programming, attention to recursion and interation, inclusion of flow diagrams and approximate solution procedures, and attention to errors in approximate calculations. In considering such changes, planners must remember the role of algebra in preparing for calculus.

A final conclusion concerning the question of manipulative or procedural skill must be postponed until research gives us some direction. The push to incorporate symbolic mathematical systems in algebra is questionable because we are not sure of the relationships between procedural knowledge and skills and the understanding of algebra. The mathematics education community needs to determine the effects on mathematical understanding of the use of symbolic mathematics systems or any other device that carries out procedures before embracing them. I predict that more procedural knowledge will be needed to learn algebra than many would believe. But research must answer before the curriculum should change.

### REFERENCES

Fey, James T., ed. *Computing and Mathematics: The Impact on Secondary School Curricula.* Reston, Va.: National Council of Teachers of Mathematics, 1983.

Fey, James T., D. Albers, and J. Jewett. *Undergraduate Mathematical Sciences in Universities, Four-Year Colleges, and Two-Year Colleges, 1975–76.* Washington, D.C.: Conference Board of the Mathematical Sciences, 1976.

Gersting, Judith L. *Mathematical Structures for Computer Science.* New York: W. H. Freeman & Co., 1982.

Maurer, Stephen. "The Effects of a New College Mathematics Curriculum on High School Mathematics." In *The Future of College Mathematics: Proceedings of a Conference/Workshop on the First Two Years of College Mathematics,* edited by Anthony Ralston and G. S. Young, pp. 153–76. New York: Springer-Verlag, 1983.

*The muMATH/muSIMP-80 Symbolic Mathematics System Reference Manual for the Apple II Computer.* Honolulu: The Soft Warehouse, 1981.

National Academy of Sciences and National Academy of Engineering. *Science and Mathematics in the Schools: Report of a Convocation.* Washington, D.C.: National Academy Press, 1982.

National Council of Teachers of Mathematics. *Computer Oriented Mathematics.* Washington, D.C.: The Council, 1963.

National Science Foundation and Department of Education. *Science and Engineering Education for the 1980s and Beyond.* Washington, D.C.: NSF and DOE, 1980.

Ralston, Anthony, and G. S. Young. *The Future of College Mathematics: Proceedings of a Conference/Workshop on the First Two Years of College Mathematics.* New York: Springer-Verlag, 1983.

Usiskin, Zalman. "What Should *Not* Be in the Algebra and Geometry Curricula of Average College-bound Students?" *Mathematics Teacher* 73 (September 1980): 413–24.

# 6

# The Themes of Geometry: Design of the Nonformal Geometry Curriculum

## Eric D. MacPherson

**F**OR several centuries we have accepted the value of a course in deductive geometry as a part of the secondary mathematics curriculum. Although other vehicles may be available, none have demonstrated the same utility for teaching precise deduction and styles of proof and, at the same time, incorporating some mathematics of later use.

It also seems to be generally accepted that despite all our attempts to keep doors open, it is somewhere around the first serious course in deductive geometry that doors slam shut. In practice, if not in theory, there is no reasonable way to do what we must do and at the same time bring along more than about half of the student population. In some jurisdictions there is considerable screening before students are permitted to enter geometry. In others, its reputation produces considerable self-screening. And in still others, the course itself is the functional screen for continuation in serious mathematics. In any event, this course, not just a theorem in it, remains the pons asinorum of mathematics.

Formal geometry's longevity can be traced to its remarkable economy. In one course, at just the right age level, we can do three things essential for further work in serious mathematics. We can introduce and develop the intricacies of proof given a set of axioms, teach acceptable styles of proof, and teach some useful mathematics. Although we may encounter changing fashions concerning these matters and make some adjustments in the course to suit them, it is unlikely that any major revisions that vitiate these objectives will have any long-term status.

It is not nearly so clear what we should be doing about geometry for *all* students before they begin the study of formal geometry—or later for students who do not select it (or are not selected for it)—or even for our selected students once formal geometry is over. This chapter sets out some guidelines for the construction of that portion of the mathematics curriculum.

My first thesis is that our principal error in designing the nonformal geometry curriculum has risen from a seemingly reasonable but ultimately destructive answer to the question of what we should be doing. Beginning with the notion that prior to the study of formal geometry we ought to do some things that prepare students for it, we have commonly gone on to ask, "What in the formal course is easy enough for us to do over here?" And that is where all the trouble starts. When we look at the geometric objects used in the formal course, we find that they are trivial, and for good reason. The theorems, problems, styles of proof and language may be far from trivial, but the objects on which they are applied, mainly lines, triangles, and circles, are boring at the kindergarten level, let alone later.

It is important to note the reason for this simplicity. As a counterexample, take the catenary. It is a fascinating curve. Students—and not just those in Saint Louis—see catenaries all around them: ropes hanging in a gymnasium, spiders' webs, chain fences, the cables on suspension bridges (well, almost), the chains hanging around their necks, and in other common objects. There is a range of interesting, productive experiments and explorations, suitable for all grade levels, that employ catenaries. But there is no way that the catenary is going to get into a first (or second) course on deductive geometry. It is too difficult. There is nothing you can prove about a catenary with only the mathematical sophistication of the tenth or eleventh grade. So it, and a hundred things like it, are not in the course, and for good reason. The raw material of a first course in deductive geometry almost *has* to be triangles and circles.

So when we ask the question in the wrong way ("What do they do in that course that we can do over here?"), the answer is, "Some terminology and simple properties of lines, triangles, and circles, and for kicks a few rectangles and the names of some other polygons." For decades, this has led to a nonformal curriculum that goes over the same tiresome triangles, circles, and rectangles for the better part of twelve years.

That was bad enough. Then in the revolution of the 1960s and 1970s, we made some changes in the deductive course. There was a heightened emphasis on precise definition and the excision of some less formal styles of proof. For example, an angle became the union of two noncollinear rays with the same endpoint; it was (at least in the text) carefully distinguished from its measure, and so on. Some of this precision was welcome. We had been a little sloppy with some terminology. But the results in the informal curriculum were devastating. Children in the elementary grades learned the distinction between rays, segments, and lines. They looked suspiciously at us but memorized that curves are curves but so are lines, and, of course, learned to find the inside and the outside of a simple closed curve. At this distance, this last must go down as one of the better mathematical jokes of the past few decades. In fairly advanced topology there is a profound theorem called the Jordan curve theorem. It proves that all closed curves, even quite pathological ones, do have an inside and an outside. The result is of some importance in more advanced topology. It is sad that someone who did not quite understand the theorem concluded that it is very important that we teach young children that ordinary closed curves have an inside and an outside.

So as not to continue to make the same sort of mistake, we need to review the impetus under which it was made. If we accept the dangerous half-truth that in preparing students for formal geometry we ought to look at that course and do what is simple enough to do "over here," we are led to little else. It is instructive to see, in toto, where it leads. Consider the chapter on informal geometry in NCTM's Thirtieth Yearbook (NCTM 1968). It is well organized and well written. But it is well over 75 percent definitions. And this is *informal* geometry!

I am certainly not the first to be repelled by the pointlessness of premature and misdirected formalism. In reaction to it, quite a different and considerably better sort of nonformal geometry was created. Teachers began to look for stand-alone activities that would at least engage students' interests. Materials were soon published on paper folding, string art, geometric designs, and geometry in nature and human artifacts. At its best, with teachers who have a strong background and who know what they are doing, this material can be a fine vehicle for learning mathematics. More commonly it becomes "Friday afternoon geometry," probably better than memorizing that a line partitions the set of points in the plane into three disjoint subsets, but otherwise of no consequence.

For all its good intents, Friday-afternoon geometry by itself is not the answer.

## THE FIRST PART OF THE SOLUTION

We begin with a proposition from the new mathematics—in fact from the new curricula. From a distance of over twenty years, we can begin to understand the curricular revolution of the sixties. Our most important motive came from the observation that every discipline has flourished because some human beings are inordinately interested in it. Not just in the facts, but also in the chase: the strategies, the sudden insights, the false starts, the new perceptions of common things, and the grand open questions. Astronomy, for example, was not created because anyone was much interested in measuring the angles between stars, their magnitudes, or their temperatures. It was invented because people look up at night and wonder what in blazes it is all about. All the careful measuring and theorizing follow.

We saw that the curriculum had become too antiseptic, too much of a preparation for a remote future that for many students never came. History had become "one damn thing after another." Science, a recitation of weights, measures, categories, constants, and laws. English, an exercise in Latin grammar. And mathematics had become too much an assemblage of skills in algebra, trigonometry, and geometry selected to enable a later course in calculus. Although some preparatory work is essential, we realized that an overemphasis on preparation drains any discipline of its lifeblood: curiosity, problem solving, frustration, and triumph. What was needed was a transfusion of the human qualities that had created the disciplines in the first place.

---

# Most of the ideas and objects of nonformal geometry should be too hard for the formal course.

---

We made some mistakes, but more often we succeeded. Mathematics, at least outside geometry, was infused with materials and methods giving greater emphasis to mathematical ways of thinking and somewhat less to "shut up and do this" algorithms and "memorize this" definitions.

It is therefore curious that nonformal geometry was not much affected by the shift. As we have seen, the main change was to replace one source of preparatory material with another. Friday-afternoon geometry was a move in the right direction, but it too often exchanged one sin for another. Romance and interest were introduced but at the price of mathematical content.

The trick is to blend the two, and it is about time we did. We must begin with what are, to the student, self-contained activities. Each should pose a problem or state an objective. An answer should be sought, and when it is found, that is the end of it. Students should rarely be tested on vocabulary or definitions. It is enough that they solve the problem or reach the objective.

This looks a lot like a prescription for Friday-afternoon geometry, and to this point it is. The teacher, however, must have a transcending set of objectives. It is here that we move beyond Friday-afternoon geometry and back into the mainstream of mathematics. In the first place, we must select activities that have a strong potential for producing both insight into the ideas of geometry and familiarity with the objects of it. We must range over the full spectrum of such ideas and objects, not just the meager set allowed in the first formal course. As a result, most of the ideas and objects of nonformal geometry should be too hard for the formal course. Second, hands-on skill with instruments should be promoted. It is still true that many important abstract ideas are partly learned somewhere between the elbows and the fingertips. And third, there should be an opportunity to introduce and use precise language. This language should be used in a natural way to increase the precision of discussions about the activity, not as an end in itself. Any twist in that direction can be guaranteed to take the heart out of otherwise intriguing explorations. In fact, it is destructive to test for *any* of the most important objectives.

## THE SECOND PART OF THE SOLUTION

There remains the problem of selecting activities that will be rich in potential for producing all these concepts, skills, and vocabulary and of suggesting how teachers can realize that potential in the classroom.

The most direct approach is simply to assemble a set of tested activities and publish them. One of the best I have seen is D. L. Bruyr's *Geometrical Models and Demonstrations* (1963). And there are others. But we have surely learned over the past few decades that considerably more than that is needed. First, it is unfair to dump a set of activities on teachers and suggest that they use them to produce concepts, skills, and vocabulary. What concepts? What skills? What vocabulary? It must be spelled out, activity by activity, what they are. And just as important, teachers must be encouraged to share the rationale behind the selection of activities. Anything less is an invitation to the teacher to accept a dependency relationship with the external "expert." The justifiable resentment that accompanies that invitation has done more than anything else over the past few decades to kill some otherwise excellent mathematics and science materials.

The critical question is, "What concepts?" It is no use listing several hundred, although it would be easy to do so. That sort of list would be unmanageable as a source of activities. We must search for a small set of pervasive ideas that run through most of what we do in geometry. Almost immediately, probably because it dominates the deductive course, we think of *congruence,* the notion that one object looks exactly like another. Removed from the context of deduction and proof it's not a very exciting theme, but it is certainly pervasive. Later in the formal course we encounter the idea of *similarity,* the notion that one object seems to be a magnified or reduced version of another, with all corresponding linear measures of the two objects being in proportion. This equally pervasive geometric theme calls up more interesting activities.

At this point the formal course is about exhausted. Given the boundary conditions within which it is created, that is not surprising, but it carries us to the question of whether or not there are further pervasive themes that, taken together, can be thought of as the themes of geometry. While I was at the University of British Columbia, two of my colleagues (Leo Rousseau and Tom Bates) and I wrestled with this question for several years. We tried out several models, looking for themes that are valid in terms of what geometry is all about and that can also be used to generate highly productive activities.

My own criterion was that if I could not find at least fifty good activities around a theme, the theme was not general enough. We ended up with nine themes meeting this criterion.

## THE THEMES OF GEOMETRY

Collectively these nine themes may be taken as characterizing geometry. If this model is useful, then the whole nonformal geometry curriculum can be woven around one or more of the themes. Obviously I think the model *is* useful, but only time will tell whether or not text authors and teachers agree.

Each theme is pervasive in geometry and therefore probably recognizable in some form, but where there is any doubt, one or two examples are given.

Here are the themes:

1. **Invariance.** *Invariance embodies the idea that when all seems to be in flux, there is something behind the scenes that does not change.* For example, in the infinite variety of triangles the sum of the measures of their angles is an invariant. The diagonals of squares are in a fixed ratio to their sides. The circumferences of circles are in a fixed ratio to their diameters. And so on. This is the most pervasive of all themes. In fact, mathematics could be defined as the search for invariants.

2. **Symmetry.** *Symmetry embodies the idea that some objects seem to repeat themselves.* Some things, a picket fence for instance, have *repetitive* symmetry. Some, like most animals, seem to be reflected across the middle. They have *bilateral* symmetry. And some will fit with themselves if they are rotated—a bottle cap, for example. This is *cyclic* symmetry.

3. **Similarity.** *Similarity embodies the idea that one object is a magnified or reduced version of another.* Trigonometry, for example, is built around similar triangles.

4. **Maximum-Minimum.** *Many situations call for seeking a maximum or a minimum.* Packagers of breakfast food seek a package shape that provides the maximum apparent size for the minimum contents, and maximum sales for the minimum cost of packaging, handling, and shelving. Builders of bridges seek maximum strength for minimum cost and weight of materials.

5. **Locus.** *Locus embodies the idea that when a pencil (or a point) moves so as to obey some physical constraint or rule, it sometimes produces interesting shapes.* A circle may be thought of as the locus of a point that remains a fixed distance from a given point. Figure 6.1 illustrates a good way of drawing an ellipse. The ellipse is the locus, or path, of $C$ (6.1b) given that $A$ and $B$ must remain on lines $l_1$ and $l_2$, respectively.

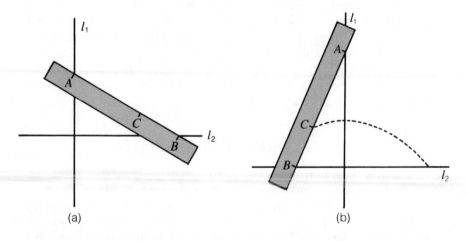

(a)                                    (b)

Fig. 6.1

6. **Congruence.** *Congruence embodies the idea that one object would be seen to match another if they were superimposed* (including superimposition by translation, rotation, and reflection).

7. **Homeomorphism.** *Homeomorphism embodies the idea that even when we are allowed to stretch, bend, or shrink a geometric object, some things stay the same so long as we do not cut it or stick together two points that were not stuck together when we began.* An old childhood puzzle provides a good example. The problem is to trace out the drawing in figure 6.2a without retracing or lifting the pencil from the paper. Whatever the solution is, it will also work on 6.2b and 6.2c because they are *homeomorphic* to the first. It is possible to go from one to another by stretching, shrinking, and bending but without cutting or gluing. It will not work on 6.2d because that figure is not homeomorphic to the others.

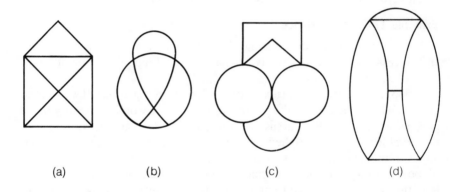

| (a) | (b) | (c) | (d) |

Fig. 6.2

8. **Limit.** *This is the idea that in geometry, as in arithmetic, some things squeeze in on a limit.* An example is to be found in the perennial question of what happens if you go half-way along a ruler, then go half the distance that is left, and so on. As we proceed, we approach a *limit*.

9. **Coordinates.** *This theme incorporates the very important idea that we can think of any geometric object as a set of points that are plotted to satisfy an open sentence.*

The first test of this model is that every significant concept of geometry can be tied naturally to at least one of the themes. Second, it must be possible to create a large number of productive activities woven around each of the themes, at every level from the primary grades to senior high. Third and most important, teachers who are familiar with these themes should be able to use stand-alone activities to give their students a thorough grounding in significant geometry and be able to evaluate and select proposed activities. Some examples of such activities follow.

## SAMPLE ACTIVITIES

Short of convincing the editors to convert the greater part of this yearbook to this purpose, it is impossible to give even one example of a well-designed activity for each theme. That is, an activity in which the main theme, related ideas, expected skills with instruments, and suitable vocabulary are identified.

Therefore, four condensed examples follow, one each from the themes of invariance, locus, similarity, and limit that illustrate what can be done. They are taken from a set of about five hundred that I have accumulated and hope to publish. These examples are all best suited for the junior and senior high school levels. I have selected them so as to maximize the chance that they are novel for even experienced teachers. The disadvantage of making such choices is that they rely to some degree on earlier explorations that are not given here. This is particularly true of the last example.

### Example 1. From Invariance

This activity calls for discovering a little-known invariant of polyhedrons. It is necessary, therefore, to have at hand several models of polyhedrons, most of them nonregular.

Suppose we consider a vertex $V_1$ of a polyhedron (fig. 6.3a). If we were to cut a slit along one edge and press the vertex flat, we would ordinarily find a gap, as in figure 6.3b. Let us call the gap the *loss* at this vertex. It is remarkable that for all polyhedrons, the sum of the losses at all the vertices is an invariant. The student's task is to find the sum of the losses for a number of polyhedrons, to discover that all the sums are about the same, to hypothesize what the invariant is, and then to test the hypothesis with additional polyhedrons. Since a large number of angles must be measured, errors of measurement introduce some uncertainty as to the value of the invariant and provide the opportunity to discuss the management of measurement errors.

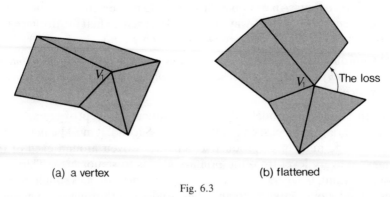

(a) a vertex                          (b) flattened

Fig. 6.3

Once students are reasonably certain of the invariant, a concave polyhedron (in which the sume of the measures of the angles at a vertex may be greater than 360 degrees) can provoke a most productive discussion. To preserve the invariant, the loss at such a vertex must be taken to be negative. The analogy with our treatment of exponents of zero, the products of negative integers, and the cosines of angles of measure greater than 90 degrees can be drawn and explored.

With hindsight, and knowing that the sum of the losses is an invariant, it is easy to find the invariant by considering a cube. There is a loss of 90 degrees at each vertex, and there are eight vertices, so the invariant is 720 degrees. It spoils the activity, of course, to let it be known at the outset that there is a single invariant or what its value is. It is therefore best to save regular polyhedrons until at least some hypotheses have been formulated.

**Outcomes**

From this activity these outcomes can be expected:

*Skills*—measuring angles, with vigorous built-in punishment for sloppy work

*Vocabulary and Definitions*—*polyhedron, regular polyhedron,* the names of some regular polyhedrons, *vertex, face, edge, measure of an angle, polygon,* the names of some regular polygons, *convex, concave, error,* and *invariant*

*Concepts*—the idea of an invariant, the use of symmetry to minimize measurements, and errors of measurement

For purposes of later discussion, some theory is needed. The following is a sketch of a proof.

Suppose we partition the surface of a sphere into $n$ "triangles." From Euler's theorem for polyhedrons, we know that $V + F - E = 2$, and we have that $F = n$. Since each triangle contributes three edges, but each edge is counted twice, there are $3n/2$ edges. Then $V = 2 + 3n/2 - n = 2 + n/2$.

On a sphere (and on any nonpathological blob), the surface will be about flat near a vertex. We will therefore measure 360 degrees at each vertex and altogether, at the $2 + n/2$ vertices, $360 \times (2 + n/2) = 720 + n \times 180$ degrees. If these were ordinary flat triangles, we should expect to find only $n \times 180$ degrees. The question is, Where do the other 720 degrees come from? They come, of course, from the fact that the "triangles" are not flat. The sum of the measures of the angles in each of them will be in excess of 180 degrees. If we add up all the excesses in all the triangles, their sum must be 720 degrees. This has long been known as the spherical excess theorem.

Suppose, now, we keep the vertices where they are and flatten out each figure to become a real triangle. Now the sum of the measures of all the angles must be just $n \times 180$ degrees, and the problem becomes, Where did the other 720 degrees go? The answer is, in the losses at the vertices.

In many ways, simply constructing nonregular polyhedrons is as productive an activity as the one summarized above. It is far from being a cut-and-paste exercise. Two little-known and remarkable invariants are involved as well as a considerable amount of elementary trigonometry.

### Example 2. From Locus

This activity calls for finding one particular kind of locus.

The student must first learn what a *pedal curve* is (usually pronounced pee'-dul). A pedal curve is always drawn *from* a point *to* some geometric figure. Formally, it is the locus of the feet of the perpendiculars from the point to the tangents to the given figure. We begin with the pedal curve from a point outside a circle to the circle.

As figure 6.4a indicates, we draw (lightly) a tangent to the circle, find the perpendicular from the point *P* to the tangent, and identify their point of intersection. Then, as in figure 6.4b, we shift to a nearby tangent and repeat the construction. The activity now stops while we argue out what would happen if we were to draw a large number of tangents between the first two. Minor errors of construction will make the conclusion more arguable than it might seem to be, but ultimately it is that the plotted points would crowd together along some path, and that if we could use *all* the tangents between the first two, the plotted points would trace out a curve of some sort.

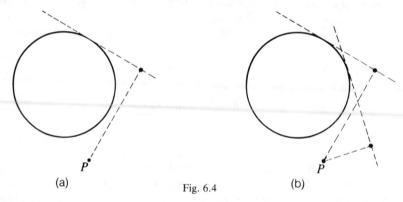

(a)    Fig. 6.4    (b)

Now the activity continues. The objective is to find out where the pedal curve goes. Students should eventually discover that it looks like figure 6.5. Note that the curve touches the given circle at two points, has bilateral symmetry, and passes twice through the given point. Each of these observations is arguable and ought to be argued at length.

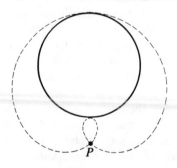

Fig. 6.5

The activity then becomes one of selecting different objects to which to draw pedal curves and differing locations for the given point. The following are all productive:

- Try drawing a pedal curve from a point *on* the circle.

- Try it with the point at the center of the circle, keeping in mind the formal theorem that the tangents to a circle are perpendicular to the radii at the points of contact.

- Having introduced earlier a way of drawing ellipses, try drawing the pedal curves to an ellipse (1) from a point outside it off an axis, (2) from a point on the ellipse on an axis, and above all, (3) from a focus of the ellipse. The outcome is startling. If ellipses are constructed as in figure 6.1, a focus may be found by placing $A$ on the intersection of $l_1$ and the ellipse and $C$ on $l_2$. $C$ will be at a focus.

- Note that at a point on a triangle other than a vertex there is a tangent. It lies along the side of the triangle. There is no proper tangent at a vertex, but we agree to draw all possible lines through the vertex that do not intersect the interior of the triangle and call them tangents. Then draw some pedal curves to some triangles. Several provocative and unexpected things happen, not the least of which is that the pedal curve is a set of connected arcs.

- Agree that a point does not have tangents. But then agree, as an extension of the sin already committed with triangles, that we will draw all possible lines through the point and call them tangents. Then draw the pedal curve from a point to a point. The result is again startling. It is explained by the formal theorem that an angle inscribed in a semicircle is a right angle.

## Outcomes

The following outcomes can be expected:

*Skills*—drawing tangents and perpendiculars, keeping nonsignificant construction lines faint, curve sketching, and drawing circles and ellipses

*Vocabulary and Definitions*—*circle, tangent, perpendicular, intersect, right angle, curve, ellipse, focus, axis, radius, bilateral symmetry, arc,* and *semicircle*

*Concepts*—the idea of a locus, some consequences of bilateral symmetry for construction, the idea of a curve as a set of points, the idea of a pedal curve, and errors of construction

## Example 3. From Similarity

The activity in the first example called for a single discovery. Once that discovery is made and confirmed, the activity is over. The second example allows for some extensions. Once students learn what a pedal curve is and master the skills of drawing them, they can draw pedal curves to additional figures to whatever extent is productive. This third example is more open ended. Once the basic idea is understood, a large number of possible applications are possible. The activity is taken from the brilliant article, "On

Being the Right Size," by J. B. S. Haldane (1956, 952–57). What is outlined below would, in fact, be spread over at least three activities.

The first observation is that for similar objects all corresponding linear measures are in proportion. There is the same ratio between any pair of similar linear measures. The second observation is that this is not true of the areas of similar figures; they are in fact proportional to the squares of the ratios of corresponding linear measures. With this preparation, it is then discovered that volumes are proportional to the cubes of the ratios of corresponding linear measures. Then we begin to explore what Haldane calls the battle of the squares and cubes.

Begin by using an overhead projector to draw similar figures on the chalkboard. (Be careful of the keystone effect, in which shapes are distorted.) It is a good plan to arrange for a ratio of about 3:1 for the first example. Establish that *all* similar linear measures on the two drawings are in this proportion. For example, the lengths $c_1$ and $c_2$ in figure 6.6 will be in the same ratio as those of corresponding sides. Use a commercial or

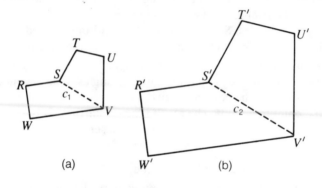

Fig. 6.6

homemade pantograph to draw further similar figures. A reasonably effective one that takes some panache to learn to use can be made by looping together identical short rubber bands (see fig. 6.7). If a pencil is placed at one

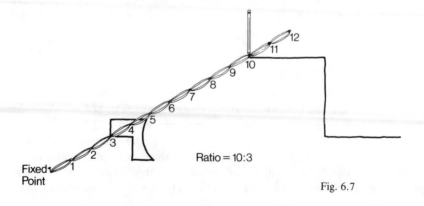

Ratio = 10:3

Fig. 6.7

knot while another knot traces out a figure, the two figures will be roughly similar and their ratio will be that of the numbering of the knots. Irregularities in the new figure can be smoothed using a hand calculator to ensure that all corresponding linear measures are in the same ratio. It is perfectly acceptable to produce blown-up copies of cartoon characters or automobiles; in fact, such drawings generate an even greater appreciation of the fact that in similar figures all corresponding linear measures are in the same ratio.

Raise the question of painting similar figures, and ask whether or not their areas will be in the same ratio as their corresponding sides. The hypothesis is most easily tested on rectangles, but a test on irregular figures using a finely squared transparent overlay is instructive. If necessary, guide the way to the discovery that the areas of similar figures are proportional to the squares of the linear ratios.

Finally, extend the problem to volume. Whatever hypotheses students have can be tested using small cardboard boxes and blocks or drawings of them.

Once the three basic rules for linear measures, areas, and volume are established, the fun starts. Begin with animals' legs. The weight of an animal depends largely on its volume. But the strength of its legs depends primarily on their cross-sectional area. So if we double the size of an animal (and by that we mean all linear measures), its weight will be increased by a factor of eight ($2 \times 2 \times 2$), but the strength of its legs will increase by a factor of only four ($2 \times 2$). Its legs will not be able to support its weight so readily. As we increase the size yet further, the animal soon comes to the point where its legs can no longer support its body. That, together with some other reasons to follow, is why there are no house-sized spiders. It also explains how quite large animals do cope. In proportion to body size, compare an elephant's legs with a spider's.

Once this basic point is made, introduce the following questions and invite the presentation of data to support hypotheses:

• The lift from birds' wings depends mainly on the area of the wings. Speculate on the proportional sizes of wings of larger and smaller birds, and collect data to test the speculations.

• Animals absorb food along the surface area of the intestine. Speculate on the comparative lengths of intestine, from earthworms to elephants.

• Should a twelve-inch pizza cost twice as much as a six-inch pizza? Do not move on too quickly. Is the twelve-inch pizza also thicker?

• Many years ago, some engineers constructed models of river deltas and dikes on scales such as 1:100 to attempt to study patterns of water flow, wave action, and silting. Explain why engineers now prefer alternative methods.

• Even a perfect scale model of an airplane does not fly at all the way the full-sized airplane flies. Why not?

• An animal's body must somehow take in enough oxygen to support respiration throughout its mass. Yet oxygen can only be absorbed across the area of its skin or lungs. How have animals adapted to this problem as their species has become larger? What does this imply about giant insects?

This activity can be continued through whatever applications interest the student.

### Outcomes

From such explorations the following outcomes can be expected:

*Skills*—measurement of lengths, areas and volumes, including the areas of irregular objects; the calculation of ratios; bibliographic skills

***Vocabulary and Definitions***—*ratio, proportion, similar, linear measures, area, volume,* and appropriate biological vocabulary

*Concepts*—similarity and its implications for linear measures, areas, and volumes; the related fact that there is no such thing as a scale model; ratio and proportion

### Example 4. From Limit

This activity from the limit theme, designed for senior secondary students, is built on three ideas developed in earlier activities.

First, students must have been introduced to the limit notion, perhaps as early as the intermediate grades, through such activities as paper folding, partitioning disks, studying bouncing balls, and the like. Figure 6.8 illustrates the kind of activity that can be used to develop the notion. A strip of paper is laid, in sequence, across the perpendiculars drawn in an angle, and the strip is marked so as to add the lengths of the perpendiculars. The sum of the lengths clearly approaches some limit.

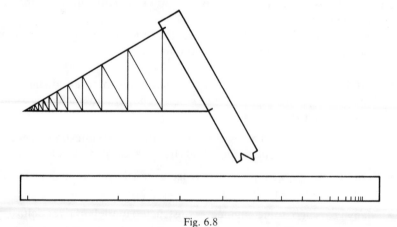

Fig. 6.8

Second, through a study of similar triangles, students should have come to appreciate the ultility of recording some triangle ratios as sines and cosines. If they have been turned off by proving trigonometric identities, a game ranking somewhere between gin rummy and snap in interest and mathematical utility, so much the worse.

Third, they must have explored tilted "rectangles" in wedges, as shown in figure 6.9, and concluded that $A_2/A_1 = d_1/(d_2\cos\theta)$. This looks a bit artificial, but in context it is an excellent arena in which to pull together similarity and some elementary trigonometry.

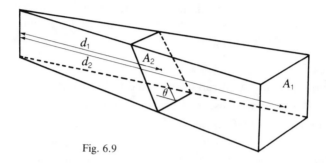

Fig. 6.9

On this foundation, the activity begins.

We wrap an open cylinder whose height is equal to a sphere's diameter around the sphere, and imagine creating a small wedge from the axis of the sphere to the cylinder, as suggested in figures 6.10 and 6.11. The challenge is to find the relationship between two areas: (1) the surface of the sphere where it is cut by the wedge and (2) the surface of the cylinder where it is cut by the wedge.

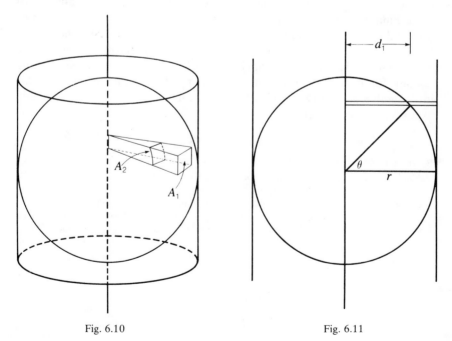

Fig. 6.10                                           Fig. 6.11

It is actually quite simple. If the indicated radius is inclined at angle $\theta$, so is the "rectangle" in the wedge. Then $d_1 = r\cos \theta$ and $d_2 = r$. With only ninth-grade algebra, it is found that $A_2 = A_1$! From here it is a very short step to imagining the entire surface of the open cylinder cut by such small wedges and using the notion of a limit to conclude that the surface area of the sphere is equal to the lateral area of the cylinder. And the lateral area of the cylinder is easily shown to be $(2\pi r)2r = 4\pi r^2$.

This is not quite the way Archimedes did it, but students who discover this fact for themselves have as much reason to be pleased as he did, and he had this drawing carved on his gravestone.

## Outcomes

The main outcomes that can be expected from this activity are:

*Skills*—sketching wedges, spheres, and cylinders

*Vocabulary and Definitions*—*wedge, angle, ratio, distance, cosine, sphere, cylinder, $\pi$, formula, limit*

*Concepts*—the ideas of limit, cosine, and the surface area of a sphere

## SUMMARY

My first recommendation is that the nonformal geometry program at any level should comprise, from the student's point of view, a set of free-standing activities, each with its own clear problem or objective. Second, the teacher should ensure that each activity is woven around some significant theme of geometry. A list of nine themes is suggested, with a short explanation of each. Finally, examples of productive activities are given, one for each of four of the themes. It is suggested that in any activity the teacher should aim to promote, in addition to familiarity with the theme, skill with geometric instruments and precise vocabulary. A diet of such geometry will be valuable not only for those students who have taken or will subsequently take a course in deductive geometry but also for those for whom this will be the only exposure to the subject.

### REFERENCES

Bruyr, D. L. *Geometrical Models and Demonstrations*. Portland, Maine: J. W. Walch, 1963.

Haldane, J. B. S. "On Being the Right Size." In *The World of Mathematics*, edited by James R. Newman. New York: Simon & Schuster, 1956.

Lockwood, E. H. *A Book of Curves*. Cambridge: Cambridge University Press, 1961.

National Council of Teachers of Mathematics. *More Topics in Mathematics for Elementary School Teachers*, Thirtieth Yearbook, pp. 323–88. Washington, D.C.: The Council, 1968.

# 7

# Computer Simulations: A Means for Integrating Realistic Problem Solving into the Curriculum

## Martha L. Wallace

SINCE the National Council of Teachers of Mathematics published its recommendations for school mathematics of the 1980s (NCTM 1980), major strides have been made toward incorporating problem solving, applications, and the hands-on use of computers into the mathematics curriculum. Publishers have added more applications exercises and problem-solving techniques in their textbooks, and teacher resource books have appeared on integrating science and mathematics (e.g., House 1980) or computers and mathematics (Elgarten, Posamentier, and Moresh 1983). At least one major computer software developer (Minnesota Educational Computer Consortium 1983) has produced software designed for teaching students how to use common heuristics in solving mathematical problems.

We have made progress in teaching mathematics with a focus on problem solving, investigating applications of mathematics in other disciplines, and using computers in the classroom. But our focus is still too narrow. We are relying too much on textbook problems and routine applications, and most computer use in the mathematics classroom is for tutorials and drill and practice.

Students must see more than just textbook problems, because problems in real life do not look like textbook problems no matter how applicable or how creatively written they are. Textbook problems usually provide only pertinent information, and students can often guess the method of solution by noting where the problem appears in the text. Real-life problems, however, come with irrelevant as well as relevant information, give no clue as to the approach that will work, and often require the analysis of huge amounts of data. Further, the problem may not even be explicit; its potential solver may first need to define the problem or formulate the question. If we are to teach

The two simulation packages described here were developed with support from the National Science Foundation and the National Institute of Education. Program listings (for the Zenith/Heathkit H89 computer) or support materials are available from the author.

students how to attack this type of problem, we must create situations that are nearly as nebulous and ill-defined as those they will encounter in real life: situations in which they must first define the question and then decide what type of data to collect, how to collect and organize the data, and how to analyze the results to reach a solution.

How do we create these situations? Ideally, we would set up physical science experiments in the mathematics classroom or send groups of students out of the school to try to help solve real community problems. One group might try to help local businesses decide how many hours to keep their shops open. Another might investigate the feasibility of adding additional parking spaces in busy retail areas. These are excellent ways to acquaint students with the types of real problems that need to be solved mathematically. They require the collection and analysis of data, a recognition of the dependence of certain variables on others, and some judgment as to what is the "best" answer.

## COMPUTER SIMULATIONS

Computer simulations are an ideal substitute for actual on-site experimentation, which is usually impractical for the average mathematics class. Simulations provide the advantages of studying realistic situations while eliminating most of the problems associated with actual experimentation. Using models that imitate the essential characteristics of a situation, students are able to investigate complex phenomena at their own level of mathematical expertise. Because they can examine the effects of changing some variables while holding others constant, they can ask themselves the type of "what if" questions that are so crucial to problem solving.

Moreover, computer simulations are an ideal way to combine problem solving, applications, and technology in the teaching of mathematics. They make possible the consideration of more complicated situations and allow students more flexibility in considering alternative strategies. They also allow simplification of the situation when necessary. In addition, the use of computer simulation to model a situation and to collect and analyze data is one of the primary uses of the computer among adult users. Let us observe two uses of computer simulations in two mathematics classrooms.

### Example 1: The Barber Shop

Ken Powell, who teaches a probability and statistics class in senior high school, is using a simulation of a barber shop to examine some problems in queuing theory (the study of waiting lines).

The first time the students used the simulation, Ken was careful to introduce concepts of queuing theory and to teach students how to use it. After defining *interarrival time* as the time between successive customer arrivals and *service time* as the time of service (in this case a haircut), he asked the students to find the *mean interarrival time* and the *mean service time* of twenty customers. Then he handed out computer disks to groups of students and described the details of the picture on the screen.

Customers enter the barber shop and take a number from the hook to the left of the barber (fig. 7.1). They sit in the waiting chairs, each placing the number under the chair. Customers are taken in turn, and a timer under the barber chair tells how much time is left for the haircut. The current clock time is shown in the upper right of the screen and the time remaining until the next customer enters the shop is on the upper left. In the display shown, customer 12 is in the chair with 2 minutes left, and customers 13 and 14 are waiting. Since the time until the next arrival is 0, another customer must be coming around the corner.

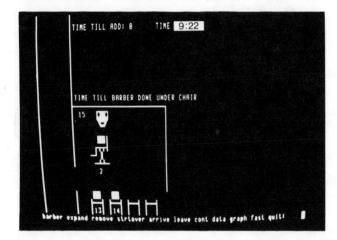

Fig. 7.1

Students were then allowed to experiment with various commands to run the simulation and were given a summary sheet of the commands. Simulations often require students to remember many commands, and Ken has found that a summary sheet by each computer facilitates the process.

That first day students had to learn how to record the data they needed. Each team of three was given a recording sheet (fig. 7.2) and practiced recording the arrival time and the time into and out of the barber chair for each customer. Very quickly they learned to start and stop the action when necessary and to distribute tasks among group members. Thus in most teams one student was operating the computer, the second was calling out readings by saying something like, "Number three arrives at 35, in at 39, out at 45. Number four arrives at 37, in at 45, out at 51." The third student was recording the data on the sheet.

After each group recorded data for twenty customers, they computed the mean interarrival and service times and then compared their results with those of the other groups. Class discussion centered on strategies for recording data and computing the means. Students also talked about why the means calculated by the various teams were close but not identical. The simulation was then set so that data were generated for 200 customers, and

| | | | | **Barber Shop** | | | | | |
|---|---|---|---|---|---|---|---|---|---|
| Customer | Inter-arrival Time | Service Time | Arrival Time | Begin Service | End Service | Waiting Time | System Time | Queue Length | Server Idle |
| 1 | 12 | 6 | 12 | 12 | 18 | 0 | 6 | 0 | 12 |
| 2 | 21 | 6 | 33 | 33 | 39 | 0 | 6 | 0 | 15 |
| 3 | 2 | 6 | 35 | 39 | 45 | 4 | 10 | 1 | 0 |
| 4 | | | 37 | 45 | 51 | | | | |
| 5 | | | 43 | 51 | 57 | | | | |
| 6 | | | 55 | 57 | 63 | | | | |
| 7 | | | 57 | 63 | 69 | | | | |
| 8 | | | | | | | | | |
| 9 | | | | | | | | | |
| 10 | | | | | | | | | |

Fig. 7.2

the means were calculated by the computer. When these values were compared with the means obtained by combining all the readings, students observed that the larger number of readings led to closer agreement.

In other sessions with the simulation, students were required to find the median length of the waiting line and the percentage of customers who had to wait for a haircut. In each case they began by entering arrival and service data on the recording sheet and then computing the other quantities they needed. As they learned about probability distributions, they used computer-constructed histograms to analyze the distribution of customer arrival and service times.

Today Ken has asked each group of students to determine the optimum number of barbers for their particular shop. Using a master program, he has prepared a disk for each group with unique patterns of customer arrival and service. Most students began the investigation by simply watching the action on the screen for a time, adding and subtracting barbers at will. With no further direction, they decide they must find a way to collect and organize data before further analysis.

Each group prepares a report to the class describing the relevant characteristics of their shop, their definition of *optimum,* and the way they approached the problem. Most decide that the optimum number of barbers means the number that provides for the least waiting time for customers but keeps the barbers as busy as possible (no barbers standing around waiting for customers). Many students feel it is also important to consider the number of customers who leave without haircuts because the waiting line is too long.

Once the question has been formulated, students must decide how much weight to give each of the factors, for it quickly becomes clear that the shortest customer waiting time means long periods of inactivity for the barbers, and the seriousness of customers leaving without haircuts depends on individual situations. They must decide how to measure customer waiting time or barber idle time and how to describe and account for differences in patterns of customer arrival or the length of time it takes to get a haircut. Most students discover that the most effective method of measuring is to record all relevant information over an adequate time span with a particular number of barbers and then to repeat the process with a different number of barbers. Some students discover that the computer can help them organize their thinking by recording much of the data and displaying graphs of some of the results.

By the time students finish this problem and present their report to the class, they have had a great deal of practice with real problem solving. They have had to define the problem, establish goals, decide which aspects of the situation were relevant, make a plan to collect and analyze data, and evaluate their conclusions. Equally as important, they have experienced the group approach to problem solving and have used the computer as a tool both in providing the simulation and in performing the calculations necessary to reach conclusions.

Investigating a real barber shop in this manner would not be feasible for this class. The time required to obtain enough readings would be prohibitive, even if a shop could be found that would allow a class of students to observe and record business patterns. Simulation allows time compression and the elimination of extraneous details. It gives students the opportunity to "hire" and "fire" barbers at will. The teacher is able to provide different initial settings for each group of students so that they are, in effect, investigating a whole town full of shops.

Another advantage of the simulation is that the same situation might provide a different investigation another day, with different parameters preset by the teacher. For example, this class or another might be asked to determine the optimum number of waiting chairs in a barber shop with a particular number of barbers or to investigate the effects of using faster barbers or changing the pattern of customers' arrival times. Introductory activities on determining mean, median, and mode could be used as well in a junior high school classroom.

## Example 2: Following the Bouncing Ball

Down the hall from Ken Powell, Diane Jackson is working with her advanced algebra students on a computer simulation of a bouncing ball. Students are working in pairs to investigate the behavior of various kinds of balls dropped from different heights (fig. 7.3). Unlike the barber simulation, this experiment could actually be done in the classroom. However, Diane prefers the simulation because she can set the program to eliminate the

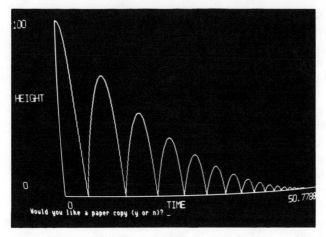

Fig. 7.3

experimental error that might obscure the results of the experiment. In addition, the simulation allows students to drop the ball from the same height on each of the planets and the moon, and to drop it from a much greater (or smaller) distance than would be feasible in a real experiment.

Students are working in pairs with one student stopping and starting the action on the screen, the other recording data. Some are using a feature of the program that automatically stops the ball at predetermined intervals; others are having the computer mark the top of each bounce.

These students, too, have had an introduction to the simulation and practice in running the program. They have tried out various options, such as computer graphing and provision for quasi-experimental error, and have developed efficient methods of performing the simulation and recording results.

Today the students are using the simulation to investigate concepts of linear and exponential functions, the linear relationship between the height of any bounce and that of its immediate predecessor, and the exponential nature of the height as a function of the bounce number. Each pair is completing an investigation guidesheet (fig. 7.4) as they work at the computer, trying different balls and drop-heights and recording the results. Most are graphing the results to determine the relationships between different variables.

This simulation can be used for many additional mathematical topics. The sum of a geometric series can be investigated by having students determine the total distance the ball has traveled after any particular bounce. This activity can serve as an introduction to finding the sum of an infinite series. Students might be directed to slow the action and observe the speed of the ball as it falls so they could try to determine instantaneous speed and compare the speed at a particular time to the corresponding slope of the distance-time graph. These activities can lead to an intuitive notion of limit and derivative. The enrichment topic of using finite differences to determine

### Bouncing Ball

Choose a ball and drop it from a convenient height so that you can see at least six or seven bounces.

1. Drop the ball and record the height of each bounce. You may wish to use a chart like the one to the right.

2. Graph the height as a function of the bounce number.

3. Graph the height of the $(n + 1)$th bounce as a function of the height of the $n$th bounce.

4. Repeat the investigation at least two more times with the same ball but with different initial heights. For each graph, plot the information from all three trials on one set of axes.

5. Repeat the entire investigation with at least two more balls. Compare your results and state your conclusions.

6. Write a formula that will predict the height of the $n$th bounce as a function of the initial height for each of the balls you used.

| Bounce Number | Height of Bounce |
|---------------|------------------|
| 0 | |
| 1 | |
| 2 | |
| 3 | |
| 4 | |
| 5 | |
| 6 | |
| 7 | |
| 8 | |
| 9 | |
| 10 | |

7. Make graphs to answer the following questions:

   a) If you drop a ball from a height of 120 cm and measure the height of the third bounce as 15 cm, how high will the ball go on the fifth bounce?

   b) Each time a certain ball bounces, it rises to three-fourths the height of the previous bounce. If the height of the fifth bounce is one meter, what was the drop-height of the ball?

Fig. 7.4

quadratic relationships might be introduced while students are trying to determine the acceleration of the falling ball (on Earth or some other planet).

## TEACHING MATHEMATICS THROUGH COMPUTER SIMULATIONS

The two classroom examples illustrate the power of computer simulation to combine problem solving, applications, and computer technology in the mathematics classroom. Computer simulation provides realistic problems for students to solve: problems that are often less than clearly defined, open-ended, and require skills from several areas of secondary mathematics. When using computer simulations, students are required to define the problem, collect data, analyze and interpret those data, and evaluate the results. They can change the conditions, make and then test intuitive guesses, and learn how to use the technology that is available to them. Teachers can present more complex problems than those possible with just textbooks, yet they can also control the parameters much more than they could in actual experiments. Further, they can assign investigations that would be impractical or impossible to do in actuality.

Few commercial simulations are available for teaching senior high school mathematics, but several teacher-produced packages are described in the recent literature. Many of them are designed to teach topics in probability and statistics. Lappan and Winter (1980), for example, simulated the trading of baseball cards to determine the probability of getting a full set. A sampling procedure was simulated by Hutcheson (1980) in a statistics class to compare results of large and small samples. The famous birthday problem, concerning the probability that two or more persons in a room have the same birthday, was investigated by Ginther and Ewbank (1982), first by hand and then by computer simulation. Woodward and Ridenhour (1982) used computer simulation as one of four ways to investigate the probability that a stick broken at random into three pieces would then form a triangle.

In an article that inspired the barber program described here, Mathers (1976) investigated a waiting line in a barber shop and asked students to consider several questions that use statistics. An experiment in extrasensory perception was simulated by Inhelder (1981), and the results were compared to those predicted by the binomial distribution. Yates (1981) and Collis (1982) both described units of instruction in probability using computer simulation. The value of pi was determined by Carlson (1981) through a simulation of the classic Buffon needle problem.

Physical experiments provide models for other uses of computer simulation in teaching mathematics, such as the examination of the behavior of a body falling with air resistance as described by Vest (1982), or the investigation of electronic resistance recounted by Travers and Gray (1981). The development of a mathematical model and simulation program for investigating the effects of differing harvesting policies on the size of a buffalo herd is described by Channell and Hirsch (1984). The study of population growth is also often used to introduce exponential functions (c.f., Dunn et al. 1978).

The mathematics of insurance was studied by Kellogg's students through a program (1981) that illustrates the illegal practice of tontine, a type of insurance policy where the last survivor of a group of persons collects the money of all the others. Roberts (1981) even used the computer to teach the process of simulation and modeling.

Many topics in senior high school mathematics can be approached by means of computer simulation. The fundamental concept of function can be illustrated by simulations that require students to look for relationships between different types of data. Manipulating one variable and measuring the effect on another helps students to understand the concepts of dependence and independence. These ideas are exemplified in the yellow-light problem described by Liao and Piel (1984). Inverse relationships can be investigated by simulating a balanced lever; radioactive decay provides an excellent example of an exponential function. Concepts in trigonometry can be made less abstract through simulations of periodic phenomena, such as a swinging pendulum.

Computer simulations provide realistic opportunities for students to learn and do mathematics. In developing and using computer simulations, we can meet the challenge of the *Agenda for Action* and integrate problem solving, applications, and computer technology into the mathematics curriculum.

### REFERENCES

Carlson, Ronald J. "Buffon's Needle Problem on a Microcomputer." *Mathematics Teacher* 74 (November 1981): 638–40.

Channell, Dwayne E., and Christian R. Hirsch. "Computer Methods for Problem Solving in Secondary School Mathematics." In *Computers in Mathematics Education,* 1984 Yearbook of the National Council of Teachers of Mathematics, edited by Viggo P. Hansen, pp. 171–83. Reston, Va.: The Council, 1984.

Collis, Betty. "Simulation and the Microcomputer: An Approach to Teaching Probability." *Mathematics Teacher* 75 (October 1982): 584–87.

Dunn, Samuel L., Ruth Chamberlain, Patricia Ashby, and Kenneth Christensen. "People, People, People." *Mathematics Teacher* 70 (April 1978): 283–91.

Elgarten, Gerald H., Alfred S. Posamentier, and Stephen E. Moresh. *Using Computers in Mathematics.* Menlo Park, Calif.: Addison-Wesley Publishing Co., 1983.

Ginther, John L., and William A. Ewbank. "Using a Microcomputer to Simulate the Birthday Coincidence Problem." *Mathematics Teacher* 75 (December 1982): 769–75.

House, Peggy A. *Interactions of Science and Mathematics.* Columbus, Ohio: ERIC Clearinghouse for Science, Mathematics, and Environmental Education, 1980.

Hutcheson, James W. "Computer-assisted Instruction Is Not Always Drill." *Mathematics Teacher* 73 (December 1980): 689–91.

Inhelder, William. "Solving Probability Problems through Computer Simulation." In *Teaching Statistics and Probability,* 1981 Yearbook of the National Council of Teachers of Mathematics, edited by Albert P. Shulte, pp. 220–24. Reston, Va.: The Council, 1981.

Kellogg, Howard M. "In All Probability, a Microcomputer." In *Teaching Statistics and Probability,* 1981 Yearbook of the National Council of Teachers of Mathematics, edited by Albert P. Shulte, pp. 225–33. Reston, Va.: The Council, 1981.

Lappan, Glenda, and M. J. Winter. "Probability Simulation in Middle School." *Mathematics Teacher* 73 (September 1980): 446–49.

Liao, Thomas T., and E. Joseph Piel. "The Yellow-Light Problem: Computer-based Applied Mathematics." In *Computers in Mathematics Education,* 1984 Yearbook of the National Council of Teachers of Mathematics, edited by Viggo P. Hansen, pp. 97–106. Reston, Va.: The Council, 1984.

Mathers, Jolly. "The Barber Queue." *Mathematics Teacher* 69 (December 1976): 680–84.

Minnesota Educational Computer Consortium. *Problem Solving Strategies.* Saint Paul: The Consortium, 1983.

National Council of Teachers of Mathematics. *An Agenda for Action: Recommendations for School Mathematics of the 1980s.* Reston, Va.: The Council, 1980.

Roberts, Nancy. "Introducing Computer Simulation into the High School: An Applied Mathematics Curriculum." *Mathematics Teacher* 74 (November 1981): 647–52.

Travers, Kenneth J., and Kenneth G. Gray. "The Monte Carlo Method: A Fresh Approach to Teaching Probabilistic Concepts." *Mathematics Teacher* 74 (May 1981): 327–34.

Vest, Floyd. "Bodies Falling with Air Resistance: Computer Simulation." *School Science and Mathematics* 75 (1982): 506–10.

Woodward, Ernest, and Jim R. Ridenhour. "An Interesting Probability Problem." *Mathematics Teacher* 75 (December 1982): 765–68.

Yates, Daniel S. "Computer-enhanced Probability." *Viewpoints in Teaching and Learning* 57 (1981): 96–113.

# 8

# Discrete Mathematics: A Unified Approach

## James T. Sandefur, Jr.

EACH summer a group of forty high school students (most of whom have just finished their junior year) is invited to Georgetown University for a six-week program in mathematical modeling. This program, originated seven years ago by Ronald Rosier under a National Science Foundation grant, is designed both to teach students important mathematical techniques and to teach them how to think mathematically. We have succeeded with our first goal by teaching topics that are considered parts of a course in discrete mathematics; that is, probability, combinations, permutations, vectors and matrices, graph theory, linear programming, game theory, and difference equations. In addition, we teach computer programming.

In teaching *mathematical thinking,* we tried to teach the students how to read a word problem, interpret it as a mathematical equation, solve that equation, and then interpret the solution in relation to the original word problem. Our efforts toward this goal were less than satisfactory.

Over the years we have attempted to overcome this problem by modifying our approach. Our solution is based on the one word *recursion;* that is, to occur again and again. Now, we first teach our students the art of recursive thinking, the most common example of which is compound interest. We then build on this theme throughout the program. At certain points, we introduce other topics in discrete mathematics (such as combinations, permutations, probability, tree diagrams, and vectors and matrices), which are then used in conjunction with recursion to do interesting (and realistic) applications. One advantage is that the students can immediately see the value of each topic; this in turn increases their interest in, and appreciation of, mathematics. The applications we present are not the standard examples usually presented to high school students. Instead, our examples come from research material in biology, genetics, and economics. By the end of our course, the students have studied the relationship between predator and prey species, the distribution of such sex-linked traits as color blindness, and the law of supply and demand as applied to the farming industry.

90

A second advantage is that this material makes extensive use of high school algebra, such as factoring polynomials and solving systems of linear equations. This use reinforces these topics as well as shows their applicability.

A number of complaints have been made about this approach to discrete mathematics. First, several mathematicians have claimed that this material is too difficult for high school students. Well, we have taught it successfully to our students, and although we are good teachers, we know that many others are better. A teacher with an interest in students and the willingness to make the effort will have little trouble teaching these concepts.

A second complaint is that we are excluding important topics in discrete mathematics. This comment comes mostly from computer scientists. Computer scientists might complain about the lack of certain topics, but we do cover their most important topic—recursive thinking. The other topics included are of the broadest general appeal. In fact, it is hard to conceive of students who would not benefit from this material, regardless of their future field of study.

The true purpose of learning discrete mathematics is to be able to set up and solve discrete mathematical models. Thus we teach a course in which the techniques and applications of discrete mathematics are taught hand in hand, as is done in most other disciplines. This leads to a cohesive course that enhances the students' appreciation of mathematics.

The following topics are our recommendations for a course on discrete mathematics:

---

**Topic A.   An Introduction to Recursion**
**Topic B.   First-Order Difference Equations**
    Part 1.   Linear Equations
    Part 2.   Nonlinear Equations
**Topic C.   Probability**
**Topic D.   Higher-Order Equations**
    Part 1.   Linear Equations
    Part 2.   Nonlinear Equations
**Topic E.   Linear Algebra**
**Topic F.   Systems of Equations**
    Part 1.   Linear Equations
    Part 2.   Nonlinear Equations
    Part 3.   Strange Attractors

---

The dependence of each topic on the preceding topics is given in figure 8.1. (A dotted line implies that although some of the material depends on the preceding topic, the material could be skipped.) These topics will be discussed in more detail in the next six sections.

This course is designed for the student who has mastered algebraic skills and is therefore ready for a more challenging course. It is independent of calculus and could be offered to students before or after they take calculus.

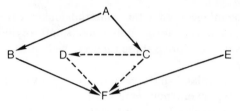

Fig. 8.1

The material is deep enough and new enough for even the brightest students to find it interesting.

## AN INTRODUCTION TO RECURSION

One of the most difficult tasks for teachers is to teach their students how to think. We have all been frustrated with students who use the wrong method on their homework problems. "Think," we say to them, but how do we train them to think? Although this question is usually difficult to answer, one type of thinking, recursive thinking, is easy to teach. In fact, in our modern society the ability to think recursively is essential, which makes it surprising that recursion is almost totally ignored in mathematics courses.

One of the simplest examples of recursion is looping in computer programming. Many of us who have taught programming have assigned the problem to write an algorithm for adding the first six integers. Many students write the following "flow chart":

$$s = 1 + 2 + 3 + 4 + 5 + 6$$

But the student who thinks recursively writes:

1. Start the sum at 1.
2. Take the next integer.
3. Add that integer to the sum.
4. If the last integer added is a 6, stop. Otherwise,
5.  go back to step 2.

This can be visualized by the flow chart in figure 8.2.

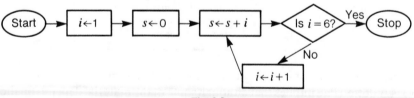

Fig. 8.2

The key to learning computer programming is to be able to use loops such as this. The job would be half done if the student was already familiar with recursion.

Computer science is not the only area in which recursion occurs. Another simple example is to consider a $1000 savings account at 7% interest compounded annually. The amount in the account at the end of the first year is the original $1000 plus interest, which is $(.07)1000 = \$70$, for a total of $1070. We can write this mathematically as

$$A(1) = A(0) + .07A(0) = 1070,$$

where $A(0)$ represents the amount of our original deposit (time 0) and $A(1)$ represents the amount in our account at the end of the first year. Continuing in this manner, we see that the amount in our account at the end of year 2 is

$$A(2) = A(1) + .07A(1) = 1.07A(1) = (1.07)1070 = 1144.90.$$

To compute the amount at the end of year $n + 1$, we would use the formula

$$A(n + 1) = 1.07A(n)$$

where $A(n)$ represents the amount in the account at the end of year $n$ (and similarly for $A(n + 1)$). To compute the amount at the end of year 6, we would use our formula above six times, just as our computer programming student used the loop six times.

To summarize, there is no area of study in which recursion would not be helpful, and there are a number of areas in which it is essential.

In order to teach recursion, teachers should give their students a large number of word problems to set up mathematically. That is, the student should learn to translate English into "Mathematicalese."

***Example 1:*** Consider a child who has a row of $n$ blocks. She starts at the left of the row and picks up one or two blocks at a time and puts them in a toy box. How many ways can the child pick up the blocks? For example, suppose she has three blocks. She can pick them up in the following three ways: $(1,1,1)$, $(1,2)$, or $(2,1)$. Here $(1,1,1)$ means she picked up one block, then a second block, and then a third block; $(1,2)$ means she first picked up one block and then two blocks.

*Solution:* Let $A(n)$ represent the number of ways to pick up $n$ blocks. As seen above, $A(3) = 3$; $A(2) = 2$, that is, (2) and (1,1).

Let us now compute $A(4)$. At her first turn, the child can pick up either one or two blocks. If, on the one hand, she picks up one block, then she has three left, and there are $A(3) = 3$ ways in which to pick them up. Thus, three ways to pick up four blocks are $(1,1,1,1)$, $(1,1,2)$, and $(1,2,1)$. If, on the other hand, the child picks up two blocks first, then she has two blocks remaining, and there are $A(2) = 2$ ways in which to pick them up. Thus two additional ways to pick up four blocks are $(2,2)$ and $(2,1,1)$. Since these are the only ways to pick up four blocks, we have

$$A(4) = A(3) + A(2) = 3 + 2 = 5.$$

It should be clear from this argument that if there are nine blocks, the number of ways in which the child can pick them up starting with one block is $A(8)$ and starting with two blocks is $A(7)$. Therefore

$$A(9) = A(8) + A(7).$$

The general formula is thus

$$A(n) = A(n - 1) + A(n - 2).$$

Using this formula, we can see that $A(4) = 5$, $A(5) = 8$, and so on. This is the Fibonacci sequence.

***Example 2:*** Consider another child with a collection of $n$ distinct blocks. He wishes to line them up in a row. How many ways can this be done? Assume the child has three blocks, A, B, and C. These can be lined up in the following six ways: (ABC), (ACB), (BAC), (BCA), (CAB), or (CBA).

*Solution:* Let $A(n)$ represent the number of ways $n$ distinct blocks can be lined up in a row. As seen above, $A(3) = 6$.

Let us compute $A(4)$. There are four blocks, A, B, C, and D. In the first position, the child can put any one of the four blocks. Thus we have four cases: Case 1 is that A is first, case 2 is that B is first, case 3 is that C is first, and case 4 is that D is first. The number of arrangements in case 4 is $(DX)$, where $X$ can be any of the $A(3) = 6$ arrangements of the three blocks A, B, and C, given above. Therefore there are six arrangements of the blocks that start with a D. Likewise, there are six arrangements starting with each of the other three letters. Thus

$$A(4) = A(3) + A(3) + A(3) + A(3) = 4A(3).$$

If we have $n$ blocks, then we have $n$ cases. In each case, since we have fixed which block comes first, we have $n - 1$ blocks left to arrange and there are $A(n - 1)$ ways to arrange them. Thus

$$A(n) = \underbrace{A(n - 1) + \ldots + A(n - 1)}_{n \text{ times}} = nA(n - 1).$$

Since $A(1) = 1$, we get $A(2) = 2(1)$, $A(3) = 3A(2) = 3(2)(1)$, and so forth. By defining $n!$ (read as "$n$ factorial") as $n(n - 1)(n - 2) \ldots (2)(1)$, we can see that $A(n) = n!$. Therefore, the number of arrangements (or permutations) of $n$ items is $n!$.

Examples such as these teach students to break problems into simpler parts, to think recursively, and to translate written statements into mathematical equations. One final example of recursive thinking that can be taught at this point is proof by induction. Simple examples would include the proof that

$$1 + 2 + 3 + \ldots + n = n(n + 1)/2.$$

## FIRST-ORDER DIFFERENCE EQUATIONS

A *difference equation* is an equation involving an independent variable (often $n$), which usually represents time, and a dependent variable ($A(n)$ in our interest problem above), which usually represents the amount of something at time $n$. The difference equation is an equation that relates the amount of something at one point in time, $A(n + 1)$, to the amount of that something at a previous point in time, $A(n)$. The simplest type of difference equation is of the form

$$A(n + 1) = rA(n)$$

Here $r$ is a given constant such as 1.07 in our interest problem above, and the equation relates the amount in our savings account in year $n + 1$ to the amount in our savings account in the previous year; that is, year $n$. This equation is called *first order* because the difference of the times $n + 1$ and $n$ is 1. It is called linear because it does not involve powers or products of the $A(n)$ terms.

Another example of a first-order linear difference equation is one that is used to describe population growth. Let $A(n)$ represent the size of a population at time $n$. Assume that the change in population during one time period—that is, $A(n + 1) - A(n)$—is proportional (with a constant of proportionality $r$) to the size of the population, $A(n)$. This is written mathematically as

$$A(n + 1) - A(n) = rA(n),$$

or, after collecting like terms,

$$A(n + 1) = (1 + r)A(n).$$

If you are given the size of the initial population, say $A(0) = 1000$, then by solving for $A(1)$, then $A(2)$, and so forth, it can easily be seen that

$$A(1) = (1 + r)1000, \ A(2) = (1 + r)^2 1000, \ldots, A(n) = (1 + r)^n 1000.$$

Thus, we conclude that populations grow exponentially.

Since observations of population growth tend to tell us that populations do not grow exponentially, we decide that something must be wrong with our model. What appears to be wrong is that the growth rate $r$ is not constant but instead depends on the size of the population. In other words, as the population increases, the growth rate must decrease because of over-crowded conditions and the lack of food. Therefore we replace $r$ in the equation above with $[r - bA(n)]$. The constant $b$ represents the amount of food available. Notice that when $A(n)$ is small, the growth rate is approximately $r$, whereas if $A(n)$ is large, the growth rate is approximately 0 or even negative (corresponding to a death rate that is higher than the birth rate). The new equation is

$$A(n + 1) - A(n) = [r - bA(n)]A(n),$$

or, after collecting terms,

$$A(n + 1) = [1 + r - bA(n)]A(n).$$

This is a first-order equation, but unlike the preceding equation it is *non-linear* because it involves the product of two terms that each contain an $A(n)$ term. For a thorough derivation of this equation, as well as an analysis of the solution, see Dorn and McCracken (1976).

Linear difference equations (and linear differential equations) are the key to analyzing many (if not most) real-world situations mathematically. Some straightforward applications that our students have enjoyed are the amortization of loans, annuities, the law of supply and demand, and compound interest.

In studying the amortization of loans, the student learns how loan institutions determine a borrower's monthly payment so that a loan can be paid off (amortized) in $n$ equal payments. See Dorn and McCracken (1976) or Sandefur (1983) for more details.

Students can study the law of supply and demand as applied to industries such as farming (where *next* year's supply depends on *this* year's prices). In this study, they learn why prices tend to oscillate. A detailed study can be found in both Goldberg (1961) and Sandefur (1983).

In each of the applications above students learn how to handle *real* applications of mathematics and not just the usual verbal "problems" given at this level. We have found that this procedure gives the students an added incentive to study mathematics, and in fact many enjoy mathematics for the first time.

Nonlinear equations are important because many important mathematical models are nonlinear. The derivation of these equations is similar to the derivation of the nonlinear growth equation given above.

The most important mathematical reasons for studying first-order linear equations are that (1) the theory behind these equations is thoroughly understood, (2) this theory is easy to convey to students. (3) many important models are linear, and (4) the key to studying nonlinear problems is based on the theory of linear equations.

The study of nonlinear equations is interesting *because* solutions *cannot* in general be given. That is, for each different starting value $A(0)$, and for each different $r$ and $b$, we must actually iterate the equation—that is, use a loop—to find out what is happening. Since this is rather unsatisfying as well as very time-consuming, we develop the technique of linearization. This is the technique of finding a linear equation whose solutions are approximately the same as the solution to the nonlinear equation.

**Example 3:** Consider the equation for nonlinear population growth with $b = 0.025$ and $r = 0.2$. The equation becomes

$$A(n + 1) = [1.2 - 0.025A(n)]A(n).$$

Notice that $A(0) = 8$ is an equilibrium value in that $A(1) = A(2) = \ldots = 8$. Let $A(n) = 8 + E(n)$. Here, $E(n)$ is the error or distance from equilibrium. Substituting into the equation gives

$$8 + E(n + 1) = [1.2 - 0.025\{8 + E(n)\}]\{8 + E(n)\},$$

or, after collecting terms,

$$E(n + 1) = 0.8E(n) - 0.025E^2(n), \text{ where } E^2(n) = E(n)E(n).$$

We now ask what happens to the solution when $A(0)$ is "close" to 8; that is, $E(0)$ is "close" to 0. In this case, $E^2(0)$ is "very" small, so we drop it from the equation, giving

$$E(n + 1) = 0.8E(n).$$

This is called *linearization*. The solution to this linear equation is $E(n) = (0.8)^n E(0)$, which tends to zero as time goes on; that is, as $n$ gets large. Therefore, $A(n)$ gets closer to 8. A computation of the actual $A(n)$ values and those computed using the linearized equation, with $A(0) = 8.5$, shows that the approximations do accurately describe the behavior of the actual $A(n)$ values:

|          |     | **Actual value** | **Approximate value** |
|----------|-----|------------------|-----------------------|
| $A(0)$   | =   | 8.5              | 8.5                   |
| $A(1)$   | =   | 8.3937           | 8.4                   |
| $A(2)$   | =   | 8.3111           | 8.32                  |
| $A(3)$   | =   | 8.2464           | 8.256                 |
| $A(4)$   | =   | 8.1956           | 8.2048                |
| $A(5)$   | =   | 8.1555           | 8.1638                |
| $A(10)$  | =   | 8.0501           | 8.0537                |
| $A(15)$  | =   | 8.0163           | 8.0176                |

In particular, we can predict that if the population above is "close" to equilibrium, that is, 8, it will remain close to 8. For more details, see Dorn and McCracken (1976) and Sandefur (1983).

By using this technique, we cannot predict exactly what will happen, but we can determine the qualitative behavior of the solutions. For example, in the nonlinear population equation we can determine under what conditions the size of the population of our species will stabilize and what the size of the population will be (8 units in our example).

This technique (which we have greatly oversimplified) is one of the most important tools of the applied mathematician. But most mathematicians will not teach this technique to the nonspecialist because they feel it is too difficult. *This is not true.* We have successfully taught linearization to high school students for several years, and most of them find it fascinating. They not only can see how mathematics is really used but can actually do it themselves.

We must note here that linearization is nothing more than computing derivatives. Since the functions are usually no more complicated than $y = 1.2x - 0.025x^2$ (which is the example above with $A(n + 1) = y$ and $A(n) = x$), most students will be able to do it, even if they have not taken calculus. Note that $y' = 1.2 - 0.05x$, and when $x = 8$, $y' = 0.8$, the same number that was in the linearized equation above.

Very nice graphical illustrations of this material can be given to reinforce these ideas. In figure 8.3, the actual values of $A(n)$ are shown. In figure 8.4, the approximate values are shown.

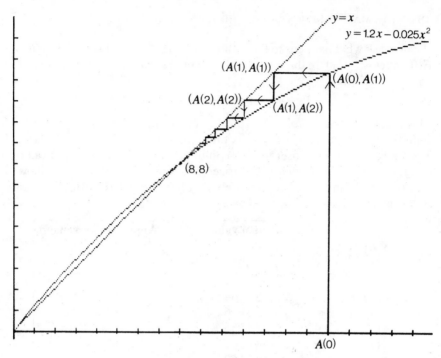

Fig. 8.3. Actual values

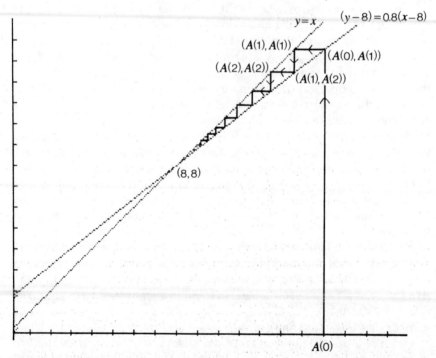

Fig. 8.4. Approximate values using the tangent line to the curve $y = 1.2x - 0.025x^2$ at the point $(8,8)$

Another topic our students enjoy is the study of *bifurcation theory*. An example of this is the study of the population growth for a species of fish. If the fish are left undisturbed, the equation that models their growth is the nonlinear growth equation considered earlier. But if we introduce fishing into our model, we get the equation

$$A(n + 1) = [1 + r - bA(n)]A(n) - c.$$

Here the constant $c$ represents a certain fixed number of the fish that are removed each year by fishing. Other than $c$, the equation is unchanged. Let us consider this equation with $r = 0.8$ and $b = 0.08$. The equation then becomes

$$A(n + 1) = 1.8A(n) - 0.08A^2(n) - c.$$

The equilibium values for this equation are found by solving the equation $x = 1.8x - 0.08x^2 - c$ for $x$. By the quadratic formula, the solutions are

$$x = 5 \pm 5\sqrt{1 - 0.5c}.$$

Since the square root of a negative number does not exist, it follows that (i) if $c > 2$, then there are no equilibrium values; (ii) if $c = 2$, then there is one equilibrium value, which is $x = 5$; and (iii) if $c < 2$, then there exist two equilibrium values. Thus if more than two units of fish are removed each time period, then there is no equilibrium and the population of fish die out; but if fewer than two units of fish are removed each time period, the fish will stabilize at the larger of the two equilibrium values.

Bifurcation theory is the mathematical study of how the behavior of some real-world systems can change as some input into the system is changed. In our example, as $c$ changes from less than 2 to greater than 2, the system goes from one that is stable to one that is disastrous. (This is why many lakes need to be restocked periodically.) Not only is this a good mathematical example, but it can also be used to give the students some insight into environmental control issues.

Along with the other topics discussed previously, we have successfully taught bifurcation theory to high school students for several years. The only difficulty is that no textbooks cover these topics. That is why the lecture notes (Sandefur 1983), which we now use in our program, were written. In fact, these notes will be expanded into a book that could be used for a course like this one.

## PROBABILITY

By teaching recursion first, a different approach can be given to the study of probability and, in particular, to the teaching of permutations and combinations. We have found that counting arguments are generally one of the most difficult concepts to explain to students. One reason for this is that the logic used is quite different from anything to which the students have been exposed. But by using recursion, we can develop counting formulas relatively easily. In example 2, for instance, we derived the formula for the number of permutations (or arrangements) of $n$ distinct items, that is, $n!$. A derivation of the formula for the number of combinations of $n$ items taken $k$ at a time can be derived similarly. See Sandefur (1983) and Tucker (1980, chap. 4).

The advantage of this approach (assuming the student has studied recursion and first-order difference equations) is that the counting arguments use techniques and logic with which the student is familiar, and thus a difficult obstacle to learning probability is avoided.

Conditional probability is another topic that is of considerable importance in applications. Conditional probability problems are of the form "What is the probability of A happening if you know that B has happened?" In genetics the problem might be phrased as "What is the probability that an offspring has a certain trait given that the parents have that trait?" By repeating this question over several generations (which is a recursive problem), we can study the long-term distribution of certain traits of a species.

## HIGHER-ORDER EQUATIONS

This topic consists first of the study of *linear* equations of the form

$$A(n + 2) = bA(n + 1) + cA(n),$$

where $b$ and $c$ are given constants. Then *nonlinear* equations (that is, equations in which we have products of terms containing $A(n + 1)$ and $A(n)$) will be studied. In these examples, the amount of whatever we are considering, $A(n + 2)$, not only depends on what happened in the previous time period (as in our previous examples) but also on what happened two time periods away; that is, in time period $n$.

The students find this material somewhat more difficult than the previous topics. This is because the study of linear equations involves both solving equations of the form

$$x^2 - ax - b = 0$$

(where complex roots are allowed) and solving systems of two linear equations with two unknowns. Although students should be familiar with each of these algebraic techniques, most students find it difficult to apply these techniques simultaneously.

The advantages of covering higher-order equations are that this topic (1) displays the need for knowing these techniques, (2) gives the students practice in using these techniques, and (3) enables the students to study interesting mathematical models.

***Example 4:*** Two of our high school students, Lawrence Letellier and Tony Pribadi, discovered a solution to the *gambler's ruin* independent of the same approach in Feller (1950). In this problem, a person bets one dollar on each play of a game (like roulette, craps, etc.) on which the probability of winning is, say, .4, and the probability of losing is therefore .6. The person plays until he or she has a total of, say, ten dollars, or until he or she is broke. If the player starts with five dollars, what is the probability the player will go broke? The idea is to let $P(n)$ be the probability the player will go broke when starting with $n$ dollars. Our problem is to compute $P(5)$.

*Solution:* The probability that players will go broke, given that they have $n + 1$ dollars, which is $P(n + 1)$, equals the probability that they will win a dollar, which is .4, and then go broke, which is $P(n + 2)$, plus the probability they will lose a dollar, which is .6, and then go broke, which is $P(n)$. This phrase when written mathematically is

$$P(n + 1) = .4P(n + 2) + .6P(n),$$

or after dividing by .4 and rearranging terms,

$$P(n + 2) = 2.5P(n + 1) - 1.5P(n).$$

This is a second-order (since time extends over two periods, that is, $(n + 2) - n = 2$) linear difference equation. We also have two pieces of information; that is, $P(0) = 1$ (players who have 0 dollars are certain to go broke), and $P(10) = 0$ (players who have ten dollars will quit playing and are certain not to go broke).

We have seen that solutions to first-order linear equations, such as $P(n + 1) = rP(n)$, are of the form $P(n) = cr^n$, where $c$ is some constant. Likewise, solutions to second-order linear equations, such as the one above, are of the form $P(n) = br^n + cs^n$, where $b$ and $c$ are some constants. By substituting $P(n) = b(r^n)$, $P(n + 1) = b(r^{n+1})$, and so on, into the equation above, we get

$$b(r^{n+2}) = 2.5b(r^{n+1}) - 1.5b(r^n),$$

or after dividing by $b(r^n)$,

$$r^2 = 2.5r - 1.5.$$

The solutions are $r = 1$ and $r = 1.5$, and therefore

$$P(n) = b(1)^n + c(1.5)^n.$$

Since $P(0) = b + c = 1$ and $P(10) = b + c(1.5)^{10} = b + 57.665c = 0$, we can solve for $b$ and $c$, getting $b = 1.01765$ and $c = -0.01765$. Thus

$$P(n) = 1.01765 - 0.01765(1.5)^n.$$

The answer to our original question is that the probability the player will go broke if she or he starts with five dollars is $P(5) = .8836$, or about 88 percent of the time. It is surprising how likely it is one will go broke, even when the odds are only slightly against one. For more details, see Feller (1950) and Letellier, Pribadi, and Sandefur (1983).

Many of the applications of nonlinear equations are from the study of the growth of populations. One application involves the study of two populations that compete for the same food. The analysis shows that if the two species have the same food requirements, then one must die out. Consequently that proves *Gause's principle of competitive exclusion*, that is, no two species can have identical food requirements and coexist. (Actually the term is *niche* requirements.) See Malkevitch and Meyer (1974) for details.

In reality, higher-order equations involve no new techniques. They are important in that they blend much of the student's mathematical background into interesting and complex applications.

## LINEAR ALGEBRA

This section introduces a powerful mathematical topic that greatly expands the student's ability to apply recursion: the study of linear algebra, or vectors and matrices. To illustrate, consider the system of equations

$$x + 2y + 3z = 10$$
$$2x - 3y + z = 1$$
$$x + y - z = 4.$$

We have two vectors $x$ and $b$, and one matrix $A$ where

$$\bar{x} = \begin{pmatrix} x \\ y \\ z \end{pmatrix}, \quad \bar{b} = \begin{pmatrix} 10 \\ 1 \\ 4 \end{pmatrix},$$

and $A$ consists of the coefficients of the unknowns, that is,

$$A = \begin{pmatrix} 1 & 2 & 3 \\ 2 & -3 & 1 \\ 1 & 1 & -1 \end{pmatrix}.$$

We can then write the system in the mathematical shorthand
$$A\bar{x} = \bar{b}.$$

The students learn the algebra of vectors and matrices, that is, how to add, subtract, and multiply these objects. Division consists of finding inverse matrices denoted $A^{-1}$. They must learn when $A^{-1}$ exists and how to find it if it does. Note that when $A^{-1}$ exists, the solution to our system of equations is
$$\bar{x} = A^{-1}\bar{b}.$$

At this point, we are suggesting that only the rudiments of linear algebra be taught; these are methods for solving systems of equations, finding inverses of matrices, and computing determinants of matrices.

One topic that is of particular importance, but that is somewhat more complex to teach, is the study of eigenvalues and eigenvectors. A vector $\bar{x}$ is called an eigenvector and a number $b$ is called an eigenvalue of the matrix $A$ if

$$A\bar{x} = b\bar{x}.$$

This is important because in this case
$$A^n\bar{x} = b^n\bar{x},$$

and thus the multiplication of matrices is simplified. The numbers $b$ are just the numbers for which the determinant of $(A - b)$ is zero, and so the determination of the numbers $b$ just involves the factoring of a polynomial. To determine $\bar{x}$, one needs to solve the system of equations

$$(A - b)\bar{x} = 0.$$

Vectors and matrices are studied so that we can study difference equations of the form

$$P(n + 1) = 2P(n) - Q(n)$$
$$Q(n + 1) = 3P(n) + 2Q(n),$$

that is, a set of difference equations in which we are considering the amounts of two objects at a certain time, say, the number of prey, $Q(n)$, and the number of predators, $P(n)$. Notice that the number of each of these species in a particular time period depends on how many of each of them there were in the previous time period. We shall discuss this example further in the next section.

## SYSTEMS OF EQUATIONS

We now deal with applications that involve several objects that are interrelated. Some applications that we have studied using different techniques are the relationships among several species of animals. In genetics we can study the relationship among organisms of the same species but with different traits. In economics, we can study the relationship among private investments, consumer spending, and government spending from one year to the next.

***Example 5:*** We now consider the *random walk*. Suppose a drunk leaves a bar. His home is two blocks to the left, and the police station is one block to his right. He will stagger one block to the left with probability .2 or one block to the right with probability .8. After walking one block, he will again walk left with probability .2 or right with probability .8. He continues in this manner until he either arrives home or arrives at the police station. (See fig. 8.5.)

Fig. 8.5

Let home be block 0 and the police station be block 3. Let $P_k(n)$ be the probability he will be at block $k$ ($0 \le k \le 3$) after he has walked $n$ blocks. Thus the probability that he will be at block 0 after walking $n + 1$ blocks ($P_0(n + 1)$) equals the probability that he was at block 0 after walking $n$ blocks (since 0 is home and once he reaches home he stays there), which is $P_0(n)$, plus the probability he was at block 1 after walking $n$ blocks ($P_1(n)$) and then walked left (.2). Thus

$$P_0(n + 1) = P_0(n) + .2P_1(n).$$

In a similar manner, we can derive the equations

$$P_1(n + 1) = .2P_2(n)$$
$$P_2(n + 1) = .8P_1(n)$$
$$P_3(n + 1) = .8P_2(n) + P_3(n).$$

By letting

$$\overline{P}(n) = \begin{pmatrix} P_0(n) \\ P_1(n) \\ P_2(n) \\ P_3(n) \end{pmatrix} \text{ and } A = \begin{matrix} \begin{matrix} P_0 & P_1 & P_2 & P_3 \end{matrix} \\ \begin{pmatrix} 1 & .2 & 0 & 0 \\ 0 & 0 & .2 & 0 \\ 0 & .8 & 0 & 0 \\ 0 & 0 & .8 & 1 \end{pmatrix} \end{matrix},$$

we have the system of equations $\overline{P}(n + 1) = A\overline{P}(n)$, which is identical to the four equations given above. Similarly to first-order linear equations and remembering that $P_0(0) = 0$, $P_1(0) = 0$, $P_2(0) = 1$, and $P_3(0) = 0$, the solution is

$$\overline{P}(n) = A^n \overline{P}(0),$$

which shows where eigenvalues and eigenvectors are useful. The determinant of the matrix $(A - b)$ is

$$|A - b| = (1 - b)(1 - b)(b - .4)(b + .4).$$

Thus we have four eigenvalues, $b = 1, 1, .4$, and $-.4$. Four corresponding eigenvectors (which are the solutions to $(A - 1)\overline{x} = 0$, etc.) are

$$\overline{x}_1 = \begin{pmatrix} 1 \\ 0 \\ 0 \\ 0 \end{pmatrix} \quad \overline{x}_2 = \begin{pmatrix} 0 \\ 0 \\ 0 \\ 1 \end{pmatrix} \quad \overline{x}_3 = \begin{pmatrix} 1 \\ -3 \\ -6 \\ 8 \end{pmatrix} \quad \overline{x}_4 = \begin{pmatrix} 1 \\ -7 \\ 14 \\ -8 \end{pmatrix}.$$

The solution is

$$\overline{P}(n) = a(1)^n \overline{x}_1 + b(1)^n \overline{x}_2 + c(.4)^n \overline{x}_3 + d(-.4)^n \overline{x}_4,$$

where $a, b, c,$ and $d$ are four constants. We can solve for these constants, since we know $\overline{P}(0)$. The solutions are (by solving four linear equations with four unknowns) $a = 1/21$, $b = 20/21$, $c = -1/12$, and $d = 1/28$. Thus

$$\overline{P}(n) = (1/21)\overline{x}_1 + (20/21)\overline{x}_2 - (1/12)(.4)^n \overline{x}_3 + (1/28)(-.4)^n \overline{x}_4.$$

Since $(.4)^n$ and $(-.4)^n$ are small when $n$ is large, $\overline{P}(n)$ is approximately $(1/21)\overline{x}_1 + (20/21)\overline{x}_2$; that is, $P_0(n) = 1/21$ and $P_3(n) = 20/21$ for large $n$. Thus the drunk will end at home 1 time out of 21 and in jail 20 times out of 21.

More complex forms of this linear system can be used to study many complex physical systems, such as the diffusion of gases through a porous membrane.

The combination of linear systems with the technique of linearization can

be used to study many mathematical models, such as the relationship between predator and prey species. There is a thorough treatment of this in
Smith (1968) and a simplified treatment in Malkevitch and Meyer (1974).

At this point, the students are able to study more complex behavior than
the above. In fact, they are able to study problems of current mathematical
interest; that is, *chaos* and *strange attractors*.

To explain, there are numerous systems of difference equations in which
the solutions $(P(n))$ behave chaotically; that is, they appear to have no
pattern. These models seem to explain many real-world phenomena. The
reason for this behavior is that linearization in some sense fails to work. This
can be demonstrated to students, and the chaotic behavior can then be
exhibited using simple computer programs.

Sometimes the behavior exhibited on the computer has a *strange* and
beautiful pattern, which is called a strange attractor. One such attractor is
the Henon attractor seen in figure 8.6. The points on this graph are the
points $(P(n), Q(n))$, where $P(n)$ and $Q(n)$ are the solutions to the nonlinear system of equations

$$P(n + 1) = Q(n) + 1 - 1.4P^2(n)$$
$$Q(n + 1) = .3P(n).$$

Mathematicians do not understand why this behavior happens. Our students have enjoyed writing programs that display this behavior, and several

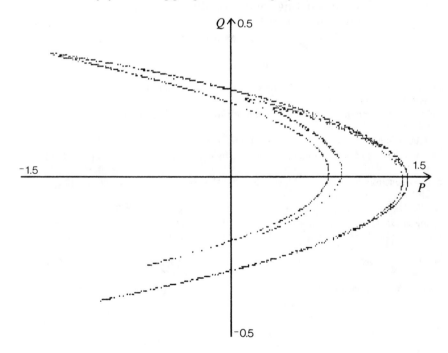

Fig. 8.6

have created science fair projects on this topic. A good introduction to this topic is found in Ruelle (1980).

Students find it interesting to see a topic that is not understood by mathematicians. This gives them an appreciation of what research mathematicians actually do.

## INSTRUCTIONAL MATERIALS

There are two disadvantages to our proposal for a discrete mathematics course. Mathematics teachers are generally untrained in difference equations, and there is a lack of instructional materials.

The lecture notes (Sandefur 1983) were written because of the dearth of material on difference equations and especially because of the lack of a text that both unifies the material given in the References and expands into the areas of bifurcation theory, difference equation solutions to Markov processes, and nonlinear systems.

The teaching of our course in discrete mathematics presents a special problem. A mathematics teacher with training in differential equations would have no trouble learning this material from the References or from a text in discrete mathematics with finite difference equations (should one be published).

For the training of high school mathematics teachers, we propose that colleges should start offering courses on difference equations and how to teach them. At present, few colleges offer such courses, and it will remain this way unless high school teachers create a demand for them.

### REFERENCES

Dorn, William S., and Daniel D. McCracken. *Introductory Finite Mathematics with Computing.* New York: John Wiley & Sons, 1976.

Feller, William. *An Introduction to Probability Theory and Its Applications.* Vol. 1. New York: John Wiley & Sons, 1950.

Goldberg, Samuel. *Introduction to Difference Equations.* New York: John Wiley & Sons, 1961.

Letellier, Lawrence, Tony Pribadi, and James Sandefur. "The Gambler's Ruin." 1983. Available from Mathematics Department, Georgetown University, Washington, DC 20057.

Malkevitch, Joseph, and Walter Meyer. *Graphs, Models, and Finite Mathematics.* Englewood Cliffs, N.J.: Prentice-Hall, 1974.

Ruelle, David. "Strange Attractors." *Mathematical Intelligencer* 2 (1980): 126–37.

Sandefur, James T. "Discrete Mathematics with Finite Difference Equations." Duplicated lecture notes, 1983. Available from Mathematics Department, Georgetown University, Washington, DC 20057.

Smith, J. Maynard. *Mathematical Ideas in Biology.* Cambridge: Cambridge University Press, 1968.

Tucker, Alan. *Applied Combinatorics.* New York: John Wiley & Sons, 1980.

# 9

# Noncareer Mathematics:
# The Mathematics We All Need

## Thomas Sonnabend

**W**HY is it that adults are so easily confused or deceived by the mathematics they encounter in their everyday lives? One reason is that our schools do not teach many of the everyday applications that adults need to know. Although we must be concerned about preparing students for careers in a highly technological society, we must also teach useful "noncareer mathematics," which all adults use as citizens and consumers. In this chapter "noncareer mathematics" will refer to the mathematics adults commonly encounter outside the workplace.

What kind of mathematics do adults need to understand and apply? They need to understand the mathematics contained in news stories and advertisements. They need mathematics to analyze the tax system, their diets, and gambling games. By understanding the geometry of design, they develop a greater appreciation of the beauty of nature and art. They need to employ mental computation and estimation in all these areas.

Secondary students do not learn the applications of mathematics that they will most commonly encounter as adults. Adults rarely use pure mathematics; they deal with mathematics in applied contexts. Yet, with the exception of consumer mathematics for the non–college bound, we teach few everyday applications. No wonder students do not understand how secondary school mathematics relates to their everyday lives!

High school mathematics has two main programs: one for college-bound students and one for non-college-bound students. Only 10 to 20 percent of all high school students will pursue mathematics-related careers. Yet, all college-bound high school students learn the mathematics whose main purpose is to prepare them for calculus. Non-college-bound high school students typically study general and consumer mathematics. In general mathematics, they have more arithmetic drill, but they do not become competent at arithmetic. In consumer mathematics, a more popular program because of its practical nature (Usiskin 1983), less common applications such as home loans, life insurance, and installment buying are overemphasized at the expense of more common applications such as budgets, taxes, and investments. Neither the college-bound nor the non-college-bound students study enough useful noncareer mathematics.

Data from the National Assessment of Educational Progress reveal the result of implementing our current curriculum. Most secondary school students possess fairly good knowledge and skills but are poor at understanding and applying mathematics (NAEP 1983). These test results are not surprising. They reflect a school mathematics curriculum that emphasizes knowledge and skills and devotes too little time to the more difficult areas of mathematical understanding and application.

This chapter will describe the most common noncareer mathematics topics that adults need. Then, a collection of noncareer mathematics units for secondary school will be presented. Finally, recommendations will be made for changing the secondary mathematics curriculum in order to make room for some of these noncareer mathematics units.

## THE FOCUS OF NONCAREER MATHEMATICS PROGRAMS

### Consumer Mathematics

Consumer mathematics helps people manage their personal finances. Adults most commonly employ consumer mathematics in budgeting, keeping financial records, banking, shopping, paying taxes, and investing. Other applications include loans and insurance. Consumer mathematics involves whole number arithmetic, mental arithmetic, percents, tables, formulas, calculators, computers, and to a lesser extent, rational numbers, integers, graphs, averages, and measurement.

### Media Mathematics

Media mathematics helps people understand and analyze advertising, news, and to a lesser degree, sports and weather. The mathematics most commonly used in advertising and news involves whole number arithmetic, rational numbers, percents, relationships between two variables, statistics (averages and surveys), and graphs and tables (Czepiel and Esty 1980).

The applications of mathematics beyond whole number arithmetic frequently involve economics or opinion polls. Rational numbers and percents most often describe rates of increase or decrease of economic variables. Relationships between variables most commonly pertain to economics (e.g., supply and demand). Statistics are used often in opinion polls and less frequently in economics applications of the mean, median, and mode. Graphs and tables illustrate data on a variety of subjects including economics, crime rates, population, the arms race, and test scores.

The sports and weather news contain the same kinds of mathematics. One also finds applications of basic probability in weather forecasts and in the odds for the outcome of sports events.

In the media, one sometimes encounters misuses of mathematics. Government officials, business people, and advertisers occasionally employ statistical deceptions. Graphs in the media may be distorted, most commonly by improperly labeling the vertical axis (see fig. 9.1).

## Other Noncareer Mathematics

In addition to consumer and media mathematics, adults apply mathematics during their leisure activities and in the home. Such applications include cooking and dieting, maintaining home and car, and playing games and sports. One's appreciation of art, architecture, and nature is enhanced by an understanding of mathematics. All these activities involve some of the same mathematics found in consumer and media applications as well as applications of measurement and geometry.

## The Mathematical Content and Processes

Noncareer mathematics principally contains applications of whole and rational numbers, percents, mental arithmetic/estimation, basic algebra, basic geometry, measurement, and statistics. Noncareer mathematics also requires such mathematical processes as induction, deduction, and a variety of problem-solving techniques (e.g., posing questions, generating an appropriate formula, and guessing and testing). This mathematics content and these processes, then, make up nearly all the mathematics most adults need to know for everyday use.

## NONCAREER MATHEMATICS TOPICS

This section will outline some specific noncareer mathematics units that can be taught in secondary school. Most of the topics in this section have the following characteristics in common:

- They involve solving word problems.
- They apply mathematics taught in grades 5–8.
- They require discussing another subject area.
- They will be more interesting, useful, or controversial than standard mathematics for most students.

The sample topics here emphasize media mathematics. Consumer mathematics units are more readily available.

**1. Topic: Mental arithmetic and estimation**

*Mathematical concepts:* rounding off, mental arithmetic, estimation, percents, field properties

*Subtopics:* mental arithmetic with rational numbers, related estimation with rational numbers, mental arithmetic with percents, related estimation with percents, computing tips

*Typical exercises*
A. Find a shortcut for computing $49 \times 20 \times 1/7$ in your head. What field property justifies your shortcut?
B. Estimate 36% of 879.

*Sample project:* Keep a record of all the times you use mental arithmetic and estimation during a given week.

*References:* Seymour (1981), Trafton (1978)

## 2. Topic: Statistical deceptions

*Mathematical concepts:* rational numbers, percents, averages, tables, and graphs

*Subtopics:* successive percentage changes, labeling of axes, percentages of different sized amounts, use of different time frames, use of different types of averages, "up to" or "as much as"

*Typical exercises*

 A. My rent went down 10% last year and rose 20% this year. Over the two years, my rent went up _____ %.

 B. President Reagan used a graph (fig. 9.1) in a speech to show how far behind the United States was in defense spending in 1982 and how the United States would close the gap by 1987. How would this graph look different if the vertical axis started at 0 instead of 200? Does the distortion in the graph shown here favor President Reagan's viewpoint?

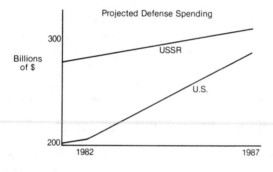

Fig. 9.1

*Sample project:* Find an advertisement that contains a significant statistical deception. Bring the ad (or a transcript) to class and explain the deception. Write the company about it.

*References:* Horwitz (1980), Huff (1954), Reichard (1974), Runyon (1981), Wheeler (1977)

## 3. Topic: Surveys

*Mathematical concepts:* percents, randomness, rational numbers, tables

*Subtopics:* constructing survey questions, reporting results

*Typical exercises*

 A. Consider the following survey question: Which category best describes your own political position?
  *a)* conservative *b)* moderate *c)* liberal *d)* none of these
  How would the results change if choice *d* is omitted? If choices *a, b,* and *c* are changed to "right wing," "middle of the road," and "left wing"?

 B. Critique the following report. On the basis of a poll on 11–14 July 1980, Gallup (1980) reported, "Public backs drafting of women." The poll asked if women in the United States should be required to serve in the armed forces. The results were as follows:

"Should women be required to serve in the armed forces?"

| Should | Should Not | No Opinion |
|--------|-----------|-----------|
| 49% | 47% | 4% |

*Sample project:* Find an article containing a poll with a significant omission, error, or biased use of data. Suggest how it could be improved.

*References:* news magazines, Runyon (1981), Wheeler (1977)

## 4. Topic: Federal taxes and the federal budget

*Mathematical concepts:* percents, formulas, decimals, tables, large numbers

*Subtopics:* types of taxes, filling out Form 1040, sources of government income, government expenditures

*Typical exercises:*

A. In 1984, the Social Security tax was 6.7% of income up to $37 800. No Social Security tax was to be paid on income beyond $37 800. Explain why the Social Security tax is regressive.

B. Which government programs had their budgets increased by more than 15% between 1984 and 1985? What percent of the total federal budget is spent on national defense? How much of every tax dollar collected comes from individual income taxes?

*Sample project:* Obtain information on a school or government budget. Analyze the budget in some detail including a discussion of trends. Evaluate the budget and suggest programs that should be cut or increased.

*References:* U.S. Bureau of the Budget (1983), U.S. Bureau of the Census (1982)

## 5. Topic: Economics

*Mathematical concepts:* tables and graphs, percents, base rates, direct and inverse variation, formulas, rational numbers, large numbers

*Subtopics:* economic indexes, supply/demand/price relationships

*Typical exercises*

A. Supply-and-demand schedule for oil

| Possible prices (per barrel) | Quantity demanded per day (million barrels) | Quantity supplied per day (million barrels) | Pressure on price |
|------------------------------|---------------------------------------------|---------------------------------------------|-------------------|
| $42 | 60 | 110 | |
| $38 | 69 | 98 | |
| $34 | 75 | 88 | |
| $30 | 80 | 80 | |
| $26 | 88 | 72 | |

Draw supply-and-demand curves on the same graph of price versus quantity. What is the equilibrium price? Fill in each row of the last column in the chart with upward, neutral, or downward. If the quantity demanded at all prices increases by 13 million barrels a day, what will the new equilibrium price be?

B. Consumer Price Index (1967 = 100)

| 1970 | 1975 | 1980 |
|------|------|------|
| 116.3 | 161.2 | 247.0 |

By what percent did consumer prices rise from 1967 to 1970? From 1970 to 1975?

*Sample project:* Choose an economic indicator and write a description of how it is computed mathematically. What are some flaws in the way the index is computed? How could it be improved? What is the significance of the index? Who is affected by it? Describe the behavior of the index over the last four years.

*References: Economic Indicators,* news magazines, newspapers, Lenoski (1981), Samuelson (1982)

## 6. Topic: World population growth and protein consumption

*Mathematical concepts:* exponential growth, percents, ratios, large numbers, decimals, doubling time, prediction, modeling

*Subtopics:* exponential growth, world population growth, protein efficiency, protein consumption

*Typical exercises*

A. The estimated population of the United States in 1983 was 234 million and the annual growth rate was 0.9%. Forecast the population for the year 2000.

B. What percentage of usable protein is lost in the process of converting vegetable protein to beef protein?

*Sample project:* Develop a plan for dealing with the world population and food crisis. For each proposal you make, estimate its impact mathematically.

*References:* almanacs, Lappe (1982), United Nations (1983)

## 7. Topic: Perspective drawing and visual perception

*Mathematical concepts:* parallelism, perpendicularity, solid geometry

*Subtopics:* limitations of our vision, basic rules of perspective, viewpoints

*Typical exercises*

A. Make a drawing illustrating one-point perspective.

B. In figure 9.2, is it farther from $A$ to $B$ or from $A$ to $C$? Answer first without measuring and then measure to see if you were right.

*Sample project:* Write a description of the basic rules of perspective. Make a drawing that incorporates some of these rules.

References: Kline (1974), Parramon (1982)

Fig. 9.2. Reprinted with permission from Wirtz (1974, 35)

### 8. Topic: Inductive and deductive reasoning

Mathematical concepts: induction, deduction

*Subtopics:* induction and its limitations, deduction and its limitations, correct vs. incorrect deduction

*Typical exercises*

   A. Make up a mathematical example of correct deductive reasoning that leads to a false conclusion.

   B. Explain how each person below uses inductive reasoning:

     *a*) a student   *b*) a mathematician   *c*) a prejudiced person

*Sample project:* For one week keep a record of all the times you use induction or deduction.

*References:* Harnadek (1976, 1980), Jacobs (1982)

### 9. Topic: Diet

*Mathematical concepts:* percents, basic algebra, ratios

*Subtopics:* calories, carbohydrates, fats, sugar, cholesterol, and protein

*Typical exercises*

   A. Daily protein consumption in grams should be about $0.43W$ where $W$ is your desired weight in pounds. How much protein do you need? How much do you typically eat?

   B. List a typical day's diet for you and compute the total number of calories and the total number of grams of carbohydrates you consume. Nutritionists recommend that we obtain 60% of our calories from carbohydrates. Examine your diet to see if you obtain a reasonable proportion of your total calories from carbohydrates. Carbohydrates have 4.1 calories per gram.

*Sample project:* A U.S. congressional committee recommends the following sources of calories in the diet: approximately 60% of calories from carbohydrates (15% sugar); 30% from fat (10% saturated); and 10% from protein. Analyze your diet and make suggestions for improving it by changes in your consumption of carbohydrates, fat, saturated fat, sugar, and protein.

*References:* Jacobson (1975), Krause and Mahan (1979), McGovern (1979)

### 10. Topic: Games

*Mathematical concepts:* probability

*Subtopics:* probabilities for cards and dice, lotteries, gambling games, backgammon

*Typical exercises*

   A. In the Maryland lottery, players try to guess three-digit numbers. One game is called "back pair." In back pair, you must select the last two digits of the winning number in the correct order. The payout is 50 for 1. What is the probability of guessing these two digits in the correct order? In the long run, what percentage of your money will you lose?

   B. In craps, what is the probability of rolling a 7 on the first roll? What is the probability of winning if you roll an 8 on the first roll? (Note for less experienced readers: this requires rolling another 8 before rolling a 7.)

*Sample project:* Select any game that involves probability and compute the probabilities of several outcomes. Suggest some optimum strategies.

*References:* Packel (1981)

### 11. Topic: Order and proportion in art, architecture, and nature

*Mathematical concepts:* symmetry, solid geometry, ratio, golden ratio, rigid motions, regular polygons, similar solids, measurement

*Subtopics:* shapes of buildings, symmetry, golden ratio, limits of size in nature, tessellations

*Typical exercises*
   A.  Describe the types of symmetry for a given building. What solids do you find in its construction?
   B.  Write the first ten terms of the Fibonacci sequence. How is it related to the golden ratio? Where does one find Fibonacci numbers in nature?

*Sample project:* Make your own tessellation drawing based on a rectangle or a parallelogram.

*References:* Bergamini (1963), Ernst (1976), Gudder (1976), Pedoe (1983), Ranucci (1977), Stevens (1974), Strache (1973), Thompson (1975)

### Other Noncareer Mathematics Units

Other possible topics for noncareer mathematics include using a calculator, computers in society, investment mathematics, budgeting, shopping, sports mathematics, and similar solids in the marketplace. Additional ideas can be found in Burkhardt (1981), Johnson et al. (1972), NCTM (1979), MAA and NCTM (1980), Rogerson (1983).

## RECOMMENDATIONS FOR CHANGE

If we are going to spend more time teaching noncareer mathematics, how will we make room in the curriculum? "If we once abandon our fatal habit of cramming the children with theorems (and procedures) which they do not understand, and will never use, there will be plenty of time to concentrate their attention on really important topics" (Whitehead 1968, 83).

School mathematics contains many unmotivated details and mechanics; instead, it should focus on the main ideas of mathematics "and let there be as many examples (of these ideas) as teachers find necessary . . . either by way of abstract particular cases or by way of application(s)" (Whitehead 1968, 80). All students should study some of the central ideas of mathematics and the most common noncareer applications of mathematics. Unnecessary details should be deleted, and more complicated mechanics should be done using calculators and computers.

What are some specific changes that should be considered for grades 7–12? As suggested in the *Agenda for Action* (NCTM 1980), all seventh and eighth graders should spend less time on "paper-and-pencil calculations with more than two digits" (p. 7) or complicated fractions.

For non-college-bound students, noncareer mathematics fits right into their high school curriculum, which typically involves further study of middle school mathematics in general and consumer mathematics courses. The emphasis of these courses should be changed from manipulations and less common applications, such as home loans and life insurance, to conceptual understanding and more common applications.

Incorporating noncareer mathematics into college-preparatory mathematics is more difficult. College-bound students do not study the mathematical content of noncareer mathematics after eighth grade. As long as current courses remain rigidly defined as algebra 1, geometry, algebra 2, and precalculus, it will be more difficult to change the curriculum to include noncareer mathematics, computers, and probability and statistics. Some of these topics now appear in those parts of the textbook that teachers usually skip.

---

## ... the three central ideas of secondary school mathematics are variable, algebraic form, and generalization.

---

Noncareer mathematics could be assigned in the form of projects, but it deserves a greater role in college-preparatory mathematics. More substantial changes in school mathematics could be made if the curriculum focused on the main ideas of mathematics and the most common applications. According to Whitehead (1982), the three central ideas of secondary school mathematics are variable, algebraic form, and generalization (p. 62). Room would be made for more applications by deleting minor topics and allowing students to employ computers and calculators for lengthy manipulations.

What are the central ideas of college-preparatory mathematics courses and what less-important topics could be deleted or dealt with primarily using computers and calcualtors? The following list represents an attempt to initiate discussion of these issues. Most of the central ideas of mathematics are based on the writing of Whitehead (1968, 1982).

### Algebra 1

Central ideas:
- Variable represents some or any number
- Variable is fundamental in theory and applications
- Generalizations of number lead to the introduction of integers, rationals, irrationals, and reals
- Number systems have fundamental properties
- Abstract ideas are needed for scientific descriptions
- Formulas have limitations when used in applications
- Graphs clarify numerical relationships

Unnecessary details:
- Contrived word problems such as coin, age, digit, and work problems (Usiskin 1980)
- Factoring to solve equations and reduce algebraic fractions
- Most of the arithmetic of algebraic fractions
- Most of the mechanics involving $n$th roots of monomials

Mechanics that calculators and computers should do:
- Solve most equations and inequalities
- Perform complicated polynomial arithmetic including fractions and roots

## Geometry

Central ideas:

- Congruence is a correspondence between two sets of points
- Congruence clarifies properties of basic plane figures
- Similarity is an extension of the ideas of congruence
- Similarity is a basis for trigonometry
- Symmetry of a figure is a correspondence of the figure to itself
- Transformations relate to symmetry, congruence, and similarity
- General properties of measurement that apply to length, area, and volume
- Abstract ideas are needed for scientific descriptions
- Euclid presents geometry in a deductive sequence
- Coordinate geometry links algebra and geometry

Unnecessary details:

- The least important theorems and proofs of obvious statements (Usiskin 1980)
- Triangle-midpoint theorem
- Theorems on intercepted arcs of secant and tangent lines
- Circumscribed and inscribed figures (Whitehead 1968)
- All proofs except for "short sequences of rigorously developed material, playing down two-column proofs" (CBMS 1982)
- The ruler and protractor postulates, concurrence theorems, and constructions (Sonnabend 1981)
- Separation postulates

Mechanics that calculators and computers should do:

- Perform area and volume computations with less-common formulas or with laborious computations

## Algebra 2/Precalculus

Central ideas:

- Development of symbolism led to important advances
- Algebraic form underlies the organization of mathematical ideas
- Coordinate geometry links algebra and geometry
- Functions and graphs are related
- Periodicity in nature can be described by periodic functions
- How triangle trigonometry and circular functions are related
- A more general definition of conic sections developed historically
- Development of imaginary numbers illustrates variable, algebraic form, and generalization
- Vectors describe essential characteristics of force and motion
- Limits of series are useful approximations
- Probability and statistics are useful in describing and predicting large-scale behavior

Unnecessary details:

- Calculations using logarithms, complex trigonometric identities, memorization of trigonometric values, the study of most trigonometric formulas beyond basic definitions, and lengthy drill of algebraic manipulation (CBMS 1982)
- Solving cubic equations by synthetic division and factoring
- Some of the memorization concerning conic sections

Mechanics that calculators and computers should do:

- Solve most equations and inequalities

- Graph more complicated functions
- Compute logarithms and trigonometric values
- Do complicated polynomial arithmetic including fractions and roots

I hope these suggestions will encourage other mathematics educators to develop their own lists of central ideas and less-important topics. Such lists will help us make more intelligent revisions in the curriculum.

## SUMMARY

It is vital for secondary school students to study the noncareer applications of mathematics that they will encounter as adults. Students learn few common mathematical applications in the present curriculum. It is hoped that the general description and the sample topics in this chapter have conveyed the flavor of noncareer mathematics. The most appropriate topics will vary according to the students and the instructor involved.

In order to add these topics to the curriculum, other topics must be deleted. This can be done by focusing college-preparatory mathematics courses on central ideas and common applications while deleting less-important topics and using calculators and computers to perform many of the manipulations. The curriculum for non-college-bound students could easily incorporate some noncareer mathematics units in place of current topics in general and consumer mathematics.

### REFERENCES

Bergamini, David. *Mathematics*. New York: Time, 1963.

Burkhardt, Hugh. *The Real World and Mathematics*. Glasgow: Blackie, 1981.

Conference Board of the Mathematical Sciences (CBMS). *The Mathematical Sciences Curriculum K–12: What Is Still Fundamental and What Is Not*. Report to NSB Commission on Precollege Education in Mathematics, Science, and Technology. Washington, D.C.: CBMS, 1982.

Czepiel, James, and Edward Esty. "Mathematics in the Newspaper." *Mathematics Teacher* 73 (November 1980): 582–86.

*Economic Indicators*. Washington, D.C.: U.S. Government Printing Office, monthly.

Ernst, Bruno. *The Magic Mirror of Escher*. New York: Random House, 1976.

Gallup, George, ed. *The Gallup Poll: Public Opinion, 1982*. Wilmington, Del.: Scholarly Resources, 1982.

Gudder, Stanley. *A Mathematical Journey*. New York: McGraw-Hill Book Co., 1976.

Harnadek, Anita. *Critical Thinking*. Books 1 and 2. Troy, Mich.: Midwest Publications, 1976, 1980.

Horwitz, Lucy, and Lou Ferleger. *Statistics for Social Change*. Boston: South End Press, 1980.

Huff, Darrell. *How to Lie with Statistics*. New York: W. W. Norton & Co., 1954.

Jacobs, Harold. *Mathematics: A Human Endeavor*. San Francisco: W. H. Freeman, 1982.

Jacobson, Michael. *Nutrition Scoreboard*. New York: Avon. 1975.

Johnson, Donovan, Viggo Hansen, Wayne Peterson, Jesse Rudnick, Ray Cleveland, and L. Carey Bolster. *Applications in Mathematics*. Courses A and B. Glenview, Ill.: Scott, Foresman & Co., 1972.

Kline, Morris. *Mathematics in Western Culture*. New York: Oxford University Press, 1974.

Krause, Marie, and Kathleen Mahan. *Food, Nutrition, and Diet Therapy*. 6th ed. Philadelphia: W. B. Saunders, 1979.

Lappe, Frances. *Diet for a Small Planet*. New York: Ballantine Books, 1982.

Lenoski, C. Gail. "The Student Price Index." In *Teaching Statistics and Probability*, 1981 Yearbook of the National Council of Teachers of Mathematics, edited by Albert Shulte. Reston, Va.: NCTM, 1981.

Mathematical Association of America (MAA) and the National Council of Teachers of Mathematics (NCTM). *A Sourcebook of Applications of School Mathematics*. Reston, Va.: NCTM, 1980.

McGovern, George. "Dietary Goals for the United States." In *Political Ecology*, edited by A. Cockburn and J. Ridgeway. New York: Times Books, 1979.

National Assessment of Educational Progress (NAEP). *The Third National Mathematics Assessment: Results, Trends, and Issues*. Denver: Education Commission of the States, 1983.

National Council of Teachers of Mathematics (NCTM). *Applications in School Mathematics*. 1979 Yearbook of the NCTM. Reston, Va.: NCTM, 1979.

———. *An Agenda for Action: Recommendations for School Mathematics of the 1980s*. Reston, Va.: NCTM, 1980.

Packel, Edward. *The Mathematics of Games and Gambling*. Washington, D.C.: Mathematical Association of America, 1981.

Parramon, J. M. *Perspective*. Tucson, Ariz.: H. P. Books, 1982.

Pedoe, Dan. *Geometry and the Visual Arts*. New York: Dover Publications, 1983.

Ranucci, Ernest, and Joseph Teeters. *Creating Escher Type Drawings*. Palo Alto, Calif.: Creative Publications, 1977.

Reichard, Robert. *The Figure Finaglers*. New York: McGraw-Hill Book Co., 1974.

Rogerson, Alan. *Mathematics in Society: The Real Way to Apply Mathematics?* Hawthorn, Australia: MIS Project, 1983.

Runyon, Richard. *How Numbers Lie*. Lexington, Mass.: Lewis Publishing Co., 1981.

Samuelson, Paul. *Economics*. 12th ed. New York: McGraw-Hill, 1982.

Seymour, Dale. *Developing Skills in Estimation*. Books A and B. Palo Alto, Calif.: Dale Seymour Publications, 1981.

Sonnabend, Thomas. "A Letter to the Editor." *Mathematics Teacher* 74 (January 1981): 7–8.

Stevens, Peter. *Patterns in Nature*. Boston: Little, Brown & Co., 1974.

Strache, Wolf. *Forms and Patterns in Nature*. New York: Random House, 1973.

Thompson, D'Arcy. *On Growth and Form*. Abridged ed. New York: Cambridge University Press, 1975.

Trafton, Paul. "Estimation and Mental Arithmetic: Important Components of Computation." In *Developing Computational Skills*, 1978 Yearbook of the National Council of Teachers of Mathematics, edited by Marilyn Suydam. Reston, Va.: NCTM, 1978.

United Nations. *World Statistics in Brief*. 7th ed. New York: U.N. Publ., 1983.

United States Bureau of the Budget. *The United States Budget in Brief—Fiscal Year 1984*. Washington, D.C.: U.S. Government Printing Office, 1983.

United States Bureau of the Census. *Statistical Abstract of the United States, 1982–3*. 103d ed. Washington, D.C.: U.S. Government Printing Office, 1982.

Usiskin, Zalman. "What Should Not Be in the Algebra and Geometry Curricula of Average College-bound Students?" *Mathematics Teacher* 73 (September 1980): 413–24.

———. "A Proposal for Reforming the Secondary School Mathematics Curriculum." Paper presented at the NCTM 61st Annual Meeting in Detroit, April 1983.

Wheeler, Michael. *Lies, Damned Lies, and Statistics*. New York: Dell Publishing Co., 1977.

Whitehead, Alfred North. *The Aims of Education*. New York: Free Press, 1968.

———. *Introduction to Mathematics*. New York: Oxford University Press, 1982

Wirtz, Robert. *Patterns & Problems*. Book F. Washington, D.C.: Curriculum Development Associates, 1974.

# 10

# Integrating Geometry into the Secondary Mathematics Curriculum

## Timothy V. Craine

**T**HE problem of geometry and its place in the secondary school curriculum continues to be a controversial issue. Over the years many proposals have been advanced to abolish the tradition of teaching geometry as a one-year course in the tenth grade. Whereas some would replace the year of geometry with something else, such as computer science, most educators would agree that some geometry is appropriate. This author is personally attracted to the unified approach to secondary school mathematics in which geometry, algebra, and analysis are taught as an integrated whole over the entire secondary school curriculum. This was the approach of the Secondary School Mathematics Curriculum Improvement Study (SSMCIS) (Sitomer 1973). However, with the exception of schools in New York and its neighboring states (see chapters 16, 17, and 19 of this yearbook), the unified approach has not caught on. Gearhart (1975) found little support among teachers for the unified curriculum, and given the resistance to radical change inherent in educational institutions, we may assume that for the moment the one-year, tenth-grade course is firmly entrenched.

This chapter is written on the assumption that the geometry course will remain in place as the tenth-grade requirement for college-preparatory secondary students, and that lacking a unified mathematics curriculum, the second-best alternative is to improve the present geometry course. A number of important issues regarding the content of this tenth-grade course must be addressed:

1. How can geometry be taught in such a way as to maintain continuity with what comes before (first-year algebra) and after (intermediate algebra, trigonometry, and analysis)? How can we avoid the common problem of students seeing geometry as a totally irrelevant hiatus in the "real" business of high school mathematics, which is algebra?

2. What should be the role of proof in the geometry course? What degree of rigor should we demand?

3. What approach should we take to teaching geometry? The standard Euclidean approach? Or more modern methods that emphasize coordinate geometry, vectors, and transformations?

4. Are students entering the tenth-grade geometry course ready for geometry on the level at which we have traditionally taught it? Or does research based on the van Hiele levels of geometric thought (Mayberry 1983) suggest that for many students much of the content is not meaningful?

This chapter addresses these questions. It presents an alternative course for tenth-grade geometry, one that incorporates a variety of approaches, traditional and modern, in a carefully developed sequence; meets the developmental needs of the students; and wherever possible integrates the content of the tenth-grade geometry course into the overall secondary mathematics curriculum.

## OVERVIEW

The syllabus for tenth-grade geometry presented here is based on a course implemented during the 1982–83 academic year at Renaissance High School, a public, city-wide, academically oriented high school in Detroit, Michigan. The course as developed was predicated on several assumptions:

1. Students entering this course have not necessarily had the informal geometric experiences that should ideally occur in the middle grades.

2. Many students entering this course are below the third van Hiele level,[1] the minimum level at which one can fully appreciate definitions and relations of class inclusion. Students who have not reached this level cannot be expected to succeed in writing proofs, a skill that requires advancing to the fourth van Hiele level. Thus proofs should be delayed until the student is ready for them.

3. High school students do not automatically appreciate a fully developed axiomatic approach to geometry or any other mathematical system. Rather, a goal of the course should be to foster such appreciation. Although it may satisfy mathematics teachers and authors of textbooks to start the course with a sparse and elegant set of postulates and proceed to develop as much geometry as one can from this set, the overall logical structure is lost to most students in this approach.

4. Students need to master new content (geometry) before being asked to master a new approach to learning (formal proofs).

5. Students need opportunities to use algebra skills learned in the ninth grade in a meaningful way. Simply including a few algebra review exercises in every unit of instruction is less meaningful than using algebra whenever possible to explain the content of the geometry being learned.

---

1. The van Hieles discovered five levels of geometric thought. Mayberry (1983) and others have validated their schema. At the lowest level, students recognize geometric figures but not their properties. At the second level, students recognize properties of figures but in isolation from one another. Only at the third level can they adequately define figures in terms of their properties and recognize relations of class inclusion (e.g., that all rectangles are parallelograms). At the fourth level, students can engage in deductive reasoning about geometric facts. At the fifth and highest level, they understand formal aspects of deduction and can appreciate indirect proof.

6. The geometry course should help prepare students for more advanced courses, such as linear algebra and calculus.

7. An eclectic approach to geometry allows for flexibility (Forbes 1973). Nevertheless, the entire course should be structured so that various topics and methods are appropriately sequenced. Topics should not be taught discretely; rather, whenever possible, the underlying unity of the subject should be revealed.

Based on these assumptions, this course is organized in the following manner. During the first semester we avoid formal proofs and attempt to cover as much content as possible. During the first six weeks our approach may be characterized as informal. We review, or in most cases cover for the first time, material that ideally belongs in the middle school curriculum. We then spend approximately four weeks studying coordinate geometry. This gives us an opportunity to expand on algebra skills and prove, using coordinate methods, several significant theorems. During the last six weeks we study transformations, and this leads to a study of congruence, similarity, and trigonometric functions.

The second semester is devoted to the development of formal reasoning. The first six weeks are devoted to studying reasoning and the role of postulates in a mathematical system. The remainder of the semester stresses the development of proof.

Each of these five major divisions is explained in more detail in the five sections that follow.

## INFORMAL APPROACHES TO GEOMETRY

At the beginning of this course, informal methods are used to introduce fundamental concepts of geometry. We avoid explicit mention of postulates and theorems and concentrate on properties of geometric figures and the relationships between classes of figures (e.g., parallelograms and rectangles). Absolute rigor in formulating definitions is not required at first but is gradually built up so that by the second semester definitions of familiar terms can be reexamined. At that point, the relationship between definitions and theorems can be appreciated. If, for instance, we accept the definition of a square as a rectangle with at least one pair of adjacent sides congruent, then the fact that all four sides of a square are congruent becomes a theorem to be proved.

As students become familiar with geometric figures, they are encouraged to study their properties through an inductive discovery approach. Such facts as "The sum of the measures of the interior angles of a triangle is 180 degrees" and "The diagonals of a rectangle are congruent" are arrived at through measurement, constructions, and paper-folding methods.

Deductive reasoning is gradually introduced as we demonstrate that the truth of certain statements necessarily follows from already established facts. In no case, however, do we attempt formal "proofs"; rather, we give an informal argument for our conclusion. Facts demonstrated in this manner include the extension of the angle sum formula from the triangle to other polygons, the development of formulas for areas and volumes, and the Pythagorean theorem.

Some space geometry is included. Whenever possible, concrete three-dimensional models are used rather than pictures of three-dimensional objects, since many students have difficulty visualizing the real thing from pictures. Topics include incidence relations, parallelism and perpendicularity of lines and planes, and the five regular polyhedra.

In addition to developing the standard area and volume formulas and the Pythagorean theorem (using an area approach), the course gives extensive practice in applying these formulas. Exercises include those in which the formula is used to establish an equation (e.g., in solving for one base of a trapezoid or the leg of a right triangle) so that students have a chance to apply algebra skills involving linear equations, literal equations, and operations with radicals. Furthermore, compound area exercises provide a challenging, but useful preparation for problems that appear on a wide variety of standardized tests (see example in fig. 10.1).

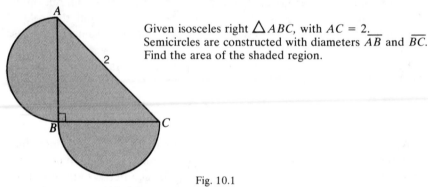

Given isosceles right $\triangle ABC$, with $AC = 2$. Semicircles are constructed with diameters $\overline{AB}$ and $\overline{BC}$. Find the area of the shaded region.

Fig. 10.1

---

## . . . coordinate proofs are less intimidating to the beginning student than formal synthetic proofs.

---

### COORDINATE GEOMETRY

The coordinate geometry unit gives students an opportunity to use and extend skills learned in ninth-grade algebra and at the same time allows them to prove significant theorems about triangles and quadrilaterals using coordinate methods. It is my experience that coordinate proofs are less intimidating to the beginning student than formal synthetic proofs.

The logical structure of this unit is based on four assumptions. The word *postulate* is avoided, since it is introduced later in the course in a more formal setting and none of the assumptions are postulates of our more formal geometry. The assumptions do, however, allow us to prove rather quickly a very rich set of theorems. The assumptions are these:

1. The $x$-axis and $y$-axis are perpendicular to each other.
2. The Pythagorean theorem and its converse are true.
3. The graph of an equation that can be written in the form $ax + by = c$ is a line (provided that $a$ and $b$ are not both 0), and any line has an equation of that form.
4. Any polygon may be placed with one vertex at the origin and one side on the positive $x$-axis.

From these assumptions, together with appropriate definitions of *slope, vector, multiplication of a vector by a scalar,* and *dot product of two vectors,* we prove six fundamental theorems of coordinate geometry. The proofs we present are not formal two-column proofs. Rather, they are arguments using algebra that is familiar to the student. The theorems are first demonstrated with specific numerical examples before the more general argument is given. The six theorems are as follows:

1. The distance formula, $d = \sqrt{(x_2 - x_1)^2 + (y_2 - y_1)^2}$ (proved from assumptions 1 and 2)
2. The midpoint formula: Midpoint = $((x_1 + x_2)/2, (y_1 + y_2)/2)$ (proved from theorem 1)
3. The equation of any nonvertical line may be written in the form $y = mx + b$ (proved from assumption 3).
4. Any line segment contained in the line with equation $y = mx + b$ has slope equal to $m$ (proved from the definition of slope).
5. Two nonvertical lines are parallel if and only if their slopes are equal (proved from theorems 3 and 4).
6. Two nonvertical lines are perpendicular if and only if the product of their slopes is $-1$ (proved from the Pythagorean theorem and the distance formula).

The last two theorems are also stated using the language and concepts of vectors. The equivalence of the two ways of stating these theorems is demonstrated:

5. **Vector approach:** Two line segments are parallel if and only if a vector of one is a scalar multiple of a vector of the other.
6. **Vector approach:** Two line segments are perpendicular if and only if the dot product of their vectors is 0.

An argument for the latter theorem is given in figure 10.2. We point out to the students that the vector approach has an advantage over the slope approach in that the statement of the theorem does not require discussing the exceptional circumstances involving lines with undefined slope (i.e., lines parallel to the $y$-axis).

The purpose of having proved these six theorems is then revealed as we use them to prove facts about plane geometric figures—particularly quadrilaterals and triangles. Students receive the list of fourteen theorems shown in figure 10.3.

For about a week we assign problems that involve proofs of these theorems. The problems are divided into three sets. In the first set, the

---

**Argument for Theorem 6 (Vector Approach)**

THEOREM 6. *Two vectors are perpendicular if and only if their dot product is zero.*

*Case 1.* One vector is vertical, in which case they are perpendicular if and only if the other vector is horizontal.

A vertical vector is represented by $(0,a)$.

A horizontal vector is represented by $(b,0)$.

So the dot product $= (0,a) \cdot (b,0) = 0 \cdot b + a \cdot 0 = 0$.

*Case 2.* Neither vector is vertical or horizontal.

Example: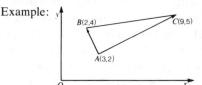

Check sides using the distance formula:
$AC = \sqrt{45}$; $BA = \sqrt{5}$; $AC = \sqrt{50}$.
$(AC)^2 + (BA)^2 = (AC)^2$

$\overrightarrow{AB} = (\Delta x, \Delta y) = (2 - 3, 4 - 2) = (-1, 2)$

$\overrightarrow{AC} = (\Delta x, \Delta y) = (9 - 3, 5 - 2) = (6, 3)$

$\overrightarrow{AB} \cdot \overrightarrow{AC} = (-1, 2) \cdot (6, 3) = -6 + 6 = 0$

The dot product of the vectors $\overrightarrow{AB}$ and $\overrightarrow{AC}$ is 0, whereas the converse of the Pythagorean theorem indicates that $\overline{AB}$ and $\overline{AC}$ are legs of a right triangle and thus $\overline{AB} \perp \overline{AC}$.

A more general argument is given by $A(x_0, y_0)$, $B(x_0 + a, y_0 + b)$, and $C(x_0 + c, y_0 + d)$.

We show that $AB = \sqrt{a^2 + b^2}$

$AC = \sqrt{c^2 + d^2}$

$BC = \sqrt{(a-c)^2 + (b-d)^2}$

Then if $(AB)^2 + (AC)^2 = (BC)^2$, $a^2 + b^2 + c^2 + d^2 = a^2 - 2ab + b^2 + c^2 - 2bd + d^2$, or $0 = -2(ac + bd)$, so $0 = ac + bd = (a, b) \cdot (c, d)$.

These steps may be reversed to demonstrate the converse.

Fig. 10.2

---

coordinates of each point are given as specific known quantities, for instance, the example in figure 10.4. In this problem the student is expected to show that $ABCD$ is a parallelogram by showing that $\overline{AD} \parallel \overline{BC}$ and $\overline{AB} \parallel \overline{DC}$ and then that $ABCD$ is a rhombus by showing that one pair of consecutive sides are congruent.

After students have demonstrated that $\overline{AC}$ is perpendicular to $\overline{BD}$, the theorem associated with this problem, theorem Rh-2, is discussed. It is emphasized that we have demonstrated *in one particular case* that the diagonals of a rhombus are perpendicular, but that we have *not* proved that perpendicular diagonals are a property of every rhombus.

In the second set of problems, variables are used for coordinates of vertices. Figure 10.5 gives an example of a problem from this set.

After working out this problem, theorem IT-2 is discussed. Here we come to the conclusion that we have proved the theorem for not just one instance

THEOREM T. *The line segment joining the midpoints of two sides of a triangle is parallel to the third side and its length is one-half the length of the third side.*

THEOREM IT-1. *The median to the base of an isosceles triangle is also an altitude.*

THEOREM IT-2. *The two medians drawn to the legs of an isosceles triangle are congruent.*

THEOREM Q. *The midpoints of the sides of a quadrilateral are the vertices of a parallelogram.*

THEOREM P-1. *Both pairs of opposite sides of a parallelogram are congruent.*

THEOREM P-2. *The diagonals of a parallelogram bisect each other.*

THEOREM P-3. *If the diagonals of a quadrilateral bisect each other, then the quadrilateral is a parallelogram.*

THEOREM R-1. *All four interior angles of a rectangle are right angles.*

THEOREM R-2. *The diagonals of a rectangle are congruent.*

THEOREM Rh-1. *All four sides of a rhombus are congruent to each other.*

THEOREM Rh-2. *The diagonals of a rhombus are perpendicular to each other.*

THEOREM Rh-3. *If the diagonals of a parallelogram are perpendicular to each other, then the parallelogram is a rhombus.*

THEOREM Tp-1. *The median of a trapezoid is parallel to its bases and its length is one-half the sum of the lengths of the bases.*

THEOREM Tp-2. *If the diagonals of a trapezoid are congruent, then two sides of the trapezoid are congruent.*

Fig. 10.3

but for all cases of isosceles triangles with one vertex at the origin and with its base along the positive $x$-axis.

Some students express reluctance to work out the details of this proof, since they do not feel as comfortable working with "letters" (variables) as with "numbers" (constants). They are ultimately convinced that the use of variables allows them to arrive at the more general result, and that as long as we accept the placement assumption (assumption 4), we can agree that the theorem is proved.

Before assigning the third set of problems, five lemmas are proved in class:

LEMMA IT. *If $P(0,0)$, $Q(a,0)$, and $R(b,c)$ are the vertices of an isosceles triangle with $PR = QR$, then $b = a/2$.*

LEMMA P. *If $P(0,0)$, $Q(a,0)$, $R(d,e)$, and $S(b,c)$ are the vertices of a parallelogram, then $d = a + b$ and $e = c$.*

LEMMA R. *If $P(0,0)$, $Q(a,0)$, $R(a + b,c)$, and $S(b,c)$ are the vertices of a rectangle, then $b = 0$.*

LEMMA Rh. *If $P(0,0)$, $Q(a,0)$, $R(a + b,c)$, and $S(b,c)$ are the vertices of a rhombus, then $a = \sqrt{b^2 + c^2}$.*

LEMMA Tp. *If $P(0,0)$, $Q(a,0)$, $R(d,e)$, and $S(b,c)$ are the vertices of a trapezoid with $\overline{PQ}$ parallel to $\overline{RS}$, then $e = c$.*

These lemmas allow us to choose the most convenient set of coordinates to

Show that $ABCD$ is a rhombus and that $\overline{AC} \perp \overline{BD}$.

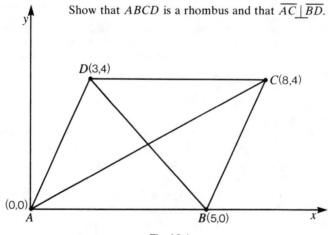

Fig. 10.4

facilitate the proof of a particular theorem. On the basis of these lemmas, students can then tackle such problems as "Prove theorem P-2." The first step is to use lemma P to set up a quadrilateral with coordinates $P(0,0)$, $Q(a,0)$, $R(a + b,c)$, $S(b,c)$. From there the proof of the theorem is similar to the proof of an exercise from the second set.

## This coordinate geometry unit bridges the gap between informal, inductive, discovery experiences and deductive proof.

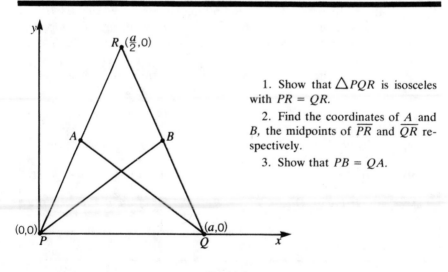

1. Show that $\triangle PQR$ is isosceles with $PR = QR$.

2. Find the coordinates of $A$ and $B$, the midpoints of $\overline{PR}$ and $\overline{QR}$ respectively.

3. Show that $PB = QA$.

Fig. 10.5

Not every one of the fourteen theorems is included in each of the three sets of exercises, but by the time students have completed all of the exercises, they are familiar with all fourteen theorems.

This coordinate geometry unit bridges the gap between informal, inductive, discovery experiences and deductive proof. During this unit students apply and extend skills learned in algebra the previous year. By the end of the unit they have not only become familiar with the coordinate plane but have surveyed a significant portion of the content of the traditional high school geometry course.

At this point in the course, a discussion of loci is appropriate. The locus definition is used to derive the equation of a circle and, if time permits, equations for other conic sections as well.

## TRANSFORMATIONS

The unit on transformations builds on the coordinate geometry unit. Transformations are approached first in an intuitive manner, using concrete models (Coxford 1973; Hirsch 1976). Miras and tracing paper are used to develop the concepts of reflection and rotation. Paper triangles are moved around on the students' desks to produce translations. Students are encouraged to make rough sketches of the image of a geometric figure under a certain transformation and to use these sketches to explore what happens when one transformation is followed by another (composition of transformations). The relationship between reflections and symmetry is established and students are asked to find lines of symmetry for common geometric figures.

Coordinate geometry is then used to formalize the notion of transformations. Rules for finding the image of a point in the coordinate plane under a given transformation are reduced to mappings of the form

$$(x, y) \rightarrow (x', y').$$

Any translation in the coordinate plane may be expressed by adding a vector $(h, k)$ to the coordinates of the point. Thus the generalized mapping for translations becomes

$$(x, y) \rightarrow (x + h, y + k).$$

Specific values of $h$ and $k$ are used in the first examples before generalizing.

Reflections about the $x$-axis are given by

$$(x, y) \rightarrow (x, -y)$$

and reflections about the $y$-axis by

$$(x, y) \rightarrow (-x, y).$$

No attempt is made to develop more general rules for reflections about other lines in the coordinate plane, since these rules become quite complex. However, more able students may go ahead and try to develop these for themselves.

The general form of a rotation about the origin is given by

$$(x, y) \rightarrow (x \cos \theta - y \sin \theta, x \sin \theta + y \cos \theta).$$

This, however, is not developed until after the students are exposed to the circular functions. At this point they can appreciate specific rotations centered at the origin, such as a counterclockwise rotation of 90 degrees. That rotation is given by

$$(x, y) \rightarrow (-y, x)$$

which they can readily verify by looking at specific points.

Armed with a set of rules for all translations and a few specific reflections and rotations, students can now engage in an exploration of the properties of these transformations. They can, for instance, sketch and calculate the coordinates of the vertices of a triangle that has undergone two transformations. Such experiences further confirm that any combination of the three rigid motions—translation, reflection, and rotation—produces another rigid motion.

Through explorations, students discover that for all three of the rigid transformations the distance between pairs of corresponding points is preserved; that is, if $A'$ and $B'$ are the images of $A$ and $B$, respectively, under one of these transformations, then $A'B' = AB$. We say that distance is *invariant* under each of these transformations.

If, however, we take the slope of the line through points $A$ and $B$ and compare it with the slope of the line through the image points $A'$ and $B'$, we find that the slope is not invariant for reflections and rotations but does remain invariant for translations.

These facts about invariant properties can be investigated on the level of specific cases, for example, What happens to the distance between $A(2,3)$ and $B(-5,7)$ under the translation

$$(x, y) \rightarrow (x + 3, y - 8)?$$

At a higher level of generality we may ask, What happens to the distance between $A(x_1, y_1)$ and $B(x_2, y_2)$ under the translation

$$(x, y) \rightarrow (x + h, y + k)?$$

In addition to translations, reflections, and rotations, transformations of the form

$$(x, y) \rightarrow (kx, ky)$$

are introduced. These are called size transformations, since they enlarge or contract a geometric figure. Properties of geometric figures undergoing size transformations are also studied.

From investigations of transformations we conclude that distance is invariant under rigid motions, whereas ratios of distances are invariant under size transformations. Perpendicularity, parallelism, and, by intuitive extension, angle measure are invariant under all four transformations.

We then define congruent figures (especially congruent triangles) as two figures such that one is the image of the other under a translation, reflection, rotation, or some combination of the above three transformations. The definition of similar figures is the same with the addition of size transformation. It then follows from the invariant properties of transformations that corresponding sides and angles of congruent triangles are congruent and that corresponding angles of similar triangles are congruent.

Corresponding sides of similar triangles are proportional, the constant of proportionality being the scale factor $k$ in the transformation mapping

$$(x, y) \rightarrow (kx, ky).$$

From this fact the trigonometric ratios in right triangles may be introduced. Since students are already familiar with the Pythagorean theorem, the law of sines and the law of cosines can be easily demonstrated, with an extension of the definitions of sine and cosine to include obtuse angles:

$$\sin (180 - \theta) = \sin \theta$$
$$\cos (180 - \theta) = -\cos \theta$$

These theorems allow students to solve any triangle, given sufficient information. In general, knowing three of its six parts is sufficient provided at least one of the parts is a side. The exception is the ambiguous case of two sides and a nonincluded angle. At this point we introduce constructions of triangles given three sides (SSS), two sides and an included angle (SAS), two angles and an included side (ASA), and two angles and a nonincluded side (AAS). Conditions for these constructions correspond to conditions that enable a trignometric solution as well as sufficient conditions to establish the congruence of two triangles. This connection is made explicit, and the idea of proving two triangles congruent, which will be developed later, is foreshadowed.

## REASONING AND AXIOMATIC SYSTEMS

By the end of the first semester, students have been introduced to a great deal of the content of the traditional geometry course and have ventured beyond to topics traditionally covered in an intermediate algebra/trigonometry course. Now they are ready to approach the subject in a more rigorous manner.

To prepare them to study geometry from an axiomatic viewpoint, we first give them a short course in elementary logic. This unit includes symbols for logical operations *not, and, or, if,* and *if and only if* ("iff"); truth tables for these operations; and patterns of inference. We stress the distinction between truth and validity.

Patterns of inference that produce valid conclusions are identified. These include *modus ponens, modus tolens,* the *disjunctive syllogism,* the *hypothetical syllogism,* and the principle of *logical equivalence.*

The most common pattern of reasoning used in geometry is modus ponens, and the most common logical relationship is *implication,* expressed by an arrow ($\rightarrow$). For that reason, special emphasis is placed on implication, particularly the different ways "$p \rightarrow q$" is translated into ordinary English. These translations include "if $p$, then $q$," "$p$ only if $q$," "$p$ is a sufficient condition for $q$," and "$q$ is a necessary condition for $p$."

We then reexamine some of the geometric content previously studied in terms of necessary and sufficient conditions. Students are asked to make lists of necessary conditions and sufficient conditions for a quadrilateral to be a rectangle. The properties of parallelograms are included in the set of necessary conditions and the properties of squares in the set of sufficient conditions. Some conditions are both necessary and sufficient, such as the defining conditions (a parallelogram with at least one right angle) and other sets of conditions that could provide alternative definitions (e.g., a parallelogram with congruent diagonals).

Having established a sounder basis for definition and some understanding of valid reasoning, we proceed to examine the role of postulates and axioms in mathematical systems. We return to the beginning of our geometry text and look at the first set of postulates and a small set of theorems (up to and including the theorem about vertical angles) that can be proved from them. One of the first theorems is that all four angles formed by two perpendicular lines are right angles. We emphasize that this does not mean the same thing as our definition of perpendicular lines (two lines that intersect to form at least one right angle) but can be proved from our definition along with preceding theorems and postulates.

This introduction to the use of postulates is followed by a unit on parallel lines and angles formed by a transversal intersecting two lines. The proofs are fairly short, and we may immediately move to examine a question of great consequence, the implications of Euclid's parallel postulate. Euclid's postulate is necessary to prove that the sum of the measures of the angles of a triangle is 180 degrees. If we accept alternatives to Euclid's parallel postulate, we get non-Euclidean geometries (hyperbolic and elliptical), in which the sum of measures of the angles of a triangle may be greater or less than 180 degrees.

We revisit the question of truth versus validity, pointing out that we are not absolutely certain which geometry is "true" for the space in which we live, but that all three geometries are equally valid. Our choice of postulates dictates which theorems will be true in the system we operate in.

## FORMAL PROOFS

The last part of the course is devoted to developing skills in writing proofs. Understanding and constructing proofs require performance at the fourth van Hiele level. The experiences of the first semester and the gradual introduction of the axiomatic method have helped bring our students to this level and prepare them to experience greater success in writing proofs.

At this point the content and presentation return to a more traditional approach. Students have already begun writing proofs in the unit on parallel lines. Now congruent triangles are studied in the fullest detail; special attention is given to writing proofs involving congruent triangles. An incremental approach to writing proofs, advocated by Hirsch (1983), is used so that many preproof experiences are given. These include completing two-column proofs by filling in missing statements or reasons, writing conditional statements for given proofs, arranging given statements and reasons in order to form a correct proof, planning proofs, and finally writing complete proofs from scratch.

Students are trained to look for the flow of the proof, asking which statements are used to prove which steps. The numbers of these statements are enclosed in brackets next to the corresponding reasons in order to emphasize this interconnection. Reasons involving implication are stated with the arrow (→). Definitions may be written with the double *iff* arrow (←→). Usually the reasoning pattern is modus ponens or, with definitions, the principle of logical equivalence. The statement of the general principle (postulate, theorem, or definition) used for the reason is the major premise; the statement referred to in brackets, the minor premise; and the new statement is justified by reason of the conclusion (fig. 10.6).

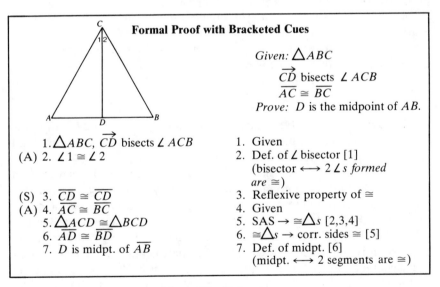

Fig. 10.6

Once facility is gained in proving statements about congruent triangles, other sections of the geometry text are studied. The sections on isosceles triangles, properties of quadrilaterals, and similar triangles can be covered very rapidly, since the content has already been introduced. Here it is useful to look at some of the theorems listed in figure 10.3 and contrast their

## Students should appreciate the unity of the subject that underlies the eclecticism of methods.

synthetic formal proofs with the analytical proofs previously studied. In some cases a student may prefer the coordinate approach (Brown 1982); in others, the synthetic approach; in still others, concepts of symmetry studied in connection with transformations. Students should appreciate the unity of the subject that underlies the eclecticism of methods.

The Pythagorean theorem, which was accepted as an assumption in the coordinate geometry unit, should be proved by one of several synthetic methods. To emphasize logical consistency, we point out to students that nothing preceding the Pythagorean theorem in our formal development can be accepted as proved if its proof depends on a theorem that has been established only by coordinate methods.

A unit on circles and relations among circles, lines, and angles is included in this last section. This includes content not previously studied and affords students additional opportunities to construct proofs of theorems using properties of congruent and similar triangles.

Depending on the interests and abilities of the students and the pace of the course, additional units may be included on inequalities, a more formal approach to loci, relationships between circles and tangents in the coordinate plane, or more space geometry.

### CONCLUSION

Although the syllabus outlined in this chapter was developed for a specific student population, the basic approach is appropriate for a wide variety of tenth-grade geometry courses for the college bound.

With a better prepared, more able group of students, one can reach a higher level of abstraction and rigor more easily. A less prepared group, however, may require more concrete examples, greater emphasis on inductive approaches, and more attention to the incremental steps toward proof.

The degree of algebraic sophistication of the students will determine the degree of formality one can use in the coordinate geometry and transformational geometry units. For example, all students should be able to follow the vector argument in figure 10.2, where specific coordinates are given for the three points. In a highly advanced class the more general argument could be given as a student homework assignment; in less able classes it could be demonstrated to the class as a whole; in still less able classes it might be given as an enrichment exercise to a select group of students so that the class as a whole does not become bogged down in the details of the argument and lose the general concept. Teachers using this syllabus should be sensitive to student feedback and adjust the level of the course accordingly. At the same time there is always room to add something with a little more mathematical sophistication not only to challenge the most able students but to push the entire class ahead. There is enough variety to create interest. Above all, the deadliness of spending a whole year of doing proofs is eliminated (and this can be especially deadly for those who don't really understand the hows and whys of proofs).

## REFERENCES

Brown, Richard G. "Making Geometry a Personal and Inventive Experience." *Mathematics Teacher* 75 (September 1982): 442–46.

Coxford, Arthur F., Jr. "A Transformation Approach to Euclidean Geometry." In *Geometry in the Mathematics Curriculum,* Thirty-sixth Yearbook of the National Council of Teachers of Mathematics, edited by Kenneth B. Henderson, pp. 136–200. Reston, Va.: The Council, 1973.

Forbes, Jack E. "An Eclectic Program in Geometry." In *Geometry in the Mathematics Curriculum,* Thirty-sixth Yearbook of the National Council of Teachers of Mathematics, edited by Kenneth B. Henderson, pp. 334–66. Reston, Va.: The Council, 1973.

Gearhart, George. "What Do Mathematics Teachers Think about the High School Geometry Controversy?" *Mathematics Teacher* 68 (October 1975): 486–93.

Hirsch, Christian R. "An Incremental Approach to Proof in Geometry." Presentation at University of Michigan Thirty-third Annual Mathematics Education Conference, Ann Arbor, Mich., February 1983.

———. *Motion in Geometry.* Lansing, Mich.: Michigan Council of Teachers of Mathematics, 1976.

Mayberry, JoAnne. "The van Hiele Levels of Geometric Thought in Undergraduate Preservice Teachers." *Journal for Research in Mathematics Education* 14 (January 1983): 58–69.

Sitomer, Harry. "Geometry in an Integrated Program." In *Geometry in the Mathematics Curriculum,* Thirty-sixth Yearbook of the National Council of Teachers of Mathematics, edited by Kenneth B. Henderson, pp. 303–33. Reston, Va.: The Council, 1973.

# 11

# A Plan for Incorporating Problem Solving throughout the Advanced Algebra Curriculum

## LeRoy C. Dalton

THE advanced algebra curriculum of the past was not completely void of an emphasis on problem solving. For years teachers have encouraged their students to use certain problem-solving strategies, such as "Use a chart or table" and "Organize and classify data," to solve mixture problems, distance-rate-time problems, work problems, and percentage problems. Also, think how often an advanced algebra teacher, in teaching trigonometry, directed a student to "work backward" in discovering how to prove an identity. Consider how often teachers suggested a trial-and-error strategy when teaching the meaning of the solution set of an equation. Can't you hear a teacher say, "Try to 'solve a simpler related problem' " or "Look for a pattern"?

Then what is wrong with what has traditionally been done relative to problem solving? First, an overall plan has been lacking for teaching problem solving in school mathematics courses, including the advanced algebra course. Second, teachers seldom gave students anything but routine problems to solve, problems that could generally be solved by some algorithm, and generally an algorithm studied in that particular lesson or chapter. This is fine for openers; once a particular mathematics concept is introduced, some practice in working with the concept should come in solving "word problems" whose solutions make use of the concept.

Traditionally, some of the best problem solving in an advanced algebra course has come from solving a collection of word problems in a chapter review or in a cumulative review. In these reviews, problem sets are usually given in which the students have to discriminate among the concepts and algorithms learned and determine which ones to apply in solving particular problems.

Beyond the word problems of the usual advanced algebra textbook, whose solutions involve one or more algorithms, come those often labeled "nonroutine" problems. These are problems whose solutions generally do

134

not involve algorithms learned in advanced algebra, or if they do, the algorithms might be ones that come much later in the logical structure of the course.

A number of teachers (some in this decade and some much earlier) have enumerated strategies that can be used to solve most of these nonroutine problems:

- List data
- Organize and classify data
- Use a chart or table
- Use a model or diagram
- Compare
- Work forward
- Work backward
- Associate
- Eliminate possible choices

- Use guess and check (trial and error)
- Look for patterns
- Solve a simpler related problem
- Generalize a solution
- Find a counterexample
- Estimate the answer
- Use operations
- Use algorithms
- Solve in several ways

Many of these strategies can also be used to solve routine problems. This gives a rational basis for introducing problem solving early in an advanced algebra course so that some of the strategies can be used in solving the routine word problems that lend practice to the algebra concepts being learned in the course. Also, since a portion of the first semester of an advanced algebra course is used for a review and extension of elementary algebra concepts, the curriculum has room here for the introduction of an overall problem-solving program.

## THE PROBLEM-OF-THE-WEEK APPROACH

Start by using a "problem of the week" approach for one year. This will give you the time and motivation to collect "good problems" and related strategies. A "good problem" possesses one or more of the following characteristics:

1. Has related problem(s) of a simpler nature that the student can recognize and solve (an idea advocated by George Polya)
2. Can be solved in more than one way within the student's background and capabilities
3. Leads the student to other similar problems
4. Contains data that can be organized or classified, tabulated, and analyzed
5. Can be solved by means of a model or diagram
6. Is of immediate interest to the student
7. Has a solution that can be generalized with either the students' present knowledge or their knowledge before completion of the course
8. Can be solved by recognizing patterns
9. Has an interesting answer

It is important that the plan and mechanics of a "problem of the week" program be well defined. A recommended plan follows:

1. *The problem*

Give each student a copy of the problem on Monday. Be sure they understand the problem and know what is asked for. Inform them that extra credit will be given on a 1–5 point scale, depending on the quality and ingenuity of their work.

2. *Possible strategies*

Occasionally give the students a hint or two, but generally discuss the possible strategies after their solutions are handed in, that is, the next Monday. Then discuss the solutions that you have discovered or read and learned about during the week. This will generally take fifteen to twenty minutes if you are well organized and prepared. Have solutions on transparencies if they are long. Hand out the problem for the next week.

3. *Solution*

Correct students' solutions during the week, and the next Monday hand back their solutions with written comments. Briefly discuss any unique solutions and give appropriate rewards, such as additional credit.

4. *Generalized solution*

Teach the students the meaning and importance of generalizing a solution. Encourage them to generalize a solution where possible and where such generalizing is within their capabilities and background. Give additional credit for generalized solutions discovered by the students. Show them how a generalized solution is obtained if it is within their ability and background to understand. Otherwise wait until they have studied the algebraic concepts necessary for arriving at the generalization, then have them do it (or possibly do it yourself, depending on the difficulty of the work and the ability level of the class).

5. *Concepts of which the generalized solution is an application*

Make a chart of where these concepts are found in the textbook so that students will not forget to include these generalized solutions at the right time.

6. *Applications of the generalized algebraic expressions*

Prepare applications of the generalized algebraic expressions ahead of time—expressions such as a sequence, series, formula, polynomial function, inequality, and so on. These applications will generally be quite direct.

To enable the reader to understand this plan more fully, the first three problems that are recommended for the first three consecutive Mondays of the school year are discussed here in detail. (All problems discussed in this chapter have been used in the author's advanced algebra class.)

*Problem:* How many squares does the given 6 × 6 square contain if the six units on each side are of equal measure?

*Strategies:*

1. If you cannot solve the proposed problem, try to solve first a simpler related problem.
2. Use a table to organize your data.
3. Analyse the data.
4. Look for a pattern.

*Solution:*

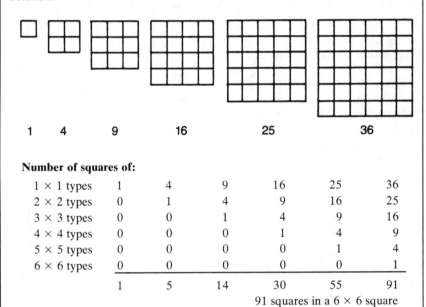

| 1 | 4 | 9 | 16 | 25 | 36 |

**Number of squares of:**

| | | | | | | |
|---|---|---|---|---|---|---|
| 1 × 1 types | 1 | 4 | 9 | 16 | 25 | 36 |
| 2 × 2 types | 0 | 1 | 4 | 9 | 16 | 25 |
| 3 × 3 types | 0 | 0 | 1 | 4 | 9 | 16 |
| 4 × 4 types | 0 | 0 | 0 | 1 | 4 | 9 |
| 5 × 5 types | 0 | 0 | 0 | 0 | 1 | 4 |
| 6 × 6 types | 0 | 0 | 0 | 0 | 0 | 1 |
| | 1 | 5 | 14 | 30 | 55 | 91 |

91 squares in a 6 × 6 square

*Generalized solution:*

Number ($n$) of units on each side of $n \times n$ square

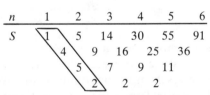

| $n$ | 1 | 2 | 3 | 4 | 5 | 6 |
|---|---|---|---|---|---|---|
| $S$ | 1 | 5 | 14 | 30 | 55 | 91 |
| | 4 | 9 | 16 | 25 | 36 | |
| | 5 | 7 | 9 | 11 | | |
| | 2 | 2 | 2 | | | |

By using a method of finite differences, we can find the general term of the sequence or an equation defining the relationship between $n$ and $S$. ($S$ = the number of squares.)

Let $S = an^3 + bn^2 + cn + d$, the defining equation for the general third-degree polynomial (cubic) function in $n$. By substituting 1, 2, 3, 4, and 5 into this equation, we determine the following expressions, which are then used to determine three rows of finite differences.

| $n$ | 1 | 2 | 3 | 4 | 5 |
|---|---|---|---|---|---|
| $S$ | $a+b+c+d$ | $8a+4b+2c+d$ | $27a+9b+3c+d$ | $64a+16b+4c+d$ | $125a+25b+5c+d$ |
| | $7a+3b+c$ | $19a+5b+c$ | $37a+7b+c$ | $61a+9b+c$ | |
| | $12a+2b$ | $18a+2b$ | $24a+2b$ | | |
| | $6a$ | $6a$ | | | |

$$6a = 2 \qquad 12a + 2b = 5 \qquad 7a + 3b + c = 4 \qquad a + b + c + d = 1$$

$$a = \frac{1}{3} \qquad 12 \cdot \frac{1}{3} + 2b = 5 \qquad 7 \cdot \frac{1}{3} + 3 \cdot \frac{1}{2} + c = 4 \qquad \frac{1}{3} + \frac{1}{2} + \frac{1}{6} + d = 1$$

$$b = \frac{1}{2} \qquad\qquad c = \frac{1}{6} \qquad\qquad d = 0$$

Substituting the rational numbers determined for parameters $a$, $b$, $c$, and $d$ of the general third-degree polynomial, we find the equation relating $n$ and $S$ to be

$$S = \frac{1}{3}n^3 + \frac{1}{2}n^2 + \frac{1}{6}n$$

The generalized sequence would be

$$1, 5, 14, 30, 55, \ldots, \frac{1}{3}n^3 + \frac{1}{2}n^2 + \frac{1}{6}n, \ldots .$$

*Concepts of which the generalized solution is an application:*
  1. Sequence
  2. Polynomial function
  3. Third-degree polynomial function (cubic function)

*Applications of the generalized algebraic expressions:*
  1. Using the general term of the sequence above, find the number of squares in an $n \times n$ square where $n$ is:
     *a*) 7
     *b*) 8
  2. Is there an easier method?
  3. Suppose $n = 30$, now which method is easier? How many squares are there in a $30 \times 30$ square?
  4. Graph the function defined by the equation

$$S = \frac{1}{3}n^3 + \frac{1}{2}n^2 + \frac{1}{6}n, \text{ where } n \in I^+.$$

In the next example, the solution involves essentially the same strategies introduced to the students after they had turned in their solutions for the first problem. This gives them an opportunity to discover that these strategies can be used and also a real opportunity to use them.

*Problem:* Find the number of downward routes from $A$ to $C$ in the $5 \times 5$ square $ABCD$.

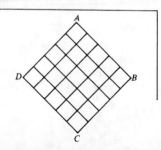

*Strategies:*
1. If you cannot solve the proposed problem, try to solve first a simpler related problem.
2. Use the grid of the 5 × 5 square as a table containing the number of routes to certain points.
3. Analyze the data.
4. Look for a pattern.

*Solution:* Using strategy 1 above, explore simpler related problems as follows:

How many different routes are there from $A$ to $E$? From $A$ to $F$? Continue with a 3 × 3 square if a pattern has not been discovered.

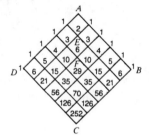

*Generalized solution:* It can be recognized that the 5 × 5 grid containing the number of routes to all points is a portion of Pascal's triangle. Thus the pattern can be projected to the line of Pascal's triangle that contains the number 252.

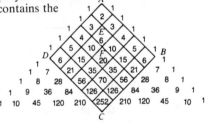

The numbers of this line can be seen to be either

*a*) the coefficients in the expansion of
$(a + b)^{10}$, using the binomial theorem—
$$1a^{10}b^0 + 10a^9b^1 + 45a^8b^2 + 120a^7b^3 + 210a^6b^4 + 252a^5b^5 + 210a^4b^6 + 120a^3b^7 + 45a^2b^8 + 10a^1b^9 + 1a^0b^{10},$$

or

*b*) the coefficients as combinations—
$$_{10}C_0 \; _{10}C_1 \; _{10}C_2 \; _{10}C_3 \; _{10}C_4 \; _{10}C_5 \; _{10}C_6 \; _{10}C_7 \; _{10}C_8 \; _{10}C_9 \; _{10}C_{10}.$$

The generalization can be seen from the following table:

| Square | Number of Downward Routes ($A$ to $C$) | Coefficient of Binomial Expansion |
|--------|:---:|:---:|
| 1 × 1 | 2 | $_2C_1$ |
| 2 × 2 | 6 | $_4C_2$ |
| 3 × 3 | 20 | $_6C_3$ |

| 4 × 4 | 70 | $_8C_4$ |
|---|---|---|
| 5 × 5 | 252 | $_{10}C_5$ |
| . | . | . |
| . | . | . |
| . | . | . |
| $n \times n$ | $\dfrac{2n(2n - 1)(2n - 2)\ldots(2n - n + 1)}{(n!)}$ | $_{2n}C_n$ |

Thus, the number of downward routes from one vertex of an $n \times n$ square to its opposite vertex is given by either $_{2n}C_n$ or

$$\frac{2n(2n - 1)(2n - 2)\ldots(2n - n + 1)}{(n!)} .$$

*Concepts of which the generalized solution is an application:*
1. Binomial theorem
2. Combinations
3. Pascal's triangle

*Applications of the generalized algebraic expression:*
   Find the number of downward routes from one vertex of an $n \times n$ square to the diagonally opposite vertex using the generalization $_{2n}C_n$ for—
   1. $n = 6$     2. $n = 10$     3. $n = 12$
   4. If $_8C_4$ is the number of downward routes from one vertex of an $n \times n$ square to the diagonally opposite vertex, what is the value of $n$?

The third of the three problems that are discussed in detail is not just a "good" problem, it is a "super" problem. Its solutions involve several strategies and several methods of solution within the students' capabilities and backgrounds, and it also contains some generalizations that students are able to discover after they have been introduced to certain concepts in the advanced algebra course. It is indeed a fun problem for the advanced algebra student.

*Problem:* Suppose that 10 people attend a party and each person shakes hands with every other person exactly once. How many handshakes take place?

*Strategies:* (Since this problem has several solutions within the student's background and capabilities, the list of strategies that might be used is longer than for most problems.)
   1. Use a model or diagram.
   2. Look for a pattern.
   3. Solve a simpler related problem.
   4. Organize and classify data.
   5. Use a chart or table.

*Solutions:*

*Solution 1* (student model). Use a circle model with 10 equally spaced points—*A, B, C, D, E, F, G, H, I,* and *J*—on the circle, representing 10 people at the party. Draw 9 chords from *A* to each other point to represent the 9 handshakes by *A*. Then, since *B* has already shaken hands with *A*, draw 8 chords from *B*, and so on, until *J* is reached. From *J*, 0 chords are drawn. Add the 9, 8, 7, 6, 5, 4, 3, 2, 1, and 0 chords (handshakes); the sum, 45, is the total number of handshakes.

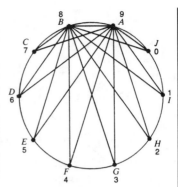

*Solution 2.* Inscribe a regular decagon in a circle and draw all the diagonals. From geometry, it is known that the number of sides of a decagon + the number of diagonals =

$$10 + \frac{10\,(10 - 3)}{2}.$$

Thus, the total number of handshakes is 45.

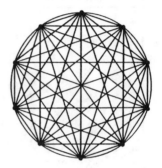

*Solution 3* (student model).

| Number of points (people) | Modle | Number of segments (handshakes) | |
|:---:|:---:|:---:|:---:|
| 2 | | 1 | 2 |
| 3 | | 3 | 3 |
| 4 | | 6 | 4 |
| 5 | | 10 | 5 |
| 6 | | 15 | 6 |
| 7 | | 21 | 7 |
| 8 | | 28 | 8 |
| 9 | | 36 | 9 |
| 10 | | 45 | 10 |

The pattern determined by differences permits a projection to *10 people* and *45 handshakes* without drawing more models.

*Solution 4.*

Find the answer from two diagonals of Pascal's triangle.

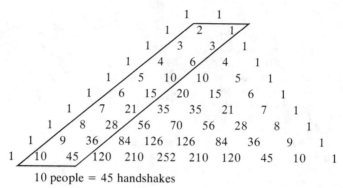

10 people = 45 handshakes

*Solution 5* (student model).

| | 1 | 2 | 3 | 4 | 5 | 6 | 7 | 8 | 9 | 10 | Number of Handshakes |
|---|---|---|---|---|---|---|---|---|---|---|---|
| 1 | X | 1-2 | 1-3 | 1-4 | 1-5 | 1-6 | 1-7 | 1-8 | 1-9 | 1-10 | 9 |
| 2 | X | X | 2-3 | 2-4 | 2-5 | 2-6 | 2-7 | 2-8 | 2-9 | 2-10 | 8 |
| 3 | X | X | X | 3-4 | 3-5 | 3-6 | 3-7 | 3-8 | 3-9 | 3-10 | 7 |
| 4 | X | X | X | X | 4-5 | 4-6 | 4-7 | 4-8 | 4-9 | 4-10 | 6 |
| 5 | X | X | X | X | X | 5-6 | 5-7 | 5-8 | 5-9 | 5-10 | 5 |
| 6 | X | X | X | X | X | X | 6-7 | 6-8 | 6-9 | 6-10 | 4 |
| 7 | X | X | X | X | X | X | X | 7-8 | 7-9 | 7-10 | 3 |
| 8 | X | X | X | X | X | X | X | X | 8-9 | 8-10 | 2 |
| 9 | X | X | X | X | X | X | X | X | X | 9-10 | 1 |
| 10 | X | X | X | X | X | X | X | X | X | X | 0 |

Total 45

*Generalized solutions:*

1. The number of handshakes is $Y$, where $Y = {}_nC_2 = \dfrac{n(n-1)}{1 \cdot 2}$ and where $n$ is the number of persons shaking hands.

2. $Y = \dfrac{1}{2}n^2 - \dfrac{1}{2}n$ can be discovered from the expression $\dfrac{n(n-1)}{1 \cdot 2}$ above or through the method of finite differences using the general quadratic equation

$$Y = an^2 + bn + c$$

in much the same way as in the first problem with the cubic polynomial function. Since it takes two people to shake hands, the value of $n$ in this development would start with 2 instead of 1.

3. The general term of the sequence

$$1, 3, 6, 10, 15, \ldots,$$

where $n$ begins with 2 instead of 1, is $1/2n^2 - 1/2n$. This general term can be found either by discovery through trial and error or by the method of finite differences described above.

4. (Student model) The series

$$(n-1) + (n-2) + (n-3) + \ldots + [n - (n-1)],$$

where $n$ is the number of persons shaking hands, generates the number of handshakes.

   The computer program below will also generate the number of handshakes ($N$) for any given number ($X$) of people shaking hands and as a bonus will do all necessary computations.

```
 1 HOME
 5 LET N = 0
10 INPUT "ENTER NUMBER"; X
15 LET F = X − 1
20 FOR Q = F TO 1 STEP −1
25 LET N = N + Q
30 NEXT Q
35 ? : ? "THE ANSWER IS"; N
```

*Concepts of which the generalized solution is an application:*
1. Combinations
2. Quadratic polynomial function
3. Sequence
4. Series

*Applications of the generalized algebraic expressions:*

If $Y$ is the number of handshakes that occur when $n$ people shake hands with every other person exactly once, find $Y$ when (use $_nC_2$):

   1. $n = 5$   2. $n = 20$   3. $n = 50$   4. $n = 100$

5–8. Repeat exercises 1–4 by using $Y = \dfrac{1}{2}n^2 - \dfrac{1}{2}n$.

   9. Find the first 12 terms of the sequence in generalization 3 above.

10. Find the number of handshakes if 15 people shake hands with each other exactly once using the generalization series in 4 above.

Two other recommended problems will be briefly discussed here. These contain interesting generalizations within the abilities of the students.

*Problem:* In how many different ways can three people divide 25 pieces of candy so that each person gets at least 1 piece? (Krulik and Rudnick 1980)

Some of the author's students solved and generalized the solution as follows:

| Number of pieces of candy | 3 | 4 | 5 | 6 | ... | 25 |
|---|---|---|---|---|---|---|
| Solutions | 1-1-1 | 1-1-2<br>1-2-1<br>2-1-1 | 1-1-3<br>1-3-1<br>3-1-1<br>2-2-1<br>2-1-2<br>1-2-2 | 1-1-4, 1-4-1<br>4-1-1, 3-2-1<br>2-3-1, 2-1-3<br>1-3-2, 1-2-3<br>3-1-2, 2-2-2 | ... | |
| Number of solutions | 1 | 3 | 6 | 10 | ... | |
| Number of solutions as a sum | 1 | 2 + 1 | 3 + 2 + 1 | 4 + 3 + 2 + 1 | ... | 23 + 22 + 21 +<br>... + 2 + 1,<br>or 276 |

Notice that the number of solutions is expressed as a decreasing sum of consecutive integers ending with *1*. Observe, also, that the first integer in that sum is 2 less than the number of pieces of candy. Thus, for 25 pieces of candy, the sum is

$$23 + 22 + 21 + 20 + 19 + \ldots + 3 + 2 + 1, \text{ or}$$

$$S = \frac{23}{2} \quad 2(23) + (23 - 1)(-1)$$

$$= \frac{(23)\,(24)}{2} = \frac{(24)\,(23)}{2}, \text{ or } \frac{(25 - 1)\,(25 - 2)}{2}, \text{ or in general,}$$

$$S = \frac{(n - 1)\,(n - 2)}{2}, \text{ where } n \text{ is the number of pieces of candy to}$$

be divided and $S$ is the number of solutions.

(Some of the students saw the resemblance of this solution to that of the hand-shake problem. When they solved this problem, they had studied arithmetic progressions and were able to see that the sum formula for arithmetic progressions was applicable here.)

---

*Problem:*

   (*a*)  Of seven coins, six are the same weight and one is lighter than the others. Given a balance with two pans for comparing weights, what is the least number of weighings needed to determine which coin is light?

   (*b*)  Of 200 coins, 199 are the same weight and 1 is lighter than the others. Given the same balance, explain how the light coin can be identified in no more than five weighings.

It works well to give problems *a* and *b* one week and the generalization problem *c* below the following week.

   (*c*)  Of *n* coins ($n > 1$), all are the same weight but one. Devise a rule for determining the minimum number of weighings needed to identify the light coin, given a balance with two pans for comparing weights.

(Parts *a, b,* and *c* are from Fisher and Medigovich [1981].)

A table can be developed and a pattern observed:

| Number $n$ of coins | 2 3 4 5 6 7 8 9 10 11 12 ... 27 28 ... 81 82 83 ... |
|---|---|
| Minimum weighings $w$ | 1 1 2 2 2 2 2 2  3  3  3 ...  3  4 ...  4  5  5 ... |

Notice that the minimum number of weighings, *w*, increases by 1 after each power of 3. The minimum number of weighings, *w*, for *n* coins is observed to be represented by the generalized expression

$$3^{w-1} < n \leq 3^w.$$

---

Of course not all "good" problems given to students fit the model illustrated here, where there has been at least one nice generalization for students to discover in each case. For example, the solution to the following problem involves a great deal of writing and analyzing of equations and inequalities, but a generalization is not in order.

---

Suppose five bales of hay are weighed two at a time in all possible ways. The weights in pounds are 110, 112, 113, 114, 115, 116, 117, 118, 120, and 121. How much does each bale weigh? (Fisher and Medigovich 1981)

At some time give the class a problem for which there are many solutions, such as the one that follows.

If two wires are attached as shown to two vertical poles of heights 10 meters and 15 meters, and the wires intersect at a point 6 meters above the ground, how far apart are the poles? (Assume an unlimited amount of wire.) (Adapted from *The Mathematical Log*, [1973; 1974]).

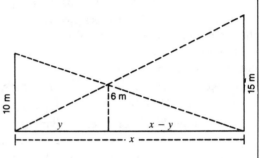

Since corresponding sides of similar triangles give the proportions

$$\frac{6}{15} = \frac{y}{x} \text{ and } \frac{6}{10} = \frac{x-y}{x},$$

both of which simplify to the equation

$$y = \frac{2}{5}x,$$

the solutions are all positive $x$ coordinates of points on the line whose equation is $y = \frac{2}{5}x$. That is, the poles can be any positive distance apart under the given conditions.

When developing and implementing a "problem of the week" program in an advanced algebra curriculum, it is helpful to have some assurance that this program will be incorporated into the required curriculum for the following year. This gives even more incentive for choosing problems carefully. It is important that "good" problems, as defined earlier, be chosen for different ability levels. Also note that if students are to be tested on strategies and techniques of problem solving, some problems must be chosen whose solutions involve certain strategies in a somewhat obvious way.

## "QUICK PROBLEM-SOLVING OPENERS"

Another way to incorporate problem solving into the advanced algebra curriculum is to start lessons periodically with "quick problem-solving openers." These are short problems to whet the student's appetite for problem solving and help establish an atmosphere for problem solving in the classroom. They may or may not be related to the particular lesson. The problems might touch on a review of a concept studied, apply or extend the previous lesson, introduce the present lesson, or preview an upcoming lesson.

For example, a problem like this one might be a quick opener when studying integral exponents:

Find all integers $x$ and $y$ such that $x^y = y^x$.

Or, when studying rational number exponents,

Verify that $\left(\dfrac{9}{4}\right)^{27/8} = \left(\dfrac{27}{8}\right)^{9/4}$.

Or, when studying real number exponents,

Verify that $(3\sqrt{3})^{\sqrt{3}} = (\sqrt{3})^{3\sqrt{3}}$.

Another day, follow up this sequence by having students conjecture what the graph of the relation defined by $x^y = y^x$ would be in the first quadrant.

Here is a quick opener when studying the solutions of polynomial equations of higher degree:

If $a,b,c, \ldots, z \in R$, *the set of real numbers,* then find $B$ in the equation
$$(x - a)(x - b)(x - c)(x - d) \ldots (x - z) = B.$$

Here is a quick opener when studying the solutions of radical equations:

Find $x$ in the equation where $x = \sqrt{1 + \sqrt{1 + \sqrt{1 + \sqrt{1 + \ldots}}}}$ .

When solving equations involving rational expressions, ask students to solve for $x$ in

$$x = 1 + \cfrac{1}{1 + \cfrac{1}{1 + \cfrac{1}{1 + \cfrac{1}{1 + \ldots}}}}$$

These latter two equations involve a similar substrategy in their solutions. Solving the radical equation, after squaring both sides once, depends on the student's ability to see that

$$x^2 = 1 + \underbrace{\sqrt{1 + \sqrt{1 + \sqrt{1 + \sqrt{1 + \ldots}}}}}_{x}$$

or       $x^2 = 1 + x$,

or       $x^2 - x - 1 = 0$.

Similarly, solving the equation involving rational expressions depends on the student's ability to see that

$$x = 1 + \cfrac{1}{1 + \cfrac{1}{1 + \cfrac{1}{1 + \ldots}}}$$

or $x = 1 + \dfrac{1}{x}$ ,

or $x^2 - x - 1 = 0$.

These two solutions rely on the student's ability to comprehend the infinite nature of each or the problem-solving substrategy of substituting what appears to be the whole for a part. Students need to become familiar with such substrategies in problem solving. If they have been introduced to the golden ratio $(1 + \sqrt{5})/2$, then they will realize an added bonus in being able to see recurrences of the golden ratio in the solution of each of these two quadratic equations. Remember, one of the criteria for a good problem is that it have an interesting answer.

## GROUP PROBLEM SOLVING

There are two effective ways to incorporate problem solving into the advanced algebra curriculum through group problem solving:

1. In one kind of group problem solving, the teacher divides the class into groups of three to five students and has each group attempt to solve either a nonroutine problem or a very unusual routine problem. Each group can delegate a person to present the group's solution on the chalkboard or overhead projector so the teacher can compare and contrast the solutions for the entire class. It is also effective to have each group solve a different routine word problem from the text and designate someone from each group to present the solution on the chalkboard or overhead projector. The student learns, even within a small group, new ways to attack problems.

2. In the other kind of group problem solving, the teacher leads the whole class as a group to individually discover the steps in the solution, including the answer. At the end of a unit on logarithms, for example, you might ask the students to find all real-number solutions of the equation

$$5 = 3^{-x} + 3^{-2x}.$$

Then ask what they observe about the exponents. Some might say that one exponent is double the other. Ask them in what other type of equation this phenomenon occurs. You hope they will say in a quadratic equation. Next, ask the class to rewrite the equation as an equivalent equation with positive exponents. Then suggest that they clear fractions. This would be a good place to stop to see if everyone has the equation that is called for.

Now ask the class to write the equation in quadratic form with $3^x$ as the variable term:

$$5(3^x)^2 - 1(3^x)^1 - 1 = 0$$

Since this quadratic equation is not factorable, suggest that they use the quadratic formula and solve for $3^x$. The result obtained should be

$$3^x = \frac{1 \pm \sqrt{21}}{10}.$$

The left side cannot be negative. Why? Thus rewrite the equation with only the positive value of the right side included:

$$3^x = \frac{1 + \sqrt{21}}{10}$$

Now ask your class to take the logarithm base 10 of both sides of the equation. Check to see that they have the equation

$$x \log_{10} 3 = \log_{10} \left( \frac{1 + \sqrt{21}}{10} \right).$$

Then ask them to solve for $x$:

$$x = \frac{\log_{10} \left( \dfrac{1 + \sqrt{21}}{10} \right)}{\log_{10} 3}$$

Finally, ask them to find a rational approximation for $x$ using their calculators.

## SUMMARY

An attempt has been made to give teachers some ideas on how to incorporate problem solving into the advanced algebra curriculum. They can prepare for this endeavor by building a successful problem-of-the-week program in their advanced algebra classes over a period of one year, with plans for incorporating this program into the required curriculum during the second year. Teachers should collect good problems, both routine and nonroutine, study problem-solving strategies, and compile a list of the most effective ones possible.

A special feature of this program is to ask students, after they solve a nonroutine problem, to generalize the solution when the algebra for this generalization comes within their backgrounds and abilities. When it does not, have them attempt to generalize the solution at the time when they have studied the necessary algebraic concepts. If this is still beyond the students' recognition and ability, the teacher demonstrates how to generalize the solution, sometimes by introducing a new procedure, such as the process of finite differences, to obtain a polynomial function or a general term of a sequence. The generalized expression is then used to build some applications of the expression. This is done with a three-pronged purpose: to emphasize the importance of a generalization, to provide a source of applications, and to give students needed experiences with the more in-depth mathematics associated with generalizations.

Two additional aids for incorporating problem solving into the advanced algebra curriculum were briefly discussed: (1) "quick problem-solving openers" to create a problem-solving atmosphere in the classroom and to include more problem-solving experiences and (2) group problem-solving procedures for further learning experiences.

This overall plan for incorporating problem solving throughout the advanced algebra curriculum could be extended across the entire four-year high school mathematics curriculum. And even though teachers may find time to plan such a program individually, it might be better for the school to sponsor a summer curriculum project in which all members of the mathematics faculty join in a cooperative planning venture.

## REFERENCES

Dunn, Angela, ed. *Mathematical Bafflers.* New York: Dover Publications, 1980.

Fisher, Lyle, and William Medigovich. *Problem of the Week.* Palo Alto, Calif.: Dale Seymour Publications, 1981.

Krulik, Stephen, and Jesse A. Rudnick. *Problem Solving: Handbook for Teachers.* Boston: Allyn & Bacon, 1980.

Mathematical Association of America and the National Council of Teachers of Mathematics. *A Sourcebook of Applications of School Mathematics.* Reston, Va.: The Council, 1980.

Mott-Smith. Geoffrey. *Mathematical Puzzles for Beginners and Enthusiasts.* 2d rev. ed. New York: Dover Publications, 1954.

Mu Alpha Theta. "Problem Solving for Fun and Profit." *Mathematical Log* 18 [University of Oklahoma, Norman] (December 1973, p. 4, problem; April 1974, p. 1, solution).

National Council of Teachers of Mathematics. *Problem Solving in School Mathematics.* 1980 Yearbook of the National Council of Teachers of Mathematics. Reston, Va.: The Council, 1980.

Polya, George. *How to Solve It.* 2d ed. Princeton, N.J.: Princeton University Press, 1957.

Saint Mary's College. *Mathematics Contest Problems.* Palo Alto, Calif.: Creative Publications, 1972.

Salkind, Charles T. *The Contest Problem Book II: Annual High School Contests 1961–1965.* Washington, D.C.: Mathematical Association of America, 1966.

Salkind, Charles T., and James M. Earl. *The Contest Problem Book III: Annual High School Contests, 1966–72.* Washington, D.C.: Mathematical Association of America, 1973.

Steinhaus, Hugo. *One Hundred Problems in Elementary Mathematics.* New York: Dover Publications, 1979.

# 12

# Mathematical Alternatives for College Preparatory Students

Joan Leitzel
Alan Osborne

**A**BOUT 45 percent of the graduating seniors in the United States enter some form of postsecondary education, and about 45 percent of this group lack the mathematical skills and understandings needed for success in postsecondary school mathematics.

Seniors in most high schools have but three curricular alternatives in mathematics:

1. Take no mathematics.
2. Enroll in a mathematics course in the non–college preparatory curriculum, such as consumer, business, or general mathematics.
3. Elect the college preparatory course that follows the one they have most recently completed.

For the student who has been only marginally successful in mathematics but who intends postsecondary education, none of these alternatives is realistic. The choices recognize neither the characteristics nor the needs of these seniors.

Through our experience in developing an alternative course for such seniors and in implementing it with over a thousand students in forty-one schools during the 1981–83 school years, we hope to focus attention on what we feel are major issues and problems in the design of the college preparatory curriculum.

## THE BASIC COLLEGE PREPARATORY MATHEMATICS PROJECT

Freshmen at Ohio State University take mathematics placement tests during summer orientation. On the basis of the scores, each student is assigned a placement level from 1 to 5. Level 1 indicates readiness for calculus; level 2, standard precalculus. Students who intend to major in science, engineering, or business need to enter with placement level 1 or 2 if they are to move immediately into the mathematics courses required in those programs. Level 3 is acceptable for most nonscience students. Levels 4 and 5 are remedial levels for all students. Level 5 students have no skills in elementary algebra; they have not yet begun to learn what is commonly regarded as college preparatory mathematics.

---

Schools participating in the [junior-year testing] program show an average increase of 40 percent in senior mathematics enrollments.

---

The freshman who enters with placement level 5 almost always needs more than four years to complete a degree. In fact, many career areas are essentially closed to students who enter with serious deficiencies in mathematics. Of the level-5 students who graduated in 1980, fewer than 2 percent graduated with majors in science-related areas. These few were mostly in the biological sciences.

In 1965, 8 percent of the freshmen entering Ohio State University had mathematics placement level 5. In 1975, 26 percent had mathematics placement level 5, and the Department of Mathematics developed a full program of remedial courses. Ohio State is an open-admissions university, admitting any graduate of an Ohio secondary school up to its enrollment limit. Under present law there is no way to exclude underprepared students. Further, the university has found no cost-effective ways to teach students with serious deficiencies. Whereas the precalculus students perform acceptably well in lecture sections of 150–200 students supported by small recitation sections, we have been successful at the remedial level only with individually taught sections of 25–30 students. Experienced teachers must be assigned to these classes. In 1977, approximately two thousand freshmen entered Ohio State with mathematics placement level 5. The cost to the university for this remedial instruction has been staggering.

One result of the concern of Ohio high schools and universities about the large number of underprepared students has been the development of a junior-year testing program. Juniors from 610 Ohio high schools participated in this program in 1983–84. Funding has been provided in the higher-education budget of Ohio that now enables any Ohio school to request the testing of its college-intending juniors.

A high school junior who takes the test is told his or her mathematics placement level and given a list of university mathematics courses that will be required in the intended major; noncredit remedial courses are identified. A student can request this information for the curriculum of any one of the state universities in Ohio. Schools participating in the program show an average increase of 40 percent in senior mathematics enrollments after the first year of participation.

The magnitude of the remedial problem, together with evidence that 46 percent of the juniors tested in 1981 placed at level 5, convinced us that there was a need for a new course for seniors who tested at the lowest level as juniors. The traditional college preparatory curriculum does not provide many options for students who have had difficulty with algebra 1. In 1981–82, with a grant from the Battelle Memorial Foundation, we began to develop an alternative course for seniors. The project staff consisted of six mathematics educators: Robert Mizer from Upper Arlington High School, Donna Fugate from Whetstone High School in Columbus, Frank Demana and Joan Leitzel from the Department of Mathematics at Ohio State, and Joe Crosswhite and Alan Osborne from the College of Education at Ohio State.

Approximately one hundred students in four classes in the two high schools were involved in the pilot year of the Basic College Preparatory Mathematics (BCPM) Project. Two of these four classes were taught by the high school teachers and two by the mathematics faculty from the university. Revised materials were field-tested in forty-one representative Ohio schools in 1982–83.

The course developed in the BCPM Project is *not* a review course. Our experience is that attempts at review are a waste of time with students who lack basic mathematical techniques and understanding; they know nothing to review. We have taken a different approach: an approach that (1) is highly numerical and makes central use of the hand-held calculator, and (2) introduces many of the mathematical concepts in concrete problem settings. Graphing is used both as a problem-solving tool and as a bridge between arithmetic and algebraic experiences.

To date, results have been quite encouraging. Of the more than a thousand seniors who studied the BCPM materials, approximately 750 were at level 5 as juniors, approximately 140 were at level 4, and 110 above level 4. Posttest data indicate that at least 80 percent of the level-5 students finished above level 5 with approximately 65 percent above level 4. Of the level-4 students, 91 percent moved at least one placement level. The performance of university freshmen at the same level in remedial mathematics was contrasted with the BCPM students on common items on chapter tests and midterm examinations. The performance on the algebraic items of 69.6 percent correct by BCPM students was significantly higher than the performance of 54 percent correct by university students; the performance on numerical items was comparable. The data suggest that remediation for university mathematics can be accomplished at least as well in the high schools as we have been able to do at Ohio State. Teachers reported that they enjoyed teaching the materials, and students exhibited no loss in attitude toward mathematics or calculators. Rhodes (1983) provides more detail concerning the evaluation of the BCPM materials. The evidence indicates that college-intending seniors who have had difficulties with mathematics at earlier school levels can learn enough mathematics to reopen career options and to decrease significantly their time of enrollment in university work.

## PRINCIPLES AND THEMES IN
## INSTRUCTION AND CURRICULUM

Six concerns guided our thinking about the design of the BCPM experience for students. Two of these, proper placement of students and their work and attendance patterns, have implications apart from the mathematics classroom. The other four are specific to what happened in the BCPM classrooms. Let us look first at placement and attendance.

### Placement in College Preparatory Mathematics Classes

The students who participated in the pilot and field-test phases of development of the BCPM materials had taken the early placement test in the winter of their junior year. This served several useful functions. First, it limited enrollment to those students who needed to begin again in their study of college preparatory mathematics. One class in the pilot phase of the program included a few students who knew enough mathematics for them to take advantage of the regular course offerings of the school. We found that these students not only showed little growth in BCPM over the year but also tended to complicate instruction because of their familiarity with some of the content. They could, and would, jump to algebraic generalizations that would rob the less-prepared student of the joy of discovery and interfere with the dynamics of group work on the mathematics. Thus, the placement testing served to assure that students had similar backgrounds.

Second, the use of the placement test helped establish a productive orientation to work on mathematics. The reality of knowing that extra mathematics courses would be required at the university before they could start a desired major and the expectation of having to pay fees for extra terms of study led students in both the pilot and field-test phases to be more purposeful and intent in study. The fact that counselors and parents were aware of the results of the testing supported a constructive work atmosphere in the BCPM classrooms. A common reaction of the guidance counselors has been that until they had the specific information relating a student's mathematical competency to the mathematical requirements for the student's career choice, they had little leverage to encourage enrollment in senior mathematics classes.

### Issues of Student Effort and Attendance

One concern in moving university remediation to the secondary schools was whether students in the secondary environment would work hard enough to make the progress they needed to make. University students at the remedial level are expected to be more highly motivated than low-achieving high school students. They pay tuition and worry about flunking out. They are in an environment where most students study. It was not clear that we would have the same leverage with high school students. However, the Early Mathematics Placement Testing program served to highlight the jeopardy of weak preparation in mathematics. Generally we were pleased by the response of students to the demands of BCPM.

Students were required to do large numbers of problems both during the class period and outside. The problems were not drill-and-practice exercises but usually required analysis and thought. In the pilot year we expected assignments to take forty-five minutes to an hour to complete. We discussed these demands with our classes during the first week and encouraged students who were not able to make a commitment to doing mathematics each day to drop the class. Early in the year students talked a great deal about the amount of time they spent on homework. Their discussions were a mixture of complaints and bragging. In time, the demands of daily assignments required no more discussion. The students seemed to become aware of their rapid progress and to know that daily homework was an essential ingredient in their learning.

Mathematics is a highly sequential discipline. Efforts to chop it into little fragments for instruction have not been successful in preparing students for collegiate mathematics. We had no greater problem in the pilot year of BCPM than the need to have all students in class every day for instruction. In one school, classes were fair game for assemblies, student council, instrumental ensembles, military recruiters, social studies field trips, and so on. We addressed the problem head on with administrators and students. In the field-test year we specifically requested that schools using the experimental course protect against this type of fragmentation.

Students believe that when they are excused from a class there is no penalty for missing it. But average and below-average students are not independent learners of mathematics. They do not yet read their texts and understand the mathematical ideas in them. They cannot reconstruct for themselves the concepts developed when they miss a class. Neither can a teacher give hour for hour in helping students understand missed work.

The custom of letting an important activity in one area cause students to miss their classes in another is out of hand in many schools. Helen Vo-Dinh (1983), an English teacher in a school near Washington, D.C., has a thoughtful essay in *Newsweek* entitled "Excuses, Excuses." She writes: "At the latest count my syllabus is at the mercy of 45 different activities sanctioned by our school system." This problem is greater for mathematics than for other disciplines because of the sequential nature of mathematics. It seems that this is one issue so important to effective instruction that mathematics teachers must go to war over it, choosing allies wherever they can be found. Far more imagination needs to be brought to the task of scheduling school activities so that class periods are not violated and academic effort can be the highest priority of our schools.

A second, related issue is the weak demands we have come to place on senior students. No year of study is more important for a college preparatory student. In the field test of BCPM, we gave the posttest during the first week in May because it was not clear that any further learning would take place for seniors in many schools. In her *Newsweek* article, Vo-Dinh writes:

> The culmination of this disrespect for intellectual effort occurs in my school when the seniors are allowed to end classes and prepare for graduation three weeks before the rest of the student body. The message which comes across is that the senior curriculum is so negligible it can be cut short.

Such scheduling does our students a disservice. The Commission on Articulation between Secondary Education and Ohio Colleges has recommended that every college preparatory student take at least three years of mathematics, including one in the senior year. We must give attention to (1) the curriculum, to guarantee that there is a suitable senior-year mathematics course for every student, (2) advising, to be sure that students are encouraged to schedule appropriate courses in the senior year, and (3) setting academic demands for seniors that realistically indicate what is ahead for them.

Now we come to the other four considerations, those specific to the BCPM classroom. We shall discuss a numerical approach to algebra and geometry, the role of graphing, problems as means, and issues of instructional style.

### A Numerical Approach to Algebra and Geometry

Most high school juniors tested in the Early Mathematics Placement Testing program have had at least one year each of algebra and geometry, and more than half were taking a second year of algebra or a more advanced course. Yet 46 percent of these students demonstrated no skills in algebra when tested. A highly numerical approach to algebra and geometry is an alternative that is effective with these students, most of whom have been only marginally successful in more formal courses. This approach, in which key mathematical ideas are first investigated through extensive computation, is possible because of the existence of low-priced, hand-held calculators. The calculator permits us to exploit the numerical basis of college preparatory mathematics. In the next few paragraphs we discuss the ways calculators have been most useful in BCPM.

1. *Entry into significant problems.* Calculators provide entry into significant problems and a way around deadly drill and practice. We are able to describe realistic problems that both interest and instruct students. Problem settings can be chosen from consumer issues, scientific phenomena, investments, inflation, population growth and decline, and situations close to students' experiences. The computation needed to solve problems in many of these settings would be forbidding without calculators. In fact, in some instances the computation would actually interfere with problem solving.

2. *Significant mathematics in spite of weak computational skills.* Calculators permit students with weak computational skills to do significant mathematics. It is often assumed that students who lack arithmetic skills will not be able to do much mathematics until these skills are developed. In BCPM we have demonstrated that such students using calculators can investigate most problem situations. They can begin graphing, and they can solve equations. Calculators also remove one excuse students have for their mistakes—computational error—and permit us to require that they produce correct numerical answers.

3. *Concrete experience to anticipate formal ideas.* Calculators permit encounters with concepts and relationships in problem settings before the concepts are formalized. For example, in analyzing the growth of a bacterial culture that has a doubling period of ten hours, BCPM students experimentally find approximations to $2^{1/10}$, $2^{2/10}$, . . . before fractional exponents are defined. They solve equations, use scientific notation, and reason with ratios in numerical settings before these concepts are formalized and algebraic techniques developed. Level-5 students can handle mathematical concepts that come out of concrete problem settings. Calculators permit this concrete experience to anticipate formal ideas.

4. *Experience with properties of numbers.* Calculators give students experience with computer logic and raise in a natural way questions about arithmetic properties, such as order of operations and exponentiation. In their first assignment, BCPM students do exercises of this type:

> **Exercise.** Write a mathematical phrase evaluated by the following sequence of key strokes:
>
> $\boxed{3}$ $\boxed{+}$ $\boxed{2}$ $\boxed{\times}$ $\boxed{5}$ $\boxed{x^2}$ $\boxed{=}$

Calculators also strengthen students' numerical intuitions. We find that level-5 students lack a sense of number order and magnitude. Investigating problems involving very large and very small numbers helps overcome this deficiency.

5. *Variables to generalize numerical relationships.* A key use of calculators is to give students the opportunity to investigate many special cases within a problem setting before introducing a variable to represent the general case. We will say more in a later section about the importance of students getting a firm grasp on the concept of *variable* early in their study of algebra. Calculators permit variables to be introduced naturally as a way to generalize numerical relationships.

> **Exercise.** Complete the following table:
>
> | Price per pound ($) | 7.20 | 8.32 | 14.24 | | 16.16 | $x$ | |
> |---|---|---|---|---|---|---|---|
> | Price per ounce ($) | | | | .97 | | | $y$ |

Because students can solve problems numerically using guess-and-verify procedures with their calculators, the formalism of writing and solving equations can be delayed until extensive numerical experience supports these procedures. For example, in BCPM students do problems of this type:

**Exercise.** Various amounts of water are added to dilute 10 liters of a 20% salt solution. Complete this chart. How many liters of water must be added to 10 liters of a 20% salt solution to give a 15% solution?

| Amount of water added (liters) | Amount of new mixture (liters) | Amount of salt in new mixture (liters) | % of salt in new mixture |
|---|---|---|---|
| 0.5 | 10 + 0.5 | 0.20(10) | $\frac{0.20(10)}{10 + 0.5} \approx 19.05\%$ |
| 1 | 10 + 1 | 0.20(10) | |
| 2 | | | |
| | | | 15% |

Before students write an equation to describe the problem above, a variable is added to the chart to give a final line that looks like this:

| Amount of water added (liters) | Amount of new mixture (liters) | Amount of salt in new mixture (liters) | % of salt in new mixture |
|---|---|---|---|
| $x$ | 10 + $x$ | 0.20(10) | $\frac{0.20(10)}{10 + x}$ |

6. *Early graphing experiences.* Calculators make possible early graphing experiences that require the plotting of large numbers of points. Then graphs come to be viewed by students as collections of points. The role of graphing in BCPM is so central that this feature is described in detail in the next section. In BCPM, graphs generalize charts and anticipate equations. Because students have calculators, the graphing of numerical relationships can precede algebra. This provides students with a visual, concrete representation of relationships that is more readily appreciated than the abstraction of an equation.

Several characteristics of the numerical approach that make algebra and geometry more accessible to remedial students could benefit all students earlier in their college preparatory courses. Problem settings could be more realistic and problems more demanding. Students could investigate large numbers of special cases before generalizing with a variable. Algebraic and geometric ideas could be approached more through computation and less through axiomatic structures. Graphing could be used to motivate and support certain algebraic concepts:

- Inequalities raise questions about where a graph is, such as above or below the axis.
- Completing the square is a procedure that identifies the vertex of a parabola.
- The division algorithm for polynomials assists in finding asymptotes for rational functions.

Large numbers of college-intending students are not learning mathematics well in their present programs. Our experience is that a numerical approach helps students who have a history of weak performance learn the mathematics they need for college entry.

## The Role of Graphing

Graphing serves as a fundamental theme for organizing instruction in BCPM. Providing a mediating step between the numerical experiences in early sections and the formalizing of algebraic concepts and notation, it gives students a second concrete representation of the generalizations that are to be expressed later with variables. Examples of specific instructional uses of graphing are given below.

1. *Concepts of number order.* One use of graphing is to address students' inadequate sense of number order and magnitude. Many of the students entering the course were not able to arrange from smallest to largest three given finite decimals between $-1$ and $1$. Graphing proved to be an effective vehicle for strengthening numerical intuitions.

Initially students needed experiences locating numbers on a number line. An important part of this experience was choosing a scale for the number line appropriate for graphing a collection of numbers. The problem of fitting a collection of numbers on a segment confined by the size of a piece of paper or having a large enough unit so that the graph was useful helped develop the sense of magnitude and order. An exercise like the following also helped students visualize the effects of exponentiation on numbers between $-1$ and $0$.

**Exercise:** Sketch a number line and graph these numbers:

$$-0.5; (-0.5)^2; (-0.5)^3; (-0.5)^4; (-0.5)^5; (-0.5)^6$$

2. *The geometry of a curve.* To develop a feeling for the geometry of a curve, BCPM took advantage of the number-crunching capabilities of the calculator. Most students entered the course with the feeling that a graph was a few points connected by a curve or by segments. Students were required to do exercises such as "Divide the interval from $-3$ to $3$ into 30 equal pieces" and then compute the 31 values for a given graph and even to insert additional values to reveal more of the character of the curve. Frequently students worked in groups to divide the labor of creating values for large sets of points for graphing. Thus they developed a strong intuition that a graph was a collection of points.

3. *Variables and functions.* Students graphed functional relationships before dealing with them algebraically. The early graphing experiences enabled students later to think of algebraic equations and inequalities in terms of their graphs so that questions about solutions could be raised in a geometric context. Exercises like the following provided a rich basis for interpretation in subsequent equation-solving lessons:

**Exercise:** Divide the interval $-4 \le x \le 4$ into 100 equal pieces.

*a*) Compute the value of $y = 1/(x^2 - 1)$ at the 101 values of $x$ that you have marked and graph the points $(x, y)$.

*b*) Describe the behavior of the graph near $x = 1$.

*c*) Use your graph to find values of $x$ for which

$$\frac{1}{(x^2 - 1)} = 1; \text{ for which } \frac{1}{(x^2 - 1)} = 0.$$

4. *Problem solving.* Graphing was used as a problem-solving tool in addition to providing a bridge between numerical relationships and their more formalized algebraic renderings. Typically in BCPM, problem situations were investigated in three ways: first numerically; then geometrically by means of graphing; and still later, algebraically. For example, the following problem was treated in each of the three settings:

---

**Problem situation.** Mary Ellen has invested $17 500, part at 9% and the rest at 7% (both simple interest).

**Numerical approach** (from chapter 2):
Complete the following chart to show several possibilities. Then find the amounts of money invested at 9% and 7% if Mary Ellen's annual interest is $1 505.

| Amount invested at 9% ($) | Amount invested at 7% ($) | Annual interest ($) |
|---|---|---|
| 4 000 | 17 500 − 4 000 = 13 500 | .09(4 000) + .07(13 500) = 1 305 |
| 8 000 | 9 500 | |
| 16 000 | | |

**Geometric approach** (from chapter 4):
Draw a graph that shows how Mary Ellen's annual interest depends on the amount invested at 9%. Use the graph to find the amount of money invested at 9% if her annual interest is $1505.

**Algebraic approach** (from chapter 5):
Let $x$ denote the amount of money invested at 9%; write an algebraic expression for Mary Ellen's annual interest. If her annual interest is $1505, find the amount of money invested at 9%.

---

Weak mathematics students often freeze when faced by a story problem. They appear to remember from elementary algebra that one should begin a solution by writing a variable—usually $x$—and then proceed to write an equation. Identifying what the variable represents and then using it to express the numerical relationships of the problem is a sophisticated approach to problem solving. Developing the numerical relationships in the form of tables, coupled with revisiting problems in the graphical setting, appears to guide the attention of learners to the relationships needed in making appropriate use of variables.

Through this approach, students were able to solve more problems. The first-semester examination included problems similar to the one above but no restrictions were placed on the method of solution. Many students elected to use a numerical or graphical approach even though at that point in the course algebraic tools and techniques were well established. Thus they were able to get started on problems without feeling blocked by their lack of control or understanding of algebraic methods. They simply tried something numerical that would get them started. Students were able to see the relationship between the numerical charts, graphs, and equations.

Another use of graphing was to enable students to solve real and significant problems for which algebraic techniques had not yet been developed. Without developing algorithms to find maximums or the idea of logarithms, the following problems were given:

> **Exercise:** Draw a graph that shows for all rectangles with perimeter 100 meters the relationship between the width of a rectangle and its area. Then determine, among all rectangles with perimeter 100, which has the largest area.

> **Exercise:** The population of Oilsville was 12 500 in 1980, and the rate of population growth was 8%. If the annual growth rate continues at 8%, in what year will the population be twice that of 1980?

This use of graphing reinforced the idea of trying to make a start on solving a problem even though an appropriate algorithm could not be remembered or had not been taught. It also served to focus the students' attention on what were to be significant concepts in later lessons.

The use of graphing as a major organizing theme in designing instruction served four primary functions:

- It helped the learner integrate concepts and ideas across several types of mathematical content rather than learning the concepts, ideas, and skills as discrete, unrelated entities.

- It extended previously developed numerical relationships, skills, and intuitions.

- Graphing encouraged and reinforced the fundamental attitude that we want to pervade problem solving: Try specific numerical cases to get started.

- The concepts of variable and function were given geometric underpinning that expedited instruction and improved learning when those topics were taught formally.

Observing students' reactions to the graphing activities in BCPM generated several questions that pertain to their earlier experiences in precollege mathematics. The two questions that follow are among the more significant.

1. *Why was the informal experience with table building and graphing so effective in generating a basis for instruction about variable and function?*

We suspect that earlier attention to developing graphical awareness of the underpinnings of the function concept with a focus on the use of dependence to deal with significant problems removes some of the significant difficulties that students exhibit in dealing with the concepts of variable and function.

We conjecture that the currently used instructional approaches and definitional bases found in texts for the precollege curriculum give insufficient attention to developing students' intuition. The learning appears to be much more complex than allowed for by many of the curricular materials and instructional approaches currently in vogue. Nicholas's article "A Dilemma in Definition" (1966) and Hight's (1968) extension of these ideas spell out alternatives to, and possible effects of, premature commitment to the strict ordered-pair definition of function without attention given to how a function may be related with a dependency rule. A number of research studies (e.g., Adi 1978; Clement 1982; Herscovics and Kiernan 1980; Hart 1980; Kiernan 1981; Rosnick 1981) can be interpreted to indicate that an understanding of variable is critical in dealing with concepts and skills associated with equation and function.

2. *Does premature closure on generalizations through the use of symbols and algebraic notation significantly curtail the willingness of students to attempt to solve problems?*

One interpretation of BCPM's use of graphing is that it is a delaying tactic interposed between numerical investigations and algebraic generalizations. Does a learner need time to allow the numerical ideas to germinate, or does the graphing experience provide an additional, needed representation of ideas critical to the algebraic formulation? On the one hand, we feel that the more leisurely encounter with generalizations was a significant, positive factor affecting performance. On the other hand, we are confident that the concreteness of the geometrical interpretations made a contribution to the learning.

### Problems: Means as Well as Ends

Problems are the means of introducing mathematical concepts and techniques in BCPM. Teachers give students situations to explore and reason within rather than giving a rule or a definition, providing illustrative examples, and saying to students, "Go thou and do likewise." Typically, the situations are not open-ended but are developed over incremental stages so that the conceptual demands do not require leaps of understanding. The thrust is more toward "try something," "explore," or "get started with what you know" than toward establishing formal heuristics or strategies for problem solving.

A major concern in using problems as a vehicle for exploring new mathematics is that problem-solving activities take instructional time, a limited commodity. This was a major reason for electing to revisit problem settings. Often a student first encounters a problem in a setting of numerical exploration, later deals with this *same* problem in a graphical setting, and finally generates algebraic techniques to deal with the problem efficiently. Because the student is already familiar with the setting, immediate attention can be given to the new mathematics.

This procedure provides several additional instructional advantages. First, it scatters learning about a concept over several days of instruction, which reinforces the ideas naturally. Learning is more stable and permanent, since revisiting the problem allows new learning to fit readily into a cognitive structure of existing concepts and skills. Second, for those students who do not fully understand the problem initially, it provides a second and, for some, a third opportunity to learn. Third, students acquire a thorough understanding of the problem setting before acquiring powerful algebraic techniques. Finally, we attempted to select problem settings that were important to understand in their own right, using settings and techniques that are important in the general educational goals of literacy. Such topics as interest and population growth should be a component of mathematical literacy.

---

A student encounters a problem in a setting of numerical exploration, later deals with this *same* problem in a graphical setting, and finally generates algebraic techniques to deal with the problem efficiently.

---

A fundamental flaw in the background of the students for whom BCPM was designed is that they have no usable concept of variable. Variables, rather than being a powerful means of representing situations or a means of capturing generalizations, are misused and misunderstood to the extent that they become a barrier to learning for some students. Students focus on learning the rule represented with variables without developing a sense of what variables represent, and consequently, what the rule represents also. The sense of confusion is great enough for some students that the use of variables appears to lead to emotional panic.

Problem solving by means of numerical exploration with guess-and-verify procedures alleviated many of the difficulties students had in acquiring the concept of variable. Many problems involved functional relationships. Calculating specific outcomes corresponding to several specific table entries and then using a variable to express the general case helped to establish the concept of variable. The variable provided a generalization that cut short computational guess-and-verify procedures. Initial use of variables in the table-building, guess-and-verify process was suggested early in the instruction but was not required until after several weeks of experience with numerical exploration and graphing.

We are confident that the concept of variable was extended and established for the BCPM students by the extensive table-building activities in the numerical exploration approach to problem solving. However, we are not sure exactly what features of instruction are critical in the teaching process. Several different decisions concerning when and how to ask students to make the generalization with variables must be made by the teacher. What role does computing each line of the table play in learning? Must the student be led to observe the regularities and patterns across rows in the table? With the prospect of a computer rather than a hand-held calculator doing the computation of table entries for the student, will table building for generalizations using variables have the same pedagogical advantage as the numerical exploration accessible with the calculator? We think these specific questions need research.

A commitment to exploratory problem solving of a numerical and graphical nature frees the preparer of instructional materials from constraints in selecting problems. Most BCPM problems embodied functional relationships. Rather than being limited to problems based on linear functions, explorations concerned with exponential and quadratic functions were undertaken early in the course. Thus, students encountered inherently more interesting applications than would have been possible within the constraints of the logical completeness that characterizes the mathematics of most courses.

### Issues of Instructional Style

The foremost issue of a methodological character concerns the use of informal methods of instruction. Formal, technical words of mathematics are kept to a minimum. In a similar manner, rules and algorithms are delayed until after students have had considerable time for inductive experiences to support the definition of the rules and algorithms. We found that students often would not attempt problems and would not use the mathematics they knew when a problem appeared to rely on their memory of a rule or definition. They would waste effort trying to remember rather than simply getting started. This behavior is a significant puzzle; what characteristics of students' previous encounters with mathematics lead to this debilitating blockage when they encounter new problems?

We found that group problem-solving techniques were particularly effective in the developmental aspects of lessons. This strategy was used partly to relieve the student from the memory blockage described above; there is always someone in a class who is able to get started. A second consideration is that many problems are time consuming. For example, many of the graphing problems required computing a large number of coordinates; splitting the task among a team reduced time to reasonable levels. The team approach resulted in students helping their peers in constructive, useful ways.

The final issue about instructional style concerns who has the responsibility for solving a problem, the teacher or the student. The exploratory problem solving that is a salient feature of the BCPM approach demands that the *student* accept the challenge of problem solving. This means that the teacher should not demonstrate or exhibit solutions but use class time for student work on problems. In the field-test year, some teachers found this natural, but others had difficulty relinquishing responsibility for showing solutions to problems. At issue is the instructional style of the teacher in promoting problem solving. Students must make problems their own if the exploratory problem-solving approach is to work. From leading students by the hand through the reading of new text material to dealing with homework exercises, teachers must reorient their own thinking and behavior to guiding the student to responsibility for the mathematics.

## REALIZING THE AGENDA FOR ACTION

The experience of developing the Basic College Preparatory Mathematics Project has yielded many insights into the problems associated with implementing the recommendations of the *Agenda for Action* (NCTM 1980). We are not only convinced that problem solving can be the focus of school mathematics (Recommendation 1) but sure that it *must* be for the older student who has a history of not being successful in previous encounters with mathematics. Problem solving that provides exploratory numerical and graphical experiences preliminary to developing powerful and encompassing rules, definitions, and algorithms offers an advantage to students in that they learn far in excess of that derived from skill- and drill-oriented emphasis on computational proficiency. The use of the calculator (Recommendation 3) makes this approach possible and is supportive of both the learning and the solving of problems.

The BCPM Project gives strong evidence that students who are college intending but have had difficulty in learning mathematics can learn enough mathematics to reopen career options and reduce the amount of time and investment required in their college programs. This would not have been possible without concerted attention to introducing an element of flexibility, a new option, into the senior high school curriculum (Recommendation 6).

BCPM was developed to respond to the needs of students entering traditional university curricula. A reevaluation of the role of calculus in the mathematics curriculum (Recommendation 6.3) might suggest that the BCPM would be even more effective in the future. The emphasis on problem solving and the discrete character of the approach that employs computational tools needs further exploration as a foundation experience for students entering nontraditional curricula in mathematics.

We find it easy to classify the BCPM Project as evidence of the good sense of many of the recommendations of the *Agenda*. However, the most intriguing factor for us is that this evidence has led to a variety of other questions about the learning and teaching of mathematics that are in need of concentrated study by researchers and developers of curricular materials for younger students in mathematics. The role of problem-solving experiences in generating an understanding of the concepts of variable and function needs careful attention. The effects of delaying formal presentation of definitions, rules, and algorithms is a major puzzle. Finally, the factors in teacher education that are important in making teachers comfortable with an exploratory problem-solving approach must be better understood.

## REFERENCES

Adcock, Al, Joan R. Leitzel, and Bert K. Waits. "University Mathematics Placement Testing for High School Juniors." *American Mathematical Monthly* 88 (January 1981): 55–59.

Adi, Helen. "Intellectual Development and Reversibility of Thought in Equation Solving." *Journal for Research in Mathematics Education* 9 (May 1978): 204–13.

Clement, John. "Algebra Word Problem Solutions: Thought Processes Underlying a Common Misconception." *Journal for Research in Mathematics Education* 13 (January 1982): 16–30.

Demana, Franklin D., and Joan R. Leitzel. *Transition to College Mathematics*. Reading, Mass.: Addison-Wesley Publishing Co., 1984.

Hart, Kathleen M. *Secondary School Children's Understanding of Mathematics: A Report of the Mathematics Component of the Concepts in Secondary Mathematics and Science Programme*. London: Mathematics Education Centre for Science Education, Chelsea College, University of London, 1980.

Herscovics, Nicolas, and Carolyn Kiernan. "Constructing Meaning for the Concept of Equation." *Mathematics Teacher* 73 (November 1980): 572–80.

Hight, Donald W. "Functions: Dependent Variables to Fickle Pickers." *Mathematics Teacher* 51 (October 1968): 575–79.

Kiernan, Carolyn. "Concepts Associated with the Equality Symbol." *Educational Studies in Mathematics* 12 (August 1981): 317–26.

National Council of Teachers of Mathematics. *An Agenda for Action: Recommendations for School Mathematics of the 1980s*. Reston, Va.: The Council, 1980.

Nicholas, C. P. "A Dilemma in Definition." *American Mathematical Monthly* 73 (August-September 1966): 762–68.

Rhodes, T. Michael. "A Study to Assess and Compare the Effects on Achievement and Attitude of Two Remediation Efforts in Mathematics by the Ohio State University." Unpublished doctoral dissertation, Ohio State University, 1983.

Rosnick, Peter. "Some Misconceptions Concerning the Concept of Variable." *Mathematics Teacher* 74 (September 1981): 418–20.

Vo-Dinh, Helen C. "Excuses, Excuses." *Newsweek*, 15 August 1983, 13.

Waits, Bert K., and Joan R. Leitzel. "An Update on University Mathematics Placement Testing for High School Juniors in Ohio." *Mathematics in College*, Spring 1985.

# 13

# The Advanced Placement Program in Calculus

John Kenelly
Patricia Henry
Chancey O. Jones

S INCE 1955, the Advanced Placement (AP) program in calculus has made available to high schools a well-organized syllabus for one or two beginning calculus courses, together with nationally graded examinations whose results are widely accepted for credit by colleges and universities. The program has grown from its early concentration in prestigious preparatory schools to one of national scope that can be found in some of the smallest and most remote high schools. This growth has been continuous and is in direct contrast with the declining school population of the last few years.

## THE CURRENT COURSES

Since the AP program began, participation has increased dramatically. Initially in the total program for all disciplines there were 1 229 candidates from 104 schools. In 1983, this number had increased to 157 973 candidates from 5 827 schools. At nine-year increments the number of calculus candidates has been 285 (1955); 7 710 (1964); 14 310 (1973); and 31 918 (1982). This is surely impressive, but if one were to forecast a nine-year doubling rate and assume that half of the secondary school calculus students who enroll in an AP Calculus course take one of the two national examinations, then it would take fifty-seven years—that is, until A.D. 2040—for the United States to have five million high school calculus students, the number currently estimated in the Soviet Union.

The number of colleges and universities that offer credit or placement on the basis of AP participation is also increasing. However, there are still college mathematics faculty members who express their opposition to "calculus in the high school." This despite evidence that the quality of the program equals or exceeds its counterpart on college campuses (Haag 1977; Dickey 1982). Moreover, the Mathematical Association of America's na-

166

tional curriculum recommendations (Committee on the Undergraduate Program in Mathematics 1981) recognizes the Calculus BC syllabus as a basis for structuring a contemporary course.

In the study by Haag (1977), AP candidates performed at a higher level than college students on the AP examination, though the grades received by the college students did *not* reflect this difference. For example, AP candidates with a grade of 3 (the lowest grade that usually receives credit) were comparable to B-level college students. Dickey (1982) compared the performance of college students and AP candidates on a general examination that did not favor either group. He found a significant difference in their performance. Even when adjustments for variations in mathematical ability were made by using the students' SAT scores, the AP candidates still performed significantly better. In other words, high school may be the *best* place to study calculus.

The Advanced Placement program is offered by the College Board, and the examinations are developed by Educational Testing Service (ETS). Mathematics has been a part of the program from the beginning, and in the first thirteen years a single calculus program was available. In 1969, the mathematics program was divided into two courses. The beginning calculus course was called Calculus AB, and the alternative course, Calculus BC, was described as more extensive and more intensive. The letter codes reflect the intended overlap of the two courses. In general terms, the AB course represents the material in a one-semester college course that gives an introductory but comprehensive coverage of differential and integral calculus. The BC course represents complete and in-depth coverage of all the topics in a single-variable calculus course. Since the introduction of the two courses in 1969, the ratio of the number of the candidates taking the Calculus AB examination to the number taking the Calculus BC exam has remained essentially constant at about 3:1 (Pieters and Vance 1961; Finkbeiner, Neff, and Williams 1971; Jones, Kenelly, and Kreider 1975).

The examinations are developed by a committee of mathematics faculty members working with the test development staff of ETS. The College Board appoints the committee, and the committee writes each year's examinations. In contrast to most national testing programs, the AP examinations have both multiple choice and free-response sections. The two parts are equally weighted, and a candidate's grade is reported on a five-point scale. The numerical scores are described as follows: 5, extremely well qualified; 4, well qualified; 3, qualified; 2, possibly qualified; and 1, no recommendation. As noted earlier, a grade of 3 or higher will usually receive college credit, and the course description booklet (College Board n.d.) contains a list of the colleges and universities that have a credit policy in mathematics. Recent score percentages are given in table 13.1. It is important to note that as the number of schools offering the program and the number of candidates taking each of the examinations have increased, the level of performance has been maintained.

TABLE 13.1
Percentage of AP Candidates at Each Score Level, 1979–1983

| Calculus AB | | | | | | Calculus BC | | | | |
|---|---|---|---|---|---|---|---|---|---|---|
| Score | 1979 | 1980 | 1981 | 1982 | 1983 | Score | 1979 | 1980 | 1981 | 1982 | 1983 |
| 5 | 13 | 14 | 14 | 15 | 15 | 5 | 24 | 22 | 23 | 24 | 27 |
| 4 | 21 | 20 | 21 | 21 | 22 | 4 | 22 | 21 | 24 | 22 | 21 |
| 3 | 34 | 35 | 34 | 34 | 34 | 3 | 24 | 27 | 27 | 28 | 27 |
| 2 | 19 | 17 | 18 | 18 | 17 | 2 | 18 | 16 | 14 | 14 | 14 |
| 1 | 13 | 14 | 13 | 12 | 12 | 1 | 12 | 14 | 12 | 12 | 11 |

The free-response, or "essay," section of the examination is graded by a group of faculty members in June at the annual reading in the Princeton, New Jersey, area. The reading session is a major part of the program, and the "readers" are the nucleus of a close-knit AP community. Hundreds of faculty members have been involved in these sessions, and the annual meetings are a major communications link in the AP program (Jameson 1980; Henry 1983).

Changes in the program are communicated through the course description booklet (College Board n.d.). Four major changes have occurred in the program:

**1969** The change from a single calculus course and examination to the two courses, Calculus AB and Calculus BC, and their respective examinations

**1982** The change from a 0–15 point scale to a 0–9 point scale in grading the individual questions in the free-response section of the examinations (The candidate's raw score is converted into the reported grade by a statistical process that maintains consistent standards.)

**1983** The change from a seven-question to a five-question free-response section; the policy of permitting, but not requiring, calculators during the taking of either of the examinations

**1985** The suspension of the calculator policy

The course description booklet describes the mathematics that is prerequisite for a sound calculus course, and each course syllabus clearly indicates the topics that should be included in each of the two AP Calculus courses. Secondary schools that are initiating AP courses should review their mathematics curriculum from the junior high or middle schools through the senior year of high school. Some of the curricular changes that have occurred in many schools giving an AP course are the offering of a first year of algebra in the eighth grade, an emphasis on functions, a move from the trigonometry of right triangles to the periodic functions of the circle, and the inclusion of more applied problems at all levels. Schools and their AP candidates are participants in a national program, and regular success by the students is a solid confirmation of the quality of the school's overall mathematics program.

## ANTICIPATED FUTURE CHANGES

The content of the two calculus courses and the specifications for the two examinations are established by the College Board's AP Calculus Development Committee and approved by the Board's Mathematical Sciences Advisory Committee. The membership of the Development Committee consists of three university faculty members and three secondary school teachers, all active in the teaching of calculus at their institutions. The committee also includes the individual who directs the reading of the examinations. This director, the chief reader, is a college mathematics professor who is appointed for a four-year term by ETS. Two senior members of the staff of ETS also serve as advisors to the committee. The committee meets at least twice each year to construct the annual Calculus AB and BC examinations and to continually monitor the content specifications of the two courses.

The committee members represent a broad geographic and institutional cross section of calculus teachers, and they serve on the committee for three years. Thus, a new secondary school teacher and a new college faculty member normally join the committee each year, and consequently the program represents the judgments of many individuals over a long period of time. At least once a year, in conjunction with its meeting, the committee conducts a miniconference for secondary school and college calculus teachers. Comments are collected from the conference participants and carefully considered in all the revisions that the committee makes in the program. In addition, the comments submitted by teachers and students at each administration of the examination are carefully considered by the committee in the revisions.

In 1983 the Advanced Placement program initiated a new calculator policy, and this policy is part of a long-term attempt by the College Board to incorporate technology changes in all of its testing programs in mathematics. The overall program efforts are coordinated by the College Board's Mathematical Sciences Advisory Committee. The use of calculators is a constant concern of the AP Calculus Development Committee, whose members made a special effort to construct examinations that would permit the optional presence of calculators. Their review of the 1983 examination results, however, caused them to effect a revision of the policy, which resulted in the release of the following statement in the spring of 1984 (College Board 1984, 12–13):

> Beginning with the May 1985 administration, the use of calculators will NOT be permitted during the administration of the examinations. Although the Development Committee believes that calculators can play an important role in a calculus course, their use on the examinations raises serious problems at this time. Some of the concerns of the Committee regarding the use of calculators on the examinations are as follows.
>
> (1) The rapid changes occurring in technology make it likely that disparities in the hardware (and software) available to students in a few years could be so

great that allowing the use of calculators would cause inequities among students taking the examinations.

(2) The results of studies done during the first administration in which calculators were permitted raise questions about whether students at this time know how to use calculators to their best advantage in a testing situation. Although the examinations were designed so that calculators were not needed, some students indicated that they had used the calculators on a substantial number of questions, and on the average, these students did less well on the examinations than did those who used the calculators very little.

Because of these and other concerns, the Committee decided to suspend, at least for the present time, the rule allowing the use of calculators on the examinations.

The report of the Committee on the Undergraduate Program in Mathematics (CUPM 1981) is especially important, since it should generate changes in the college calculus courses. The report specifically calls for a heavier emphasis on numerical methods and "calculus models," as well as a revision of the coverage of sequences and series. The recommendations ask for a decrease in the emphasis on integration techniques and a reexamination of the coverage of differential equations. The Calculus Development Committee will closely follow the effect of these national recommendations. To the extent that the recommendations succeed in modifying the typical university calculus courses, the changes will be incorporated into the AP syllabus.

The coverage of differential equations, sequences and series, and other advanced topics is frequently reviewed by the committee. In particular, the candidates' performance on questions on these advanced topics for a nine-year period (1969–1977) was studied by the staff at ETS in 1977. This internal report showed that these questions contributed significantly to the students' scores. Thus these advanced topics are an essential part of a student's preparation in the Calculus BC course. The coverage of differential equations is only intended to be an introduction to these techniques, and a complete in-depth treatment should be reserved for a later course in differential equations. The differential equations section of the course will continue to be carefully monitored by the committee. Calculus BC teachers should stay attuned to the changes that will be communicated in the future editions of the course guide. The changes are shaded and highlighted when they first appear.

Since the course was introduced in 1969, Calculus AB has been maintained as an appropriate course for secondary schools to use when they first introduce their AP Calculus program. Through the years the course coverage has received only small modifications, the most recent change being the inclusion of simple integration by parts and l'Hôpital's rule. The committee will continue to make careful adjustments in the course specifications, and AP teachers should always have a current edition of the course description booklet. It should be noted that the free-response and multiple-choice sections are used to give any one examination full coverage of the topics in the syllabus, and it should be emphasized that the committee's long-term policy will continue to be as follows: *Every topic that appears in the syllabus must be tested in either the free-response or the multiple-choice section of the examination within any three-year period or the topic will be dropped from the course description.*

## CALCULUS AS A MAINSTREAM COURSE

There are legitimate questions being raised today about the role of calculus in the general curriculum (Ralston and Young 1983), and its position should be carefully reviewed. The CUPM report (1981, 35) defends the calculus course by saying that "the language, spirit and methods of traditional calculus still permeate mathematics and the natural and social sciences." It notes that the course is "historically rich, is filled with significant mathematical ideas, is tempered through its demonstrably important applications, and is philosophically complete" (p. 36).

---

## Calculus is a cornerstone in an individual's personal development in the use of quantitative methods.

---

The study of mathematics provides an opportunity for the individual to reason abstractly, to model, and to deduce the subtle consequences of basic assumptions. To this end calculus asks the simple question, "How do things change?" The answers are astonishing in their completeness, their complexity, and their wide range of applications. Calculus is a cornerstone in an individual's personal development in the use of quantitative methods.

Unfortunately, the course occasionally degenerates into a collection of mechanical procedures and a codification of techniques. In this event the material is open to serious criticism and appropriately vulnerable to external attack. However, when it is presented with a conceptual approach that incorporates understanding and avoids meaningless pendantic rigor, the material gives the student a mature ability to use quantification methods. A similar amount of intellectual growth is seldom, if ever, achieved by the same amount of course work in any other mathematical subject.

In the past, the calculus course was considered "essential" for science and engineering students. Today the quantification of dynamic models permeates all the professional areas, and the course is equally important in the business and social sciences. The course unifies all its prerequisite material into a collection of concepts and methods that have universal applicability. In the study of limits and continuity, students are required to refine their understanding of basic functional properties and the way that mathematics deals with the quantification of input/output devices and cause-and-effect numerical relationships. In the study of the derivative, the students see the results of numerical investigations of dynamic events, and as a by-product they are introduced to the rich area of optimization. Almost as a sage's lesson in life—"What is the best that you can do within these restrictions?"—students are introduced to a wealth of applications that involve maximum and minimum values.

The circular and exponential functions have real substance and importance when students see their place in growth and decay problems and cyclical processes. In the simple fact that $y = \sin x$ gives $y'' = -\sin x$, students note that nature's basic cycle is described as one whose *driving force is the negative of its current state.* Here in clear terms the students see how, for example, cattle population sizes drive the cyclical market prices of cattle. That is, excess supply gives low prices, and farmers reduce their herds. These reductions lead to inadequate supply and high prices. The driving value (populations) and the derived value (prices) are directly opposite to each other. This suggests that the best time to enter the cattle market is when it is the least popular and the worst time is when it is the most popular. Thus the public's intuition is misleading and correctly noted in the old adage, "If everyone's doing it, it's wrong." The end product is a student's better understanding of the fundamental processes of nature.

Admittedly the course's material will be changed dramatically in the future, and technological changes may add substantial sections on numerical methods. However, the course is broad enough to absorb these changes and important enough to survive.

## ALTERNATIVES TO CALCULUS AS A MAINSTREAM COURSE

Serious consideration is being given to the increased role that discrete mathematics should be given in the college-level curriculum, and calculus is being challenged as the mainstream introductory course in college-level mathematics (Ralston and Young 1983). The debate can be oversimplified into the question, "Should continuous processes be replaced by discrete processes in the mainstream mathematics course at the college-entry level?" A successful academic tradition and the fact that calculus methods permeate the natural and social sciences justify the denial. (The affirmative position is outlined by Ralston in chapter 3 of this yearbook.)

Proponents on all sides of the current curriculum arguments readily recognize the importance of discrete *and* continuous methods being part of every technical student's background, and today's debate centers on the order and sequencing of the calculus course and courses in discrete methods. On the one hand, the existing calculus course is a refined and coherent body of important mathematical methods intimately related to a wide array of technical courses. The course has a keystone role in every technical curriculum. It represents many decades of topic selection and curriculum refinements. But it can be said that many of the sections on manipulative techniques are justified only by *tradition*. On the other hand, it is argued that discrete methods are essential in the new computer-related areas of mathematics and that *space must be found* for their inclusion in freshman mathematics courses.

Even though curriculum changes are slow and major shifts are evolutionary, it is safe to say that discrete mathematics will play an increasing role in all mathematics courses. Discrete methods may replace significant parts of the traditional calculus sequence, but it is premature to envision them replacing the course completely. In that event, the solution would create an equivalent problem because most of the arguments for one side's inclusion are equally appropriate for the other.

## THE ROLE OF THE CALCULATOR IN A CALCULUS COURSE

The calculator can play a particularly strong role in learning calculus. For example, the concept of a limit can be more readily grasped when a student can evaluate the behavior of a function as a value is approached by using small incremental steps, leaving the cumbersome evaluation to a calculator. This is illustrated in figure 13.1.

---

In most elementary calculus texts an intuitive argument is given for the limit of trigonometric functions. Students can more readily accept the limit values if they are assigned to evaluate the function under consideration for increments of $x$ increasingly close to 0.

1. Look at $\lim\limits_{x \to 0} \dfrac{\sin x}{x}$ by completing the chart:

| $x$ | $-0.5$ | $-0.3$ | $-0.1$ | $-0.01$ | $0.01$ | $0.1$ | $0.3$ |
|---|---|---|---|---|---|---|---|
| $\dfrac{\sin x}{x}$ | | | | | | | |

2. Look at $\lim\limits_{x \to 0} \dfrac{1 - \cos x}{\sin x}$ by completing the chart:

| $x$ | $-0.5$ | $-0.3$ | $-0.1$ | $-0.01$ | $0.01$ | $0.1$ | $0.3$ |
|---|---|---|---|---|---|---|---|
| $\dfrac{1 - \cos x}{\sin x}$ | | | | | | | |

3. In each example what does it appear the limit should be?

---

Fig. 13.1

Numerical approximations obtained from algorithms such as the trapezoidal rule and Simpson's rule have traditionally been a part of the calculus course. With a calculator, viable solutions to realistic problems can be obtained, and an instructor can assign a sufficient number of problems to deepen understanding without overburdening the students. The concepts of exact and approximate answers and average and relative error become more meaningful when the student can readily calculate them, as in figure 13.2.

The area under the curve $y = x^2$ from $x = 1$ to $x = 3$ is given by

$$\lim_{n \to \infty} \sum_{i=1}^{n} (1 + i\,\Delta x)^2\,\Delta x, \quad \text{where} \quad \Delta x = \frac{2}{n}.$$

1. Evaluate the upper sum:

$$\sum_{i=1}^{n} (1 + i\,\Delta x)^2\,\Delta x, \quad \text{where} \quad \Delta x = \frac{2}{n}$$

for $n = 4, 8, 16$.

2. Evaluate the lower sum:

$$\sum_{i=0}^{n-1} (1 + i\,\Delta x)^2\,\Delta x, \quad \text{where} \quad \Delta x = \frac{2}{n}$$

for $n = 4, 8, 16$.

3. Evaluate the area by taking the limit of the sum.

$$A = \lim_{n \to \infty} \sum_{i=1}^{n} (1 + i\,\Delta x)^2\,\Delta x, \quad \text{where} \quad \Delta x = \frac{2}{n}$$

4. Compare the error and relative error for each of the upper and lower sum approximations at $n = 4$, $n = 8$, and $n = 16$.

Fig. 13.2

As hand-held calculators become more sophisticated, their role in calculus instruction will increase. It is true that calculators will have more built-in algorithms whereby answers can be obtained by merely punching in appropriate constants. This is not a new situation for mathematics instructors to handle. We have always complained of courses and texts where students are handed a formula and instructed to "plug in" values when the concepts involved are not clearly understood. However, when using an algorithm, students should verify the accuracy of the answer, and this act affords teachers many meaningful teaching opportunities. Calculators with built-in algorithms are usually programmable to some degree, and calculus offers many types of problems in which students can develop their own algorithms and enter them into the machine.

As noted previously, the 1983 AP Calculus examinations allowed the use of calculators for the first time. The tests were carefully developed in anticipation of calculator usage. Candidates taking these tests were afterwards asked questions about their use of calculators. Approximately 72 percent of the candidates said that they had a calculator available. Even though only 21 percent used a calculator on more than four of the forty-five multiple-choice questions, some indicated that they had used a calculator on more than half of the questions. These students did less well on the examination than those who used the calculator very little. The grading of the five essay questions revealed no discernible advantage or disadvantage to students whose papers indicated calculator usage.

It appears that in most calculus classes the role of a calculator is that of a tool to aid in calculations and not a substitute for problem solving.

## THE ROLE OF muMATH IN FUTURE CALCULUS COURSES

Computer software developments now include packages such as muMATH that manipulate symbolic expressions. Computer algebra has arrived. The programs are able to manipulate fractions, factor and reduce algebraic expressions, construct the derivatives and antiderivatives of functional representations, and symbolically solve certain differential equations. The results are impressive and accurate. So we are left with the inevitable question of how these procedures will change the teaching of mathematics.

Two previous developments come to mind: (1) the readily available square root key on small, inexpensive calculators and (2) the machine translations of foreign languages. In discussions about the changes that we can anticipate, it would be well to keep these outer extremes in mind. In the example of the square root, the paper-and-pencil algorithm for obtaining a numerical result was included in the mathematics curriculum, but the theoretical content was poorly understood and seldom adequately explained. The availability of inexpensive pocket instruments has appropriately removed the square root algorithm from the curriculum.

In the calculus course several units give an exact parallel to the square root analogy. Many of the dreary sections on techniques of integration are included so that future engineers can derive a numerical result, but their theoretical content is typically given only cursory treatment. The best example might be integration by partial fractions. Very few, if any, calculus classes give this unit anything but the briefest theoretical explanation, but students are drilled, drilled, drilled in the technique. It would be safe to say that small pocket instruments with a definite integral key would be welcomed by practitioners, who would readily calculate integral values without a second thought about "the good old days." Another example is the unit on half-angle substitutions to reduce rational trigonometric expressions.

However, parts of the study of calculus also bring up images of the machine translation of languages. Here, the computer is very capable with mechanical substitutions but the rich subtleties are lost. As a result the final product is not acceptable. Parts of calculus have *understanding* as their primary goal, and they will not be replaced. In the section on graphing functions, we should remember that the goal is the understanding of functional processes and not the simple act of "getting the picture." Here, modern graphics packages will readily display the graphs of the function and its several derivatives; but unless students understand what their innerconnections suggest, the pretty pictures are just that! This calculus unit will change to incorporate much more discussion about the graphed functions and spend less time on the actual graphing. Perhaps this is the way that the material should have been presented all along.

The section on applications of Riemann sums will also experience significant changes. Too often students get the idea that volumes of revolutions are the ends in themselves, when in fact the unit should be a rapid and varied collection of applications of the Riemann sums. Maybe the impressive graphics packages and other software will give everyone freedom from details and a chance to set the tone of the course on understanding.

## SUMMARY AND CONCLUSIONS

The Advanced Placement calculus program has proved itself a cornerstone of excellence even in periods when excellence was not the major theme in education. Literally hundreds of thousands of capable students in the courses have had a rich experience that has been a rigorous part of their mathematical development. At the same time improvements in the overall mathematics program in participating secondary schools has been an additional benefit of the program. The program has been a major force in the attempts to increase the professional interaction between college faculty members and secondary school teachers.

The calculus course and all of mathematics are in a state of significant change, but the Advanced Placement program has in place a maintenance structure that will not only keep it stable but also enable it to adjust to the future.

### REFERENCES

College Board. *Advanced Placement Course Description—Mathematics*. New York: College Board, published annually.

Committee on the Undergraduate Program in Mathematics. *Recommendations for a General Mathematical Science Program*. Washington, D.C.: Mathematical Association of America, 1981.

Dickey, Edwin M., Jr. "A Study Comparing Advanced Placement and First-Year College Calculus Students on a Calculus Achievement Test." Doctoral dissertation, University of South Carolina, 1982.

Finkbeiner, Daniel T., John D. Neff, and S. Irene Williams. "The 1969 Advanced Placement Examinations in Mathematics—Complete and 'Unexpurgated.' " *Mathematics Teacher* 64 (October 1971): 499–516.

Haag, Carl H. *Comparing the Performance of College Students and Advanced Placement Candidates on AP Examinations*. New York: College Board, 1977.

Henry, Patricia. *Grading the Advanced Placement Examination in Mathematics 1983*. New York: College Board, 1983.

Jameson, Robert U. *An Informal History of the AP Readings 1956–76*. New York: College Board, 1980.

Jones, Chancey O., John W. Kenelly, and Donald L. Kreider. "The Advanced Placement Program in Mathematics—Update 1975." *Mathematics Teacher* 68 (December 1975): 654–70.

Pieters, Richard S., and E. P. Vance. "The Advanced Placement Program in Mathematics." *Mathematics Teacher* 54 (April 1961): 201–11.

Ralston, Anthony, and Gail S. Young, eds. *The Future of College Mathematics*. New York: Springer-Verlag, 1983.

# 14

# The Gifted Math Program at SUNY at Buffalo

## Betty J. Krist

THE State University of New York (SUNY) at Buffalo is offering in cooperation with area schools a program for gifted (top one percent in ability) and highly motivated secondary school mathematics students. The central feature of this program is that each September a new group of seventh-grade students embarks on a full six-year school/college mathematics program at this university. The SUNY Buffalo program is most closely modeled after the Mathematics Education for Gifted Secondary School Students (MEGSSS) project (Kaufman, Fitzgerald, and Harpel 1981; Harpel 1983) in Saint Louis, Missouri. Both programs use the Elements of Mathematics (EM) texts developed as part of the Comprehensive School Mathematics Project and are organized in a similar manner for the first three years of the program. However, the Buffalo program is quite different in years four through six. Other similar EM-based programs exist in Baltimore County (Maryland), Broward County (Florida), and Portland (Maine). These programs do not have the strong university-community bond of the SUNY Buffalo program.

### OPERATION OF THE PROGRAM

Nominations of sixth-grade students are accepted early each calendar year from school principals or directors of area public, parochial, and private schools as well as from individual parents. Parents of nominated students are invited to attend informational meetings before student screening is begun. Nominated students take a series of tests including the PSAT "College Board" mathematics sections, the Watson Glaser Critical Thinking Appraisal, a syllogisms test, and a mathematics aptitude test. Since we have resources for about sixty new students each year, the students having the top sixty scores on the testing are invited to participate with their families in individual interviews. The purpose of the interview is not further screening of the student but further scrutinizing of the program by the family so that expectations and responsibilities are understood and the important communication channels are established. Although the number of students tested fluctuates a great deal from year to year, the test scores of ae itted students do not.

Accepted students study mathematics at the university two afternoons each week during the academic year. Beginning classes meet from 3:30 to 5:30 P.M. Mondays and Thursdays. In order to avoid conflicts with other school activities, classes at higher grade levels meet from 6:30 to 8:30 P.M. on those same days. These classes replace the student's regular school mathematics program, and that time is set aside for him or her to meet the heavy work load of this program. Sometimes early dismissal is also arranged so that students can commute to the university to attend classes on time. Parents are responsible for transportation.

Although much of the curriculum of the first four years of the program addresses school content, university-level mathematics, such as logic and abstract algebra, is introduced in the first year and increases in proportion each year. On successful completion of this college-level work with grades of A or B, this course work may be converted (as a parent option) to regular university mathematics credit through the university's Division of Undergraduate Education. Thus, for example, a seventh-grade student would participate for the equivalent of eight university credit (contact) hours, one hour of which could be converted to university credit for the work he or she did in mathematical logic, the other seven hours representing school-level work. By the end of grade 10, students can accumulate four university credits. In grades 11 and 12 they can obtain an additional sixteen credits for work in calculus and discrete mathematics. Thus students can obtain twenty hours of university mathematics credit (not just advanced standing) and begin their traditional undergraduate studies on at least a sophomore level in mathematics.

Grades and other progress reports are communicated directly to schools and parents. A school system liaison committee with representatives from each district keeps communication lines open, provides program evaluation, and addresses intraschool problems.

This year represents the fifth year of the Gifted Math Program (GMP). Though no students have gone on to university yet, discussions with current students indicate most of them will not be mathematics majors. Nevertheless, their work in GMP has given them a solid mathematics background and increased scheduling flexibility for their collegiate studies.

## THE CURRICULUM

The textbooks used in the first four years of these classes include the *Elements of Mathematics* (EM) (Books 0, I, II, III, and Problem Book B), published by Harper & Row. This text series was developed specifically for gifted students by an international team of mathematicians and school mathematics teachers with support from the National Institute of Education. The series does not simply accelerate mathematics instruction; rather it integrates school and college mathematics, the specifics of school mathematics fitting into the more general conceptual setting of college mathematics. Logic and powerful notation are important parts of this program. Trials in Saint Louis and other communities have suggested that gifted students have little difficulty with the formality in which the ideas are presented. "Book" 0 (whose sixteen chapters are themselves each book length) provides a carefully designed junior high school transition to this more formal discourse. Book 0 and the later volumes are taught in parallel during the first three years of the program so that students are doing college-level work even as early as grade 7. An *EM Problem Book* also provides students with opportunities to address original, challenging problems.

Some idea of the curriculum of GMP I–IV (school grades 7–10) may be gained from the content listing of the EM texts in use (fig. 14.1).

In addition, grade 9 students study from *Karel the Robot* (Pattis 1981). In grade 10 students also study from a manuscript by Donald Stover and

|  |  |  | Grade |  |
|---|---|---|---|---|
| **Book 0** | **Intuitive Background** |  |  |  |
| Chapter | 1 | Operational Systems | 7 |  |
|  | 2 | The Integers | 7 |  |
|  | 3 | Sets, Subsets, & Operations with Sets | 7 |  |
|  | 4 | Ordered $n$-tuples | 7 |  |
|  | 5 | Mappings | 7 |  |
|  | 6 | The Rational Numbers | 7 |  |
|  | 7 | Decimals and an Application of the Rationals | 7 |  |
|  | 8 | An Introduction to Probability | 7 |  |
|  | 9 | An Introduction to Number Theory | 7–8 |  |
|  | 10 | Algebra in Operational Systems | 8 |  |
|  | 11 | Algebra of Real Functions | 8–9 |  |
|  | 12 | Geometry: Incidence and Isometries | 8–9 |  |
|  | 13 | Geometry: Similitudes, Coordinates, and Trigonometry | 10 |  |
|  | 14 | Topics in Probability and Statistics | 9 |  |
|  | 15 | Topics in Number Theory | 9 |  |
|  | 16 | Introduction to Computer Programming | 9 |  |

|  |  |  | Grade | University Credit |
|---|---|---|---|---|
| **Book** | **I** | **Introductory Logic** | 7 | 1 hr. |
|  | **II** | **Logic and Sets** | 8 | 2 hr. |
|  | **III** | **Introduction to Fields** | 9–10 | 1 hr. |
| **Problem Book B** |  |  | 8–12 |  |

Fig. 14.1

Gerald Rising (the codirector of our program), which surveys precalculus mathematics and provides many exercises, including computer applications.

In grades 11 and 12, students enroll in the following regular SUNY Buffalo courses: in grade 11, Calculus 1 and 2; in grade 12, Introduction to Discrete Mathematics 1 and 2. Special sections of these courses are created for GMP students.

The following examples of student assignments should provide insight into the elevated expectations of the program:

*Grade 7.* In order to give students a taste of how mathematics (and arithmetic in particular) affects important political and social decisions, their work with decimals culminates with an exploration of the tax policy in the

---

**The [EM] series does not simply accelerate mathematics instruction; rather it integrates school and college mathematics.**

---

imaginary country of Sikinia. Students are asked to imagine they are members of the Sikinian House of Representatives, which has agreed to raise 2.4 billion kulotnicks (the Sikinian monetary unit) through taxation. Two versions of a uniform income tax plan and two versions of a progressive tax plan have been presented to the legislature. Arguments for and against each proposal have also been mounted. For homework students are asked, "Devise a tax plan of your own for Sikinia and prepare a paper defending your reasons for promoting it" (Book 0, chap. 7, p. 87).

*Grade 8.* As mentioned previously, students begin work for which they are eligible for college-level credit early in the program. In one review section, students are asked, "In the theory of commutative groups, show that the following statement is a theorem:

$(\forall x, y, z)\, [x * y = n \rightarrow (x * z) * y = z].$" ($n$ is the identity for $*$) (Book 2, p. 234)

*Grade 9.* Geometry is based on transformations. Throughout the program students are encouraged to be creative and have good reasons for their statements. For homework students are asked: "$a$) Explain why no scalene triangle has any rotative symmetries. (*Hint:* Remember that rotations preserve distance.) $b$) Explain why no triangle having exactly one reflective symmetry has any rotative symmetries. (*Hint:* Show that such a triangle has two sides with equal lengths and a third side of a different length. Then argue as in part ($a$))" (Book 0, chap. 12, p. 184).

*Grades 8–12.* Students are assigned a specific number of problems each year from the Problem Book. They can choose whichever problems they wish, accumulating points according to the difficulty of the problem and the correctness of the solution. Some typical problems:

**1 point.** No person has more than 300 000 hairs on his head. The Capital of Sikinia has a population of 300 001. Can you assert that there are two persons in the city having the same number of hairs on their heads? (p. 20)

**3 points.** Find the smallest natural number with the following property: If you transfer the leftmost digit to the right-hand end, the new number will be 1½ times the old number. (p. 14)

**5 points.** Is there any way to pack 250 $1 \times 1 \times 4$ bricks into a $10 \times 10 \times 10$ box? (p. 38)

The philosophy underlying Book 0, which teaches school mathematics, is to develop abstractions from everyday experience. Numbers, points, functions, and groups are objects that can be thought about and from which discoveries can be made. Topics are discussed in an intuitive, heuristic way. Students explore the genesis of mathematical ideas and use concrete objects (manipulatives and drawings) to help them understand and use these ideas.

Books 1–3 provide students with the logical machinery to make complex mathematical arguments formally and rigorously. The style of writing in these later EM books and the problems in them are modeled after the style found in college-level mathematics books and articles. We hope to prepare our students to think, read, write, and talk as contemporary mathematicians and contemporary users of mathematics do. We also hope to have students recognize not only that personal struggle with a problem is an important mathematical activity but also that mathematics is a social enterprise with discussion, argumentation, thesis, and antithesis.

## OBSERVATIONS

We currently have 250 students enrolled. Our experience has convinced us that several aspects of our program, embedded in the curriculum, are absolutely necessary.

The program capitalizes on the unique abilities (e.g., the ability to abstract) of these bright young people and would be inappropriate, even at a slower pace, for their less able classmates. It is challenging so that students learn to deal with the frustrations and rewards of answering questions once viewed as unanswerable. The instruction concerns itself not only with the content being learned but also with guidance and firm encouragement for good work habits and study skills, good English, and good behavior. The program involves a long-range commitment to excellence by students, teachers, and parents. When the going gets rough, as it does, the students must have appropriate support and direction.

Many very bright youngsters have no sense of problem solving even though they do their standard schoolwork exceptionally well. Often they have never been challenged by a problem that requires more than a few moments of reflection and are entirely lost when their first attempts meet with failure. For some, this challenge is responded to by withdrawal. In this program, class time is often spent in considering problems that have more than one answer or different kinds of solutions to the same problem. We encourage students to become epistemologists, to gain a good sense of their own thinking and the individual differences among students in the program. Many activities are specifically designed to encourage students to talk and listen to one another. They gain not only insight into mathematics and problem solving but some assurance that they are different, not weird.

---

## . . . the detail, seriousness, and precision of formal logic aptly characterizes the appeal and intrigue of mathematics for most of these students.

---

When students do problems incorrectly or carelessly, their errors are corrected and they revise their work until it meets a formidable yet reasonable standard. Talented students want to be taken seriously. They desire verification when they are correct and explanation when they are wrong. We seek to give them opportunities for knowledgeable dialogue.

These students are observant and have fine memories. One can mount a most thought-provoking discussion by merely asking students their ideas about numbers or geometric shapes or how ideas are put together. Our program has convinced us that the detail, seriousness, and precision of formal logic aptly characterizes the appeal and intrigue of mathematics for most of these students.

Any strong program for talented students moves them beyond the standard secondary school content to university-level work. For such work, they should perform to university standards and get university credit. This does not imply that fourteen-year-olds should be in college classes, for there they also may not receive instruction geared to their ability. Bright teenagers are just that, and forcing them to be diminutive adults is robbing them of many important aspects of their childhood. Their school programs should encourage them to be in extracurricular activities, sports, and clubs. They need friends of their own age. The stereotype of bright children being uninterested in children's activities is almost universally wrong.

### SUMMARY

This program was mounted because we at the university believe that it offers specific advantages to each of its constituencies:

**For students**
- To study high-quality mathematics
- To accelerate their study of mathematics
- To interact with other gifted youngsters

- To meet an intellectual challenge beyond what they are accustomed to find in their school program

**For parents**

- To enrich the academic program of their gifted children
- To help focus more of their children's attention on serious academic studies
- To provide a substantial portion of their children's college education—up to about a sixth—at far less expense

**For the schools**

- To provide a strong program for an important group of students whom they are not able to serve as well by other means

**For the university**

- To provide an appropriate community service, thus "showing the flag" to a significant student and parent population
- To involve students of very high ability in its mathematics programs
- To encourage these high-quality students to continue their studies here
- To have a favorable impact on other universities through students who continue their mathematics studies elsewhere

**For society**

- To respond to the serious shortages in scientific personnel projected for the decade ahead by national commissions

In conclusion, we welcome dialogue. More detailed information is available on request from our project office at 560 Baldy Hall, SUNY at Buffalo, Buffalo, NY 14260.

### REFERENCES

*Elements of Mathematics Books 0, 1, 2, 3, Problem Book B*. New York: Harper & Row, 1975.

Harpel, Jim. "Project MEGSSS." *Mathematics Teacher* 76 (April 1983): 286.

Kaufman, Burt, Jack Fitzgerald, and Jim Harpel. *Mathematical Education for the Gifted Secondary School Student: MEGSSS in Action*. Saint Louis: CEMREL, 1981. (ERIC Document Reproduction Service No. ED 226 960)

Pattis, Richard E. *Karel the Robot*. New York: John Wiley & Sons, 1981.

Stover, Donald F., and Gerald R. Rising. *Precalculus with a Computer*. Available in manuscript form from the Gifted Math Program office at SUNY Buffalo.

# 15

# A Special School in North Carolina

Steve Davis
Phyllis Frothingham

TEACHERS who accompany students to mathematics field days, mathematics contests, and science fairs often wish they could bottle the atmosphere and take it back to their school. These gatherings of talented students who have similar interests are characterized by energy, excitement, enthusiasm, and the healthy interaction of peers. There is little question that peer interaction among talented students can be a tremendous asset for a teacher and a school. At activities such as contests and field days, teachers are witness to the effects of talented students discovering that there are others with similar interests. One of the primary benefits is the opportunity for the gifted to be part of a group. Too often they are on the sidelines. With a supportive peer group and in a friendly learning environment, the traces of insecurity and doubt that lie below their surface energy and enthusiasm can be addressed. It is sad that for many of these outstanding students the association lasts only for a few days or possibly for a few weeks during the summer.

## BACKGROUND

In North Carolina action was taken in 1978 to confront this problem. The inspired leadership of the governor and the support of the General Assembly combined to establish the North Carolina School of Science and Mathematics (NCSSM). The school has a student body of 400 eleventh and twelfth graders with special ability and interest in science and mathematics. These students pursue a demanding two-year high school curriculum with an emphasis on science and mathematics in a residential setting.

The students are accepted through a lengthy admissions process that seeks potential rather than achievement. The result is a diverse student body of talented students with a wide variety of backgrounds and interests. Creating a learning environment for such students, which means building on their energy, nurturing their curiosity, arousing their creativity, and addressing their insecurity and doubt as well as the differential between academic

184

maturity and social maturity, is a special challenge for an educator. It is, however, a challenge the faculty and staff enjoy meeting. Of course, the reality on a daily basis is hard work—hard work for teachers, resident advisors, counselors, administrators, and students; but it is a reality that results in a special sense of accomplishment each June.

---

The result is a living and learning environment filled with vitality and energy, with student helping student, with teachers returning in the evening to help . . .

---

This unusual school has the opportunity to build on the atmosphere that develops when talented students are brought together. The result is a living and learning environment filled with vitality and energy, with student helping student, with teachers returning in the evening to help students, with students pursuing independent study projects, with students accepting the challenge of working in a university research laboratory at one of the four local universities, and with students volunteering for community service projects. Among the group are, on the one hand, students who find each day a tremendous academic challenge, but it is a challenge they wish to meet. On the other hand, there are students who find the course work interesting but easily mastered, so they undertake independent study and projects.

All students find special opportunities in science and mathematics and face special demands in these courses. During their two years in residence, each must take three years of science and two years of mathematics, including what is generally called "fourth-year mathematics." Each student must also meet a computer competency requirement.

### THE CURRICULUM

Since the backgrounds of the students are diverse, the mathematics department offers a wide variety of courses. A brief description of the mathematics curriculum will suggest the breadth and depth of the program and how it provides each student with a challenge, yet a challenge that can be met.

*Algebra* establishes the fundamentals of algebra found in first- and second-year algebra. The course is designed for able students who do not have a good background in first-year algebra.

*Algebra 2 and Trigonometry* is a solid course in this essential subject. The best way to describe the course is to say that "we finish the book."

*Algebra 2 and Introduction to Analysis and Finite Mathematics* is a fast-paced course covering two years of mathematics in one year. Students enroll in calculus following this course.

*Algebra 3* is designed for students who have completed second-year algebra in their home school but who do not demonstrate a sufficient mastery of the subject to enter the Introduction to Analysis and Finite Mathematics course.

*Introduction to Analysis and Finite Mathematics* covers the important topics of precalculus mathematics and a number of topics from finite mathematics that are growing in importance as computers become more prevalent in our society. The course de-emphasizes topics such as trigonometric identities and factoring to include topics such as algorithms, mathematical models, and approximations of experimental data. Also available is a special version of this course that moves at a rapid pace and includes additional topics. Both versions focus on problem solving and are designed to increase the mathematical sophistication of the student.

Two of four one-semester courses—*Survey of Finite Mathematics, Number Theory /Mathematical Logic, History of Mathematics,* or *Statistics*—are elected by students who have experienced difficulty in Introduction to Analysis and Finite Mathematics. Instead of teaching a watered-down calculus, the school prefers to provide the students an opportunity to prepare themselves for the mathematics used in many applications (finite mathematics and statistics) or to explore interesting topics that can challenge a broad range of students.

*Calculus 1 and 2* is essentially the BC syllabus. Also available is a version of this course that moves rapidly through the standard syllabus and includes additional topics such as numerical algorithms, a more detailed treatment of parametric equations, and mathematical models.

*Calculus 3* is a one-semester course in the calculus of several variables.

*Linear Analysis* is a semester course that treats the theory of first- and second-order linear difference and differential equations. These ideas are combined with matrix theory and the study of finite-dimensional vector spaces to analyze problems related to interest rates, the spread of disease, population growth, and probability.

*Topics in Discrete Mathematics* is a one-semester course designed to follow Calculus 3. It provides students an opportunity to explore important areas of mathematics that are not usually treated at the high school level. Topics in this course include combinatorics, linear programming, game theory, and analysis of algorithms.

*Advanced Mathematical Topics* provides a student with an especially strong background an opportunity to study a topic in depth. The study results in a formal presentation and the writing of a paper.

*Introduction to Logo* is a one-semester computer course, which is graded satisfactory-unsatisfactory.

*Introduction to Pascal* is another one-semester computer course, also graded satisfactory-unsatisfactory.

*Independent Study* is an important part of the curriculum. Projects in computer-related areas are the most popular, but a number of students elect to explore areas of mathematics in independent study. Recent completed projects include a Logo interpreter; a Lisp interpreter; IGOR, a machine language simulator; GRAPHPAD, a general-purpose graphics utility; and the implementation of Turtlegraphics for a Pascal compiler.

A few students each year do work to support the administrative use of computing. This ranges from implementing a data management system to making templates for applications of electronic spreadsheets.

Either computer course offered fulfills the graduation requirement. Each focuses on the applications of computers, organized approaches toward solving problems, and the programming language. To graduate, students are required to demonstrate the ability to use the computer as a tool. For example, they must demonstrate the ability to use word processing and to use commercial software (or their own programs) for processing data acquired in an experiment. This is not a burden for NCSSM students. Computer offerings are very popular and are supported by a truly marvelous computer facility. NCSSM has a variety of microcomputers and a large minicomputer (a VAX-11/750). Students have access to the equipment from early morning to curfew (ten or eleven o'clock in the evening), and the facility is available on weekends. Interdisciplinary use of the computer is encouraged. For example, the computer may be used in processing data from a biology experiment or in word processing for a French term paper. The school is dedicated to providing students with the best computing facility possible.

Placing juniors at their correct level in the mathematics curriculum is of critical importance. The total NCSSM school program almost always represents a major change from the student's previous school experience, and the typical junior, faced also with increased academic demands, has great difficulty in managing time. Teachers are faced with the challenge of distinguishing between problems of background, problems of ability, problems of organization, and problems of study efficiency. These problems also mean that there must be a large number of course offerings for juniors in order for them to find their proper levels. Seniors present less of a problem, since they share a common experience of having had teachers who focus on problem solving, a graphical approach toward problems, and a continuing examination of what is taught, how it is taught, and how it integrates advances in technology. In classes of juniors and seniors, it is very easy to identify juniors during the first semester. This is not nearly so easy by May.

Members of the mathematics faculty can best be described as teachers-learners. Each year topics are chosen for a series of faculty seminars, and students observe teachers working together on problems, sitting in on a colleague's classes, or studying a topic with a student as part of an independent study project. Teachers in the nation's high schools often have little professional contact with one another. In contrast, the colleagueship among teachers at NCSSM is real and is viewed as a key ingredient in the development of a vital and active faculty.

## BEYOND THE CURRICULUM

No quick portrait of this school for eager and motivated students would be complete without mentioning that the school has a broader charge than providing a marvelous learning experience for 400 juniors and seniors. The school is also charged with serving the state. Faculty members are invited to speak at meetings statewide on a regular basis. Outreach activities are extensive and consume a large percentage of faculty time. During the summers, the school conducts workshops for teachers, both on the school's campus and at sites spread across the state. Also, NCSSM serves as a clearinghouse for materials and information on computer software. Its institutional membership in the Minnesota Educational Computing Consortium (MECC) allows school districts across the state to enroll as client members and thereby purchase MECC software at significant discounts.

The school also develops curriculum materials that are used to instruct students in other schools. Teachers at NCSSM realize that they have an excellent opportunity to test new approaches and new topics in classes of motivated and talented students and are dedicated to finding new and improved methods of learning and teaching that are adaptable to all schools.

It is becoming increasingly clear that NCSSM students who return home to visit former schools and discuss their present course work with former teachers are having an impact on local schools' curricula. To enhance this effect, NCSSM sponsors a visiting instructor program. Teachers from across the state are selected to spend one year at NCSSM, teaching a reduced load and developing materials for their home schools. This program is a tremendous success for all concerned—teachers, home districts, and NCSSM.

In conclusion, it might be appropriate to mention again that it is difficult to describe the energy and motivation of all connected with the school—students, faculty, residential staff, and administration. Yet, the excitement is apparent even to casual visitors. Much is the result of an atmosphere of challenge. Some students must struggle to meet the high standards. Some must look outside the classroom for significant challenges. Others have problems initially in adjusting to a heavy work load or to a residential learning environment. All these adjustments pose challenges for students and teachers, yet these challenges are met in a friendly, supportive, and enthusiastic learning environment where no school awards for achievement are given, where there is no class ranking, and where all graduating seniors wear honor cords.

The result is a school that serves both the students and the state well. It is an idea other states are studying.

# 16

# Let's Teach Mathematics: A Case for Integrated Mathematics Programs

## Warren B. Manhard II

**A** CERTAIN amount of interest is now being generated in the United States for programs of integrated mathematics in secondary schools. A growing number of educators are finding that the traditional algebra-geometry-algebra or the less popular algebra-algebra-geometry sequences are not as satisfactory as once thought. Although the algebra-geometry-algebra sequence has many excellent attributes, a program of secondary mathematics in which the various topics are blended together is gaining serious consideration. In the East, for example, about one-third of the New York State school systems offer an integrated curriculum of secondary mathematics as an alternative to the standard curriculum (see chapter 17), and in Massachusetts several high schools have such programs as their only curriculum.

Various catchwords are used for this type of program, such as *integrated, blended, unified,* and so on, and whereas each of these may mean something different to each author, for our purposes we shall consider these terms synonymous.

As opposed to an algebra-geometry-algebra sequence, an integrated program is constructed by taking the topics of secondary mathematics and assembling them in some order to span a three-year time period. (The notion is easily extended to the fourth year.) From this point of view, one can compare the structure of the two programs. The algebra-geometry-algebra program is usually seen as a sequence of three distinct courses, whereas an integrated program is often viewed as a single course studied over a three-year period.

### PHILOSOPHY AND ADVANTAGES

Although essentially the same topics may be covered, the philosophy behind the two programs is considerably different, and it would be helpful to preview the differences before going further. First, algebra-geometry-algebra programs tend to separate the branches of mathematics, so that students feel they are studying two distinct subjects with little connection between them; integrated programs try to stress the underlying themes of secondary mathematics and exemplify these themes through various topics, not subjects. Mathematical problem solving requires a certain amount of free thinking unfettered by an association with a particular subject. Thus, students studying *mathematics* rather than algebra or geometry are less likely to feel bound to a particular approach when looking at a new problem. Second, integrated programs are more likely to spiral the important skills and concepts of mathematics when arithmetic, algebra, geometry, and perhaps statistics are studied each year because the emphasis is on the development and enlargement of these central ideas rather than on the presentation of any particular subject. Third, integrated programs may be more sensitive to problems of student readiness in that the study of each subject is spread out over a longer period of time. Thus, students may work on formal geometry for as long as three years. This benefits students who are not mathematically mature enough for the demands of the traditional tenth-grade course. Fourth, integrated programs are usually more flexible in that topics may be easily interchanged, lengthened, or shortened. Geometry, for example, may be taught for more than a year, or less, as desired by the faculty. This flexibility is largely due more to a freer attitude among the teachers than to any practical reason, and it provides greater opportunity for creative curriculum development. Finally, since the various themes of mathematics are stressed in each course, students should be better able to reason both sequentially and holistically and be more appreciative of the interrelationships among the different parts of mathematics.

## Eliminates Compartmentalization and Rigid Approaches to Problem Solving

Algebra-geometry-algebra programs usually tend to compartmentalize mathematics. From the titles of their courses students know that they are studying either algebra or geometry, and it is not uncommon for them to develop a preference for one or the other. Moreover, if problems are posed, students tend to try to apply the mathematics they are currently learning in seeking a solution. They balk if a teacher tries to use algebra in a geometry course or vice versa. More serious is compartmentalization among the faculty. Although each of us should not be denied our preferences for certain topics, it is too easy to see ourselves as a "geometry teacher" or an "algebra teacher" and assume certain biases in the selection of methods for problem solving. At its worst a faculty may find itself divided into camps where "algebra teachers" don't communicate with "geometry teachers" or vice versa. At its very least, as with some foreign language departments, such divisions may present scheduling, retraining, or even RIF (reduction in force) problems in the event that an additional "geometry teacher" is needed but an "algebra teacher" must be let go. Thus, a major feature of an integrated program is that it largely eliminates compartmentalization among both students and faculty.

Students should be encouraged to attack any new mathematical problem with all the resources available to them, regardless of the topic being studied at the moment; the ability to free-think is essential. By its very nature, an integrated program more easily encourages realistic problem solving because neither the faculty nor the students see themselves as being confined to a particular subject when exploring a problem.

### Capitalizes on a Spiral Approach

A second major advantage of an integrated program is its increased opportunity to spiral through different topics. A major weakness of the algebra-geometry-algebra program, the fact that a year and two summers separate algebra 2 from algebra 1, causing many skills to be lost through lack of practice, is largely eliminated in most integrated programs. The algebra topics are spiraled through all three years. Skills are maintained and continually reinforced. Therefore, time spent on review is minimized.

As an example, consider how factoring might be spiraled through an integrated curriculum. With the possible exception of some use in the unit on circles, geometry is largely free of factoring, so the skill may be lost during the geometry year. After the multiplying and factoring unit, the first course in an integrated program would follow with the simplification of rational expressions and the solution of quadratic equations by factoring, as is usual for an algebra 1 course. However, the second course would continue with quadratic equations and functions, advanced factoring, more rational expressions, and then operations on irrational expressions (predominantly square roots), where the simplification of quotients using the conjugate would be introduced. Early in the third course students would see factoring again while studying operations on expressions of complex numbers. Later, factoring would be used in solving exponential and logarithmic equations, quadratic equations in the unit on circles, and in proving trigonometric identities. Of course, it also plays a prominent role in the study of analytic geometry and conics. Because factoring comes up in many units of each course, students see it as a central skill of mathematics. More importantly, since it spirals through all the courses, students may find that what they have not mastered in a previous course, they can learn in the present course.

As another example, consider the concept of congruence. Students usually think of congruence as a geometric idea. Building on work done at the elementary and junior high school level, where the students have done slide-flip-rotate exercises with geometric figures, a unit in the first course of an integrated program at the secondary level would begin with the graph of $y = x$ and discuss the rotation $y = mx$ and the concept of slope. Translations would be revisited with graphs of $y = 2(x - 1)$ and $y + 3 = 2x$, leading to the point-slope form of the line (fig. 16.1).

Students might then explore graphs of $y = |x|$ and $y = |x + 1|$ and compare $y = (x - 2)^2$ with $y = x^2$ and observe the slides involved (fig. 16.2).

In the second course the study of congruent triangles would begin with more slide-flip-rotate exercises (students with this training rarely make

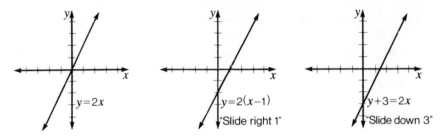

Fig. 16.1

errors matching corresponding parts), since this forces visualization of the objects involved and develops space perception. Overlapping triangles are easily separated, and students have less difficulty with drawings of three-dimensional figures. (See fig. 16.3.)

Students see the algebraic connection in a later unit when they graph such relations as $|x| + |y| = 4$ and $|x - 1| + |y| = 4$ and realize that a "slide" is involved. The relation $y = -|x|$ is easily seen as a "flip" of $y = |x|$ about the $x$-axis. In the third course, the notion of stretching and shrinking parallel to the $x$-axis or $y$-axis would be emphasized with the students comparing the

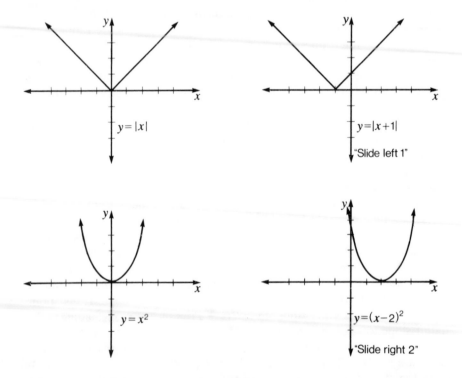

Fig. 16.2

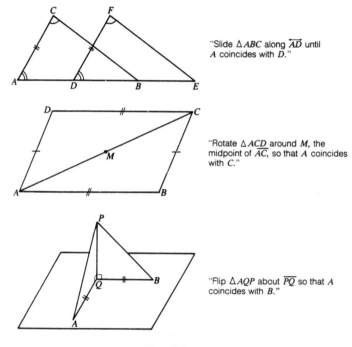

"Slide $\triangle ABC$ along $\overleftrightarrow{AD}$ until $A$ coincides with $D$."

"Rotate $\triangle ACD$ around $M$, the midpoint of $\overline{AC}$, so that $A$ coincides with $C$."

"Flip $\triangle AQP$ about $\overline{PQ}$ so that $A$ coincides with $B$."

Fig. 16.3

graph of $y = 4x^2$ with the graph of $y = x^2$. When the graphs of other conics are introduced, $4x^2 + (y - 1)^2 = 4$ can be compared with $x^2 + y^2 = 4$ from an algebraic *and* geometric point of view. After studying periodicity, students can, with careful preparation, handle transformations of trigonometric functions in the unit on circular functions and can more quickly sketch $y = 2 \sin 3(x - 1)$ from $y = \sin x$ by identifying the stretch factor of 2 in the $y$-direction, the shrink factor of 3 in the $x$-direction, and the slide of 1 to the right for the function given. In the fourth course, the concept of transformation would be extended to include an introduction to the algebra of rotations by graphing ellipses such as $x^2 + xy + y^2 = 6$ and by studying the matrices involved in such linear transformations. The idea is that the concepts of congruence and transformation cycle through each course and students continually review and build on previous learning.

As a final example, the development of the concept of proof should not be left solely to the geometry teacher. However, it does little good for students to prove sometimes obvious and trivial facts in an algebra 1 course as preparation. If a mathematics faculty believes in the importance of proof as a logical and explicit mathematical argument, then the notion can be introduced in the first course by expecting students to write each step of an algebra exercise clearly and by giving points for justifying each step. This can be done in the unit on simplifying expressions, but it is also very natural in the unit on solving linear equations where the use of the associative property of addition and the addition and multiplication properties of equality can be made explicit. The idea is that mathematics teachers of integrated programs tend to teach the concept of proof in both algebra and geometry units naturally and endeavor to point out to students various similarities and differences of approaches. Since algebraic proofs occur in the same course as geometric proofs, they are easily accepted by the students, and proof is seen as a central idea of all of mathematics.

## Anticipates Differences in Student Readiness

Another major advantage of many integrated programs has to do with the notion of "readiness." Research on learning tells us that there are different stages of learning, that students must advance through these stages sequentially, and that students mature at different rates. The algebra-geometry-algebra program assumes that all students are ready for, say, a relatively abstract course in geometry by grade 10, or age fifteen. Whereas elementary and junior high school programs now consider some informal geometry, many do not adequately prepare students for the formal course because teachers by and large do not view mathematics as integrated. Arithmetic and prealgebra dominate the pre–high school mathematics curriculum. The full year of first-year algebra, devoid of geometry, does nothing to heighten this readiness. Thus, students are not as developed geometrically as they might be. Students need to be aware of most of the facts and relations of geometry *before* they start the formal study. Usually, they are not. More importantly, to help them develop both hemispheres of the brain concurrently, we need to force them to think geometrically, to see some situations holistically as opposed to sequentially. As an example, they need to ask why the diagonals of a rectangle are congruent whereas those of other parallelograms are not. What is so special about the rectangle, and why? There is no need for formal proofs here, just exploration and exposure to thoughtful analysis and logical thinking. Yet virtually no opportunity for this development is given to ninth graders in the year just before their formal course. An integrated program that includes some informal geometry with first-year algebra would help correct this problem.

One aspect of readiness is the necessity for skills and concepts to develop sequentially; a second is the speed at which this development, commonly called maturity, takes place. It is not unusual for capable but less mathematically mature students to flounder through the formal geometry course. The variation, algebra-algebra-geometry, attempts to address this situation by delaying the study of geometry for all students. However, an integrated program usually spreads the study of formal geometry over several years in order to minimize the problems for relatively late mathematically maturing students. Further, assuming the students are capable, relatively good grades can be maintained through success in other parts of the course.

## Permits Greater Curricular Flexibility

Another attribute of integrated programs is flexibility. What is inherent in the study of geometry that makes it natural for the course to be exactly one year long? Nothing. It is more likely that the study of geometry was cut and pruned in order to be exactly a year long than that it was pumped up to fill a year. But is a year the right amount of time to spend on geometry? The same could be asked of other courses except that geometry, of all the courses, seems to stand alone in the curriculum. An integrated program tends to allow the various units to assume their optimum lengths more naturally. Judgments regarding the lengths of units may be made according to their relative importance by considering the depth of understanding expected, the difficulty of the skills and concepts involved, and the total time allotted. Thus, an integrated program might allow more or less time to be spent on any given topic than might be usual.

Topics can be easily interchanged. What might at one time have seemed to be a natural order of topics may later appear to be awkward. Topics should be continually reexamined, and in an integrated program changes can usually be made easily. A classic example of this, again from geometry, is the decision of one publisher to place the study of parallel lines before the study of congruence as opposed to the more usual order. Because the focus in an integrated program is on a topic rather than a subject, these types of changes are easily made as teachers see a better way of helping students learn.

A third aspect of flexibility has to do with the relative ease of removing obsolete topics and inserting new ones. Calculators are changing the logarithms unit dramatically—so too with certain parts of trigonometry. These changes allow room to do more with statistics, say, or linear programming, as the needs of the school population dictate.

Integrated programs may stimulate creativity among the faculty. It is not unusual to hear, as teachers mingle at conventions, "Our school uses the _____ series; what series does your school use?" Certainly, schools should use the best resources that their limited funds can purchase. But there is the danger that the books become the curriculum. To the degree that this happens, the potential for curriculum development among the faculty lessens. Students accustomed to using two or three or even four books in a course rarely question the curriculum. However, teachers using such an array must continually question what they are doing and why they are doing it. Does the course, as a course, make sense? What are the goals of the course? Are my lessons achieving these goals?

Apart from the written curriculum, the most important aspect of teacher creativity occurs in the sequence of daily lessons as teachers continually guide students in seeing interrelationships among topics. These interrelationships are frequently surprising and often are noticed spontaneously, as when a student comes up with a clever way of looking at a routine exercise or when students see that a cross-section of a cone can be expressed as an algebraic equation. Calculus students first wonder at the relationship between trigonometry and logarithms, two seemingly independent topics, when they study the integral of the tangent function. Thus, it is natural to study inequalities and absolute value along with points, rays, and segments. The difference is not so much in content as in the attitude of the teacher toward mathematics. Students are consistently encouraged to try to transfer previous learning to the topic at hand.

## Fosters a Broader Conception of Mathematics

Finally, we must consider the aesthetics. Most of us teach mathematics because we are relatively good at it and enjoy its inherent beauty. This beauty extends not only from the internal logic of the subject but also from its immense power and scope. We try to convey these features to our students mostly by letting them learn these things for themselves but also by pointing out to them the aspects of logic, power, and scope as they occur. An integrated program can demonstrate the interconnectedness of mathematics—in a way other programs cannot—well before students see this for the first time in a calculus course. They see it simply because this attitude is continually stressed throughout the courses. Although not understanding it fully, most students can begin to appreciate the natural weave of that fabric we call mathematics.

## SCOPE AND SEQUENCE OF AN INTEGRATED PROGRAM

Before discussing a particular program at Newton South High School, it is necessary to know that as a comprehensive high school we offer five mathematics tracks, of which four are college preparatory. At the top of our program is an honors sequence leading to the Advanced Placement Calculus AB and BC examinations; this program will not be discussed here. Most of our students take one or the other of the next two tracks, and it is the higher of these two (the second track) that will be outlined in the following pages. The lower (third track) is similar but less intensive and theoretical. The fourth track is an alternative program in which students study essentially the same material using worksheets instead of textbooks; the teaching techniques are also different. The basic math sequence (fifth track) is for students who are either not ready for, or not interested in pursuing, a college preparatory program.

The second-track program presently consists of Math 1 (algebra 1) followed by an integrated two-course sequence, Math 2 and 3. We start off the Math 2 course with factoring and rational expressions because these topics are familiar to the students from their work in Math 1. Then the study of formal geometry is begun with a review of the basic definitions and postulates, particularly those dealing with segments and angles. The addition, subtraction, multiplication, and division of radical expressions follows, which allows time for the concepts of geometry to be absorbed. The remaining units beginning with triangle congruence proofs more or less alternate between algebra and geometry topics. An outline is listed in figure 16.4.

The topics from Math 2 should be recognizable from their headings, with the possible exception of the graphs of relations unit. As indicated earlier, we ask students to graph $y = x^2$, $y = \sqrt{x}$, $y = 1/x$, $y = 2^x$, and $y = |x|$, thus reviewing in a different setting calculations involving real numbers. These equations and their graphs become "heads of families," and students see the graphs of $y = x^2 + 1$ or $y = |x - 1|$ as slides of $y = x$ and $y = |x|$, respectively, and $y = -|x|$ as a flip of $y = |x|$, thus tying in the slide and flip of the congruence unit. (Algebraic rotations are left for the senior course.) The unit concludes with extensive exploration of the graphs of $|x| + |y| = 4$ and $x^2 + y^2 = 16$ and their many variants. We find that students need considerable practice with graphing as a precursor to the sharp analysis and quick sketching of curves needed for the analytic geometry units and calculus courses that follow.

The major algebraic theme of our Math 3 course is functions. Some teachers prefer to start the course with the functions unit (as shown in fig. 16.5); others insert the unit later as a way of tying together ideas developed during the course. The unit contains definitions of a function, domain, range, function notation, graphing, addition and composition of functions, and inverse functions.

The circular functions unit includes right triangle trigonometry and ends with double-angle formulas. The study of circular functions and trigonometry continues in the senior course. Since not all our top college-

---

| **Math 2** | | **Math 3** | |
|---|---|---|---|
| (Weeks) | | (Weeks) | |
| 4 | Polynomials, factoring, and rational expressions | 2 | Functions |
| 1 | Summary of geometric facts | 3 | Areas and special right triangles |
| 1 | Angles and triangles | 3 | Exponents and logarithms |
| 2 | Radicals and exponents | 3 | Similarity |
| 4 | Congruence | 2 | Complex numbers |
| 2 | Coordinate geometry (and proofs) | 3 | Sequences and series |
| 3 | Indirect proof and geometric inequalities | 2 | Circles and spheres |
| 2 | Statistics | 7 | Circular functions (first half) |
| 1 | Perpendicular lines and planes in space | 1 | Areas of circles and sectors |
| 2 | Graphs of relations | 2 | Solids and volumes |
| 2 | Systems of equations | 2 | Permutations and combinations |
| 3 | Parallel lines and quadrilaterals | 2 | Probability |
| 1 | Parallel lines and planes | 32 | |
| 4 | Quadratic equations and functions | | |
| 32 | | | |

| Fig. 16.4 | Fig. 16.5 |
|---|---|

bound students take Math 4, we feel it is desirable to have this unit in the junior course as a common experience for these students.

For many years we were a three-year high school, and these two courses in various curriculum levels constituted the core of our program. With the addition of the ninth grade to our school, Math 1 came under our roof essentially unchanged as a junior high school algebra 1 course. By the time this chapter is published, the course will undoubtedly have undergone several changes. First, a three-week unit in BASIC is part of each of the seventh- and eighth-grade programs, and it is natural that these units should be built on and expanded. Second, the facts, relations, and concepts of elementary and junior high school geometry must be continued in the ninth grade as a bridge toward the formal study of geometry. Finally, too often neglected in this country is the early introduction and continued study of statistics. Our proposed outlines for Math 1 and Math 4 are shown in figures 16.6 and 16.7.

| **Math 1** | |
|---|---|
| (Weeks) | |
| 1 | Review of introduction to BASIC |
| 3 | Numbers, operations, and properties |
| 3 | Algebraic expressions and polynomials |
| 4 | Solution of linear equations and inequalities |
| 3 | Statistics |
| 4 | Algebraic products, factoring, quadratic equations |
| 4 | Rational expressions |
| 3 | Geometric facts and relationships |
| 5 | Ordered pairs, graphing, and variation |
| 2 | Systems of linear equations |
| 32 | |

Fig. 16.6

| **Math 4** | |
|---|---|
| (Weeks) | |
| 3 | Algebra of vectors |
| 3 | Vector geometry of the line |
| 5 | Circular functions (second half) |
| 2 | Polar coordinates |
| 3 | Mathematical induction, sequences, series |
| 3 | Polynomials (graphing, factor theorem, etc.) |
| 2 | Probability |
| 4 | Analytic geometry (including rotations of conics) |
| 2 | Matrices |
| 2 | Statistics (with probability) |
| 2 | Space vector geometry |
| 31 | |

Fig. 16.7

We like to take a look at circular functions in the senior course from a different point of view, and so vector algebra and geometry come first. The other topics of Math 4 should be more or less recognizable from their titles.

Most of our teachers have experience using computers, and so problems in the various units of each course that lend themselves to analysis by computer are explored according to teacher preference. The team teaching each course meets regularly to share ideas. Students interested in the further study of computer science beyond that given as part of these mathematics courses can take one of three introductory computer science courses. These are graded pass/fail and meet twice a week for the year. The best students are encouraged to take the advanced course, which may be followed by the Advanced Placement course in computer science.

## CONCLUSIONS

Since our entire mathematics program is integrated, we have no control group within the school against which we can check the performance or attitudes of our students. We do have three indicators that suggest that our program is at least as good as those of surrounding communities, most of which offer the algebra-geometry-algebra sequence. Our graduates returning from college report that their preparation in mathematics is at least as good as, and sometimes better than, those of their classmates, presumably comparable students. Although SAT scores in mathematics have declined somewhat across the nation during the last ten years, the scores of our students have held steady at their former competitive level. Finally, as a suburb of Boston, Newton is a community largely made up of professionals, many of whom are professors at nearby colleges and universities; therefore the population watches diligently over the quality of education its youngsters receive. In general, the community has been highly supportive of its schools, and no question or criticism has come up concerning the integration of the topics of mathematics.

The program is not without its problems, however. The major one involves transfers into and out of our system. Hardest hit are juniors who come into our school with a full year of geometry but without a comparable foundation in algebra. We place such students in the junior course in the curriculum somewhat below their natural level, and teachers give additional help with the algebra as needed. There is a math lab for extra help, and tutoring is available, but these students sometimes have a hard go of it. Although we have less experience with juniors moving out of our school, many solve their problem by taking both geometry and algebra 2 in their junior year. A second problem is the limited choice of textbooks on integrated mathematics written in the United States and in American style. Schools unable to match the available textbooks to their programs may have to issue each student two or even three books, which can be costly at the beginning. The textbook situation seems to be improving, however.

Integrated programs have the potential to accomplish more than the standard algebra-geometry-algebra sequences. By trying to break down artificial boundaries between topics, such programs encourage students to draw from all previous mathematical learning. The programs spiral through the more significant topics, thus maintaining important skills and deepening central ideas. Topics can easily be lengthened or shortened, rearranged, or substantially changed. An integrated program may help the student appreciate better the underlying logic, power, and scope of all the various parts of mathematics.

# 17

# New York State's New Three-Year Sequence for High School Mathematics

Fredric Paul
Lynn Richbart

N OT since the late 1950s and early 1960s has mathematics education received so much public attention. The post-*Sputnik* enthusiasm for reforming mathematics at the secondary level has returned.

Although we in the mathematics education community have been seeing and reacting to many recommendations by various organizations, the report that really caught the public's eye was *A Nation at Risk: The Imperative for Educational Reform,* by the National Commission on Excellence in Education (1983). Later in that year the College Board (1983) published *Academic Preparation for College: What Students Need to Know and Be Able to Do.* This report was part of the board's ten-year Educational Equality Project. Each of these reports discussed many aspects of schooling, from the length of the school day to the amount of homework required. Recommendations in the area of mathematics are summarized by Usiskin in chapter 1 of this yearbook.

We in New York State were pleased to see most of the recommendations included in these reports, since we had embarked on similar revisions some ten years earlier. But before we describe our development of a new mathematics sequence for grades 9–11, let us first identify several aspects of New York State's unique educational system.

In New York the state board of education is called the Board of Regents. From their name comes the title of our statewide testing program of Regents examinations. Regents examinations are final exams prepared for over twenty state courses of study. All schools in the state are expected to make general use of Regents examinations, and almost all public and private schools do. Because of this, most schools in the state follow the state curricula on which the exams are based. New York has no textbook lists; local schools are free to use any materials they wish in order to best meet the needs of their students within the framework of the syllabus.

## COURSE DEVELOPMENT

An ad hoc committee of mathematics educators was called together by the Bureau of Mathematics Education in June 1972. Their charge was to develop an outline of a secondary mathematics program to possibly replace the traditional program.

The committee's product was a three-year curriculum outline that attempted to bring together the various branches of mathematics that usually are treated as independent year-long courses. The program avoided the traditional sequence of the teaching of algebra for a year, geometry for a year, and algebra/trigonometry for a year. Instead, it integrated algebra, geometry, trigonometry, probability/statistics, and logic into a comprehensive three-year program. A large percentage of the traditional content was maintained, although rearranged. In addition, the topics of probability/statistics and logic, which have been recommended by various national curriculum committees, were included. Units on mathematical systems and transformation geometry were also added. The program was designed to develop from the practical and experimental to the more abstract. It looked at mathematics in terms of being useful and practical to more than engineers and mathematicians but at the same time laying the needed foundation for these and other technical areas of study. A complete outline of the program is included at the end of this chapter.

An experimental version of the first year's program, Course I, was developed during the following months. In October 1973 all secondary schools in the state were notified that a pilot program was to begin in September 1974 and volunteers were needed. This and a second letter of explanation and further details sent to responding schools in December 1973 resulted in a large number of volunteers. Of these, forty were selected to participate in the pilot program. They were chosen so as to represent all areas of the state and reflect rural, urban, and suburban settings, large and small. In addition, those selected were directed to choose their students as randomly as possible from average (based on Regents examinations) students. Honor sections were not to be used for the pilot sample.

Course I was taught in these schools during the 1974–75 school year. Since no single text was available, pilot teachers developed their own materials and shared them. After the first year, revisions were made and the revised program was used in 1975–76. During the summer of 1976, three pilot teachers were hired to assist with writing a second revision, which was then printed as a syllabus. Their work was influenced by a comprehensive questionnaire returned by all Course I teachers. Similar activities were conducted for Courses II and III in succeeding years. Each course was taught twice and revised twice before the syllabus was printed.

In January 1977, the printed syllabus for Course I was distributed to principals in all the state's junior and senior high schools. The principals were informed that they could begin the course of study in the fall of 1977 as an alternative to the traditional mathematics sequence.

During 1977–78 three demonstration centers were established for the new program. Funding for these centers was provided by ESEA Title IV-C federal funds. Each center had to submit evidence concerning the success of its program. Evidence showed that students in the new course had better results on common examinations and greater retention of the previous year's work than those in the traditional course. Moreover, a higher percentage of students took all three years of the new program than had previously completed the traditional program.

Once established, these three centers provided information, assistance, and in-service programs to schools wishing to begin the new program. Each year the centers were oversubscribed with schools wanting to embark on the new program.

As growth continued, there was a need to inform colleges about the program. In October 1978 the department sent a short note to directors of admissions of New York State postsecondary institutions to make them aware that more and more students' transcripts would be showing the new course of study. At the same time it assured them that, like the traditional program, the curriculum did follow national curriculum recommendations.

To keep the mathematical community abreast of the status of the new curriculum, presentations about it were made at statewide and regional meetings as well as at several NCTM conferences. Articles on the program appeared in state and national mathematics education journals.

As the program grew, locally developed materials were no longer sufficient. Fortunately, three companies have now published texts that are fully based on the three-year sequence—Charles E. Merrill (Bumby and Klutch 1982), Amsco (Dressler, Keenan, and Gantert 1980), and Houghton Mifflin (Rising et al. 1981).

## EVALUATIVE STUDIES

Any change meets a certain amount of reluctance, and this program is no exception. Every effort was made to include all essential aspects of the traditional high school mathematics curriculum. Certain topics have been shifted, and additions to the curriculum dictated a de-emphasis or deletion of some topics. Right triangle trigonometry has been removed from grade 9 and incorporated into the trigonometry unit of Course III. Euclidean geometry with synthetic proof has been retained, but the number of theorems has been reduced and the concept of required theorems determining a specific sequence has been eliminated. A focus on specific types of problems, such as motion and investment, has given way to a general problem-solving approach.

The report of the Conference Board of the Mathematical Sciences (National Advisory Committee on Mathematical Education 1975) reflected many of the ideas of New York's new curriculum, such as integrating statistical ideas throughout the curriculum at all levels; the focus on developing abilities in problem solving, logical reasoning, and critical thinking; and new and imaginative approaches to teaching geometry in high school. The new curriculum follows the philosophy of NCTM's *Agenda for Action,* providing flexibility and motivating students to continue in mathematics.

The most common concern, primarily from those with no experience in the program, was that it didn't seem to provide as strong a background as the traditional program. Once the pilot period was over, the program was offered to students at all ability levels. Some of these students progressed successfully through the three-year sequence, a fourth-year program, and Advanced Placement Calculus. Individual schools studied standard examination results and carefully monitored the students.

---

## Results . . . supported the contention that the principal concepts of the traditional program were not sacrificed in the new sequence.

---

Several specific studies were done using PSAT or SAT scores. We realized that these examinations tested the material of the traditional program and did not address several of the newer topics. It was hoped that students in the newer curriculum would do as well on these tests as those in the traditional curriculum and thus show that none of the essential aspects of the older program had been sacrificed while many important concepts had been learned but not tested. On the 1976 PSAT, the mathematics scores of the two groups were not significantly different.

In 1978 the Educational Testing Service (ETS) conducted a similar but much more sophisticated study of PSAT scores of students in both programs based on 1977 results. This involved 365 experimental (new program) students and 935 control (traditional program) students. A preliminary report, published in April 1979, concluded that a student who enrolls in the alternative program has "no practical disadvantage over a student of similar ability who participates in the Regents (traditional) program" (Braswell 1979).

To test the consistency of these findings, the Testing Division of the New York State Education Department designed a study that resulted in the selection of twenty-four pairs of schools: twenty-four teaching the traditional curriculum and twenty-four teaching the new sequence. Schools were paired on grade 11 enrollment and the percent of students passing the Regents comprehensive examination in English. Thus the schools teaching the traditional mathematics and schools teaching the new-sequence mathematics for at least three years were made up of students of comparable ability with no mathematics bias. The study involved 7293 students and provided the department with mean $(\bar{x})$ SAT mathematics and SAT verbal scores as shown in table 17.1.

TABLE 17.1
SAT Mean $(\bar{x})$ Mathematics and Verbal Scores

| Program | $\bar{x}$ Mathematics Score | $\bar{x}$ Verbal Score |
| --- | --- | --- |
| Traditional curriculum | 489.79 | 441.95 |
| New sequence | 491.08 | 443.70 |

A $t$ test showed that the two groups did not differ significantly. The results were consistent with the previous ones and supported the contention that the principal concepts of the traditional program were not sacrificed in the new sequence.

## COLLEGIATE REACTION

Reaction to the new curriculum from the collegiate level has been generally positive. The Seaway Section of the Mathematical Association of America conducted a study of the new program through a committee of six professors. One was quite critical because he thought algebra had been slighted in terms of days allotted to algebraic topics. The other five members of the committee were far less critical and were, in fact, supportive of many areas of the program. One professor stated, "After our meeting, I expected to be very critical of the proposed sequence, but I was surprised to discover that I have little to criticize. . . . As a teacher of freshman calculus, I won't have any problems with students who have been through this sequence."

The PTA of a Long Island district that had been teaching a few sections of the new sequence was concerned about how engineering schools would react to the course. The PTA Council sent out letters to engineering schools across the nation with this inquiry: "Would our students, wishing to enroll in your school of Engineering, Practical Mathematics, be properly educated in Mathematics to be classified as a freshman student?" Comments from the colleges ranged from "Yes" and "This type of program could well be an improvement on the usual high school mathematics curriculum" to the following:

> We have these materials and think they are generally quite good. A student who has learned the mathematics of that full sequence would be well-prepared for beginning calculus and could move directly into our sequence required of science and engineering students.

These three reactions came from colleges in Connecticut, Virginia, and Ohio, respectively. After seeing the results, the PTA Council supported the school's decision to move totally to the new sequence.

## STATEWIDE EXPANSION

Figures from the state's Basic Educational Data System showed a steady voluntary movement to the new program. In 1977, the first year that all schools could offer Course I, 7587 students enrolled. In 1983–84, over 79 000 students were registered in Course I. Enrollments in Courses II and III were over 39 000 and 23 000 students, respectively.

With the program growing and evaluation results positive, it was not surprising that in February 1983 the State Education Department published a proposed phase-in schedule for the whole state. The proposal, which was passed by the Board of Regents in 1984, called for the last traditional ninth-grade algebra Regents examination to be given in January 1988. Thus *all* students in the state beginning a mathematics sequence in the fall of 1987 will be enrolled in Course I of the new program.

The statewide adoption of the sequence will eliminate the few problems that have accompanied student transfers within the state. For those from out of state, some problems will still exist.

Our experience has shown that students moving from the new sequence to a traditional program have very few problems. As one can see by looking at the complete outline, all the fundamentals of the traditional program are there. A problem may arise, for example, if a student comes to a traditional algebra program in late October or early November after working primarily on logic and probability/statistics in the new sequence. Although this doesn't happen often, it is possible, since the state does not dictate the order in which topics are presented by the local schools. When transfers to the traditional program occur over the summer, after the completion of full courses, the problem is minimal.

Transfers into the new sequence are similarly affected by timing. Obviously students have to catch up in those topics that are new to them. The spiral approach that is used gives them this opportunity.

## COURSE CONTENT

Although the entire curriculum outline is included at the end of this chapter, it may be useful to focus on at least one topic to show how it is spiraled through the three years. Probability, which is mentioned in every curriculum report of late, is a good example.

In Course I, students are exposed to the concept of probability and use the counting principle and permutation formulas in probability applications. In Course II, combinations are discussed as well as permutations with repetition. These lead to probability questions in this area. In Course III, work with the binomial theorem and the probability of exactly $r$ successes in $n$ trials completes the spiral. To illustrate these concepts, the following probability questions are taken from past Regents examinations in the three courses.

### Course I

A bag contains 2 green marbles, 4 blue marbles, and 5 red marbles. If one marble is drawn at random from the bag, what is the probability that it will be green?

### Course II

A vase contains 4 yellow roses, 3 pink roses, and 5 red roses. What is the probability that a combination of 3 roses will have either all roses of the same color or one rose of each color?

### Course III

If the probability of a team's winning is 2/3 and the probability of its losing is 1/3, what is the probability that the team will win exactly 1 of 4 games?

## CONCLUSIONS AND REMARKS

Recent national educational reports on desired curricular changes in school mathematics have been consistent with the direction taken by New York State. Our 1972 ad hoc committee of mathematics educators did an outstanding job. With the possible exception of the recommendations concerning computers, New York's "Three-Year Sequence for High School Mathematics" appears to have correctly predicted the recent trends in high school mathematics.

Probability and statistics, which is mentioned in every report, is taught throughout the sequence. No longer is the topic reserved for those few juniors or seniors who might have time in their schedules. Now, all students in this new sequence are exposed to these topics and are shown their importance in a comprehensive mathematics program.

Although computers are not mentioned directly in the outline, it is hoped that the work done with probability/statistics and logic will be of value in this area. However, no curriculum should be considered perfect. As soon as a document is printed, some modifications may be desirable, and our program is no different. Plans for the modification of the program described here have already begun.

For those considering the implementation of a new mathematics curriculum, we offer the following advice:

• Try to keep as many of those individuals and groups affected as informed and involved as possible.

• Keep all lines of communication open, and initiate progress reports as often as possible.

• Expect criticism. Constructive critiques will be of value—if not immediately, then later when program modifications are needed.

• Don't be afraid to publish a document because certain areas are constantly changing. If you wait until the technology revolution is over, you may wait forever.

• Be prepared to modify your product after a very short time.

## COURSE OUTLINES

### COURSE I

**I. Logic**
 A. The sentence
  1. Truth value
  2. Open sentences
  3. Replacement set
 B. Formation of sentences
  1. Negation
  2. Conjunction
  3. Disjunction
  4. Conditional
 C. Truth tables, tautologies
 D. Related conditional sentences
  1. Converse
  2. Inverse
  3. Contrapositive
  4. Examples from mathematical and nonmathematical sources
 E. Biconditional

**II. Aspects of Algebra and Geometry**
 A. Review of operations with positive and negative rational numbers; application of properties of the rational number system
 B. Addition and multiplication of monomials
 C. Solution of linear equations and inequalities
 D. Geometric sets
  1. Discussion and classification of geometric sets
  2. Angle measure and classification
  3. Use of protractor
  4. Area—parallelogram, triangle, rectangle, trapezoid
  5. Volume—prism, rectangular solid
  6. Applications—including problems involving rate of change
 E. Ratio and proportion
  1. Percent as a ratio of a number to 100
  2. Solution of proportions
  3. Similar polygons
 F. Real numbers—beyond the rationals
  1. Examples of numbers that are not rational
  2. Rational approximations of irrational numbers
  3. Operations with radicals
  4. Pythagorean theorem
  5. Circle formulas
  6. Volume of right circular cylinder, cone, sphere
 G. Multiplication of binomials

### III. Probability, Permutations, and Statistics
A. Discussion of the term *probability*
B. The counting principle
C. Elementary combinatorics
  1. Permutations
  2. Urn problems
    *a*) With replacement
    *b*) Without replacement
  3. *n* factorial
D. Investigation of events whose probabilities must be determined empirically—idea of stabilization of relative frequency
E. Introduction to statistics
  1. Discussion of the term *statistics*
  2. Need and justification for statistics
  3. Sampling techniques
  4. Graphical representation and interpretation, histograms
F. Some measures of central tendency
  1. Mean, median, mode
  2. Quartiles
  3. Mathematical and nonmathematical examples

### IV. Rectangular Coordinate System
A. Graphs of linear functions
B. Analytic solution of systems of linear equations
C. Graphic solution of linear inequalities in two variables, systems of linear inequalities

---

## COURSE II

### I. Logic
A. Review of material on logic from Course I
B. Laws of reasoning: laws of contraposition, detachment, syllogism, and disjunctive inference; negative of conjunction, disjunction (De Morgan's laws); applications
C. Quantification: universal and existential quantifiers; notation; negation of quantified statements; counterexample

### II. Mathematical Systems
A. Investigation of finite mathematical systems: computation and equation solving; binary operation; identity and inverse; closure; commutativity and associativity in these systems
B. Groups: definition, reinvestigation, and reclassification of systems studied thus far
C. Discussion of group theorems and applications
D. Fields

### III. Euclidean Geometry
    A.  Discussion of the foundations of an axiomatic system; undefined terms, definitions, axioms, and theorems
    B.  Discussion of specific terms and assumptions in proofs of theorems concerning—
        1.  Betweenness and congruence
        2.  Parallel lines
        3.  Similarity
    C.  Constructions

### IV. Analytic Geometry
    A.  Review of material on rectangular coordinate system and graphing from Course I
    B.  Distance formula, midpoint of a line segment, division of a line segment, and problems involving area
    C.  Slopes of parallel and perpendicular lines
    D.  Equations of a straight line: point-slope and slope-intercept forms
    E.  Locus: definition; locus of points equidistant from two points, three points, two parallel lines, at a fixed distance from a point (circle), equidistant from a fixed point and a fixed line (parabola); equations of circle and parabola
    F.  Proof by analytic means

### V. Solution of Quadratic Equations
    A.  Review of the solution of quadratic equations by factoring; solution by graphing
    B.  Completing the square
    C.  Derivation of the quadratic formula
    D.  Graphical and algebraic solution of a quadratic and linear equation simultaneously
    E.  Application to cases with rational and irrational roots

### VI. Probability, Permutations, and Combinations
    A.  Review of material on permutations from Course I
    B.  Permutations of $n$ things taken $n$ at a time with repetition
    C.  Combinations of $n$ things taken $n$ at a time, $r$ at a time
    D.  Probability involving combinations

## COURSE III

### I. Complex Numbers
    A.  Further study of the real number system
    B.  Extension of algebraic techniques
    C.  Introduction of the complex number system
    D.  Quadratics with complex roots
    E.  Absolute value: equations and inequalities

### II. Relations and Functions
    A.  Definitions and properties

B. Exponential and logarithmic functions
C. Common logarithms and computation

### III. Circular Functions

A. Further work with the geometry of the circle
B. Circular functions and their graphs
C. Trigonometric identities and equations
D. Applications to area, law of sines, law of cosines, right triangle trigonometry

### IV. Transformation Geometry

A. Review of mapping
1. Definitions, one-to-one mappings, identity mappings, inverse mappings
2. Some geometric examples
B. Line reflections
C. Translations
D. Rotations
E. Isometrics
F. Applications to group theory

### V. Probability and Statistics

A. Review of previous work with probability, combinatorics
B. Probability of exactly $r$ successes in $n$ trials
C. The binomial theorem
D. Review of previous work with statistics
E. Measures of dispersion
1. Range, mean absolute deviation
2. Variance
3. Standard deviation
F. $\Sigma$ notation

## REFERENCES

Braswell, James S. *Performance on the PSAT/NMSQT New York Students in the Integrated Mathematics Program vs. New York Students in the Regents Program.* Preliminary report. Princeton, N.J.: Educational Testing Service, April 1979.

Bumby, Douglas R., and Richard J. Klutch. *Mathematics: A Topical Approach,* Courses 1, 2, and 3. Westerville, Ohio: Charles E. Merrill Publishing Co., 1982.

College Board. *Academic Preparation for College: What Students Need to Know and Be Able to Do.* New York: The Board, 1983.

Dressler, Isidore, Edward P. Keenan, and Ann X. Gantert. *Integrated Mathematics,* Courses 1, 2, and 3. New York: Amsco School Publications, 1980.

National Advisory Committee on Mathematical Education. *Overview and Analysis of School Mathematics, Grades K–12.* Reston, Va.: National Council of Teachers of Mathematics, 1975.

National Commission on Excellence in Education. *A Nation at Risk: The Imperative for Educational Reform.* Washington, D.C.: U.S. Department of Education, 1983.

Rising, Gerald R., et al. *Unified Mathematics,* Books 1, 2, and 3. Boston: Houghton Mifflin Co., 1981.

# 18

# Applied Mathematics:
# A Three-Year Program for
# Non-College-Bound Students

Donald L. Chambers
Henry S. Kepner, Jr.

AMERICAN high schools urgently need to develop mathematics programs more appropriate to the needs of non-college-bound students. The three-year program of instruction described here includes elements of arithmetic, algebra, geometry, and statistics; it can be successfully taught to students who have previously had no mathematics instruction beyond computation.

The failure of existing programs to meet the needs of non-college-bound students, and many college-bound students as well, was recognized by the Conference Board of the Mathematical Sciences (1982, 4–5), which observed:

> For the many students in secondary school who are not specially talented in mathematics and not headed for careers in science or technology, current programs are a source of discouragement, anxiety, and repetition in a dull "basic skills" program which serves them poorly.

The College Board (1983, 19), which usually concentrates on recommendations for college preparation, recognizes that

> all people need some knowledge of mathematics to function well in today's society. Mathematics is our indispensable language of science and technology, as well as business and finance. All people, therefore, need some fluency in this language if they are to contribute to and fare well in our contemporary world.

In 1980, NCTM recommended that all students study mathematics for three years in grades 9–12. (NCTM 1980, 20). Recognizing the inadequate program for non-college-bound students, the Council called for the de-

---

The authors wish to express their appreciation to Stephen Leinwand, Mathematics Consultant, Connecticut Department of Education, for his valuable assistance in the preparation of this chapter.

velopment of new courses appropriate to their needs. The National Commission on Excellence in Education (1983, 24) also recommended that "new, equally demanding mathematics curricula . . . be developed for those who do not plan to continue their formal education immediately" and suggested three years of mathematics as a requirement for graduation.

The seriousness of the problem is indicated by patterns of enrollment in present courses. Nationwide, about 71 percent of 17-year-olds have completed one semester of algebra; 52 percent, one semester of geometry; and 38 percent, one semester of algebra 2 (NAEP 1983). Usiskin (1983) estimates that only about 20 percent of each graduating class, those who are college bound into (1) natural science or other majors requiring mathematics beyond calculus or (2) institutions with highly competitive admissions, are well served by the present high school program.

Usiskin (1983) has outlined a three-year program for non-college-bound students. In "A Proposal for Reforming the Secondary School Mathematics Curriculum" he recommends one year of consumer mathematics, one semester of applied algebra, one semester of applied geometry, one semester of computers, and one semester of statistics. He suggests that calculator and computer skills replace complicated paper-and-pencil arithmetic and algebra, that geometry include little or no proof, and that applications be emphasized throughout the program.

In "New Directions for General Mathematics," Chambers (1983) reported on a project to develop a three-year program for the same population. A statement of general goals and a topic outline for the first year were presented. The philosophy and content of these two sets of recommendations are completely compatible. The major distinction appears to be that Usiskin prefers a sequence of discrete courses whereas Chambers and his colleagues favor a unified, or integrated, approach.

The limitations of the two proposals are that Usiskin's recommendations contain few specifics beyond those mentioned above and Chambers made recommendations for the first year only. This chapter extends Chambers's previous recommendations to the second and third year. That three-year program is referred to as the Applied Mathematics Program.

## GOALS

The program's goals for arithmetic, algebra, geometry, statistics and probability, and problem solving are discussed in the next five sections.

### Arithmetic Goals

The emphasis in the arithmetic strand of the Applied Mathematics Program is on the understanding of numbers and their representations and the use of calculators to solve numerical problems. Consistent with the recommendations of the Conference Board, students learn any whole number facts not previously learned and informal mental arithmetic strategies. There is a

---

There is a heavy emphasis on estimation and approximation . . . skills . . . essential to the efficient use of calculators.

---

heavy emphasis on estimation and approximation. These skills are essential to the efficient use of calculators.

Students should learn to estimate the results of all computations, and estimation strategies should be explicitly taught. They should also learn to determine whether an estimate is sufficient or whether a precise answer is required. When a precise answer is needed, students should learn to decide the most efficient method from among three choices: the use of mental arithmetic, a calculator, or a pencil-and-paper algorithm.

Procedures for solving routine problems are explicitly taught. By "routine problem" we mean customary applications of arithmetic in one-step, multiple-step, and rate problems usually referred to as verbal or story problems. Students select the appropriate problem-solving procedure from among the ones they know.

In using calculators, students become acquainted with conventions regarding the order of operations and the use of memory features. They also become aware of rounding and truncating errors and the interpretation of the display. The most outstanding example of the latter occurs when 0.9999999 appears as the result of $\boxed{1}$ $\boxed{\div}$ $\boxed{3}$ $\boxed{\times}$ $\boxed{3}$ $\boxed{=}$. As early as possible, students should be introduced to scientific notation and have access to calculators with a scientific notation capability for problem-solving activities involving very large or very small numbers.

Materials available for the development of the arithmetic objectives include *Applying Arithmetic* (Usiskin and Bell 1984), *Algebra through Applications with Probability and Statistics* (Usiskin 1979), and *Experiences in Mathematical Ideas,* volume 1 (NCTM 1970). Appropriate calculator activities can be found in *Calculator Activities for the Classroom* (Immerzeel and Ockenga 1977) and *Problem Solving with the Calculator* (Jacobs 1977). The Agency for Instructional Television has created a twelve-part series, "Math Wise," for general mathematics in ninth and tenth grades. Several of those programs address the arithmetic goals of the Applied Mathematics Program.

Many commercially prepared general mathematics and consumer mathematics texts can be adapted as instructional materials for this program. But it is important when using them to keep in mind the goals of the program and to select material judiciously.

### Algebra Goals

In the Applied Mathematics Program the development of algebra proceeds from intuitive notions about arithmetic to generalizations involving variables and then to more formal algebraic manipulations. The topics are spaced throughout the three-year sequence and developed and reviewed in the context of applications in geometry, probability, statistics, and other areas.

The program contains many of the topics traditionally included in the first-year algebra course but deletes topics that can be justified only as preparation for second-year algebra. Content and emphasis are consistent with the recommendations of Usiskin (1980; 1983) and others. Only elementary work with rational expressions and trinomial factoring is included. Traditional word problems are de-emphasized, and greater attention is given to applications involving formulas, proportions, and statistics.

The first-year work is designed to help students use algebraic expressions and equations to represent information obtained from a variety of settings. In particular, algebraic representation is used to generalize arithmetic patterns already observed or reported. Students also learn to use expressions in describing relations found in problem-solving situations and data collected in statistical settings.

Whereas the first year focuses on representing relationships through the use of variables, the second year stresses the study of equivalent representations. Initially, students translate equivalent word statements into algebraic ones. Then the algebraic statements are studied for their equivalency—for example, "the perimeter of a square is the sum of the lengths of its sides" ($s + s + s + s$) and "the perimeter of a square is four times the length of a side" ($4s$).

Graphing skills are developed during the first year through the construction of graphs for statistical data and number patterns. During the second year, students do extensive graphing of linear relationships along with other relations. After basic work on graphing points and linear equations, students use one of the many computer software programs that reinforce the relationships between a linear equation and its graph. Many of the typical practice sets with paper and pencil lead to skills in solving equations or constructing graphs, but the tedious calculations required to locate points often cause students to miss the interrelations between equation and graph.

The third year is characterized by the use of linear inequalities in applications. Students start with simple inequality statements that can be derived from everyday statements. Later, skills on solving linear inequalities are developed after the corresponding skill has been developed with equations. Graphing inequalities is an important tool in describing word statements of applications and reporting solutions to problem-solving activities.

Also in the third year, students are introduced to polynomial functions. First, through graphing, they can observe basic properties of polynomials of the form $y = f(x)$. Later, using computer graphics software packages, they analyze the graph that corresponds to a given function.

Trinomial factoring is demonstrated in the third year but is not practiced for mastery. The goal is to make students aware that $(x - 5)(x + 7) = 0$ is a form of a quadratic equation that shows that 5 and $-7$ are solutions. This concept is intended to complement work on solving quadratic equations through the use of the quadratic formula. The formula is presented and practiced without proof.

Students work with trigonometric functions through applied settings. They solve algebraic equations with trigonometric terms, and in addition, they study the sine, cosine, and tangent functions and contrast their range and periodicity with polynomial functions.

Throughout the second and third years, the use of algebra in problem solving is a dominant focus. The construction of an open sentence or graph as the representation of a problem relationship is a major goal. In examining data collected or patterns observed, the student is encouraged to write an algebraic representation where possible.

Text material for the algebra component can be extracted from algebra texts prepared for low-achieving students. The recent interest in prealgebra courses has produced materials that can be readily adapted. The prealgebra texts that include arithmetic, algebra, geometry, and statistics in an integrated format are especially appropriate. Other suitable materials include *Algebra through Applications with Probability and Statistics* (Usiskin 1979), *Elementary Algebra* (Jacobs 1979), *Unified Mathematics* (Rising et al. 1981), and *The Search for Pattern* by Sawyer.

### Geometry Goals

The goals of the geometry component of the Applied Mathematics Program are very similar to those of many K–8 mathematics programs. The reason for their inclusion here is twofold. First, as O'Daffer has observed, "It is not uncommon to find that even though the text material used by an elementary school teacher includes a number of geometry topics, the teacher will skip much of it" (1980, 91). Second, although most students of high school age are able to recognize triangles, squares, rectangles, circles, cylinders, spheres, and cubes, their knowledge of properties of figures and properties of relations among figures is unsatisfactory. According to the *Results from the Second Mathematics Assessment of the National Assessment of Educational Progress* (Carpenter et al. 1981, 58), "The majority of 13- and 17-year-olds were not able to apply the Pythagorean theorem to solve routine problems nor were they able to apply properties of similar triangles in problem situations." A report on results from the Third Mathematics Assessment is no more encouraging: "The concepts and skills underlying geometry and measurement do not appear to have been learned very well. For example, only about half of the 13-year-olds and three-fourths of the 17-year-olds could calculate the area of a rectangle when given its length and width" (NAEP 1983, 18).

The most important distinction between the geometry program proposed and the geometry course as presently offered is the de-emphasis of the axiomatic method and proof. This allows the elimination of many traditional theorems, since their only value is to serve as lemmas for the axiomatic development of other theorems. There is a corresponding increased emphasis on the intuitive development (based on measurement, in many cases) of properties and relationships and their application to real-world problems. Applications involve concepts of perimeter, area, and volume and the use of congruent and similar triangles to determine measures.

---

## The Turtle Geometry feature of the Logo language is very effective for integrating geometry concepts and computer concepts.

---

Formulas for area and volume are developed intuitively and are applied to a variety of regular and composite figures. Methods for estimating the area and volume of irregular regions are taught, and strategies for increasing the accuracy of the estimates are studied.

Tangrams and geoboards are used to develop other measurement properties—for example: *Figures with equal areas do not necessarily have equal perimeters.* Generalizations for maximizing area given a fixed perimeter or other specifications are also investigated.

The study of congruence and similarity is also related to real-world problems. Students learn to use properties of congruence and similarity to determine measures without measuring. This is an opportunity to apply arithmetic and algebra skills in a new setting.

The Turtle Geometry feature of the Logo language is very effective for integrating geometry concepts and computer concepts. Having learned to recognize a square, for example, students became familiar with its measurement properties by instructing the turtle to make the sequence of moves that results in forming a square. The formation of a triangle can be achieved only through an awareness that the sum of the measures of the angles is 180 degrees. This should be learned through experimentation, not through proof. Paper folding can also be used to develop such geometric relationships as *The base angles of an isosceles triangle are congruent,* and *The diagonals of a square are perpendicular bisectors of each other.*

The collection of activities described by MacPherson in chapter 6 of this volume is ideally suited for the geometry component of the Applied Mathematics Program. Appropriate text materials include *Geometry in Easy Steps: An Informal Approach* (Cox 1983) and *Geometry: A Model of the Universe* (Hoffer 1979).

### Statistics and Probability Goals

The Applied Mathematics Program highlights the role of statistics and probability in everyday life, the concepts needed to apply and interpret problems involving statistics and probability, and an appreciation for the significant role of statistics and probability as advocated by Pereira-Mendoza and Swift (1981, 3). The statistics and probability units are developed in a problem-solving mode. A question to be answered or a problem to be solved always initiates the study of a new concept or technique. To answer the question, a student must decide what information is needed and determine whether or not that information is available. Must information be generated through experimentation, survey, or resources? How can that information be organized into a form that can be more readily interpreted with respect to the stated task? Finally, how can the results be reported clearly to a given audience? These statistical projects always conclude with a communication of the results to others.

In *Educating Americans for the Twenty-first Century,* the National Science Board Commission on Precollege Education in Mathematics, Science and Technology (1983, 43) expressed its concern that "discrete mathematics, elementary statistics and probability should now be considered fundamental for all high school students."

In the first year the focus is on collecting and organizing data. Data are collected in a variety of situations including surveys, physical experiments, and resource materials. Class discussions center on identifying the question to be answered and methods for collecting appropriate data. After data have been gathered, students work on varied approaches to present the data clearly to others. Primary sources for this and other statistical activities are *Statistics by Example* (Mosteller et al. 1973), *Statistics: A Guide to the Unknown* (Tanur et al. 1972), materials from the Schools Council Project on Statistical Education (1981), *Teaching Statistics and Probability* (NCTM 1981), and *Exploring Data* by Landwehr and Watkins, a unit prepared for the ASA-NCTM Joint Committee on the Curriculum in Statistics and Probability. The best reference for statistics modules is the ASA Quantitative Literacy Project (Dorothy Perreca, Project Coordinator, 806 15th St., NW, Washington, DC 20005).

Questions of sampling, which come up early in the attempts to collect data, are developed throughout the statistics sequence. Randomness, bias, and the variability of samples are explored.

After collecting or receiving data, students develop ways to organize the data for summary and description. Of particular interest in descriptive statistics are the tabular and pictorial representations of the data.

The recent techniques of constructing stem-and-leaf plots (similar to histograms) and box-and-whisker plots are of value to the student in organizing data and showing important pieces of information (Liebetrau 1981, 27–29). Other descriptive information, such as central tendency (mean, median, and mode) and dispersion (range, quartiles, and deviations), are also used by the students. Although most of these descriptive statistics are developed in the first year, the standard deviation is presented later when there is adequate algebra background to interpret the formulas as well as grasp the idea. Through collecting, organizing, and describing data, students develop skills for reading and interpreting summarized data.

Students are also introduced to some of the potential misuses of statistics. Through applied situations, they can focus on such fallacies as definitional problems (*poverty, slow learner*), shifting statistical definitions, improper comparisons, measurement problems (the use of numbers to represent properties), and misleading charts. Campbell's book, *Flaws and Fallacies in Statistical Thinking,* is the best single source of such examples.

Probability is introduced through experiments involving counting successes in a finite set of trials. Results from replications of the same experiment are discussed. Emphasis is placed on listing the sample space. Without this skill students have difficulty determining probabilities of more complex events later.

Although permutations and combinations are major components of probability theory, these concepts must be developed through listings and tree diagrams in numerous examples before introducing the standard notation used in traditional probability units. Care must also be taken to keep these counting techniques from becoming too abstract because of their notational complexities.

Through the construction of frequency distributions for a large number of varied settings, students learn to recognize probability distributions that approximate normal, biomodal, rectangular, skewed, and J-shaped distributions.

In the third year, students study correlation through experimental data and scatter diagrams. With the assumption of linear correlation, they study examples of data with correlations ranging from $-1$ through 1. Scatter diagrams are matched with correlation coefficients calculated using a computer program (Matsumoto 1981, 126–34). Although students do not calculate a correlation coefficient using a formula, they do study the differences between correlation and causation.

Familiarity with scatter diagrams leads to the construction of trend lines drawn by eye. Students use trend lines to extract interpolations and extrapolations from existing data, learning to consider the limitations of extrapolations and interpolations in these situations.

In the final year, students explore decision making with statistics. The first major concepts are sampling, sampling distributions and their variability, and distribution of sample means in relation to the original population distribution. These are considered through experimentation and recording results of sampling activities. From activities on sampling, Kissane (1981, 184) suggests:

> Students should get a strong intuitive feel for the important results:
> - The means of a set of samples cluster around the mean of the population.
> - The larger the sample, the closer the clustering.
> - If a single sample mean is used as an estimate of the population mean, larger sample sizes lead to smaller likely errors.

After experimenting and making these observations, students explore hypothesis testing. They learn to construct a null hypothesis, state the alternative hypotheses, and identify the possible decision cases (e.g., *Reject the null hypothesis when the null hypothesis is true*). Through varied examples, students discuss the possible consequences of making each decision. Finally, they conduct hypothesis-testing experiments in laboratory or survey settings.

In addition to sources identified previously, *Statistics, Concepts, and Controversies,* by D. Moor, and the ASA-NCTM Joint Committee unit *Information from Samples: Yes-No Populations,* by J. Swift, provide valuable resources on hypothesis testing.

## Problem Solving Goals

Problem solving is an integral part of the Applied Mathematics Program, and specific segments are devoted to teaching problem-solving skills and strategies. In addition, problem solving is included in every topical unit in the form of applications.

Calculators are an important part of the problem-solving strand. Students use calculators in varied problem-solving settings, many of which involve applications of arithmetic, algebra, geometry, or statistics. The major goal of making the calculator a tool in problem solving is to help the student focus on the problem-solving process and to worry less about computation. The Iowa Problem-Solving Project, *Modules on Using the Calculator,* is a valuable source of such activities. For information, write Earl Ockenga, Iowa Problem Solving Project, Price Laboratory School, Cedar Falls, IA 50613.

---

The attempt is made to break the learned expectation that all mathematics is assigned one day and completed the next day.

---

Students practice a small set of specific problem-solving strategies in the program. Major skills include *guess and test, make a chart and table, find a simpler problem, write a mathematical sentence,* and *obtain relevant data.* Over the three-year program, these strategies are developed in a variety of settings. Problem-solving strategies and mathematical content are *not* taught simultaneously but rather presented as tasks in themselves when first developed. They appear again later in applications of mathematical content already presented.

Starting in the first year, short problem-solving units develop student skills in using such strategies as guess and test. Students address small problems that can be solved using this technique. Problems from the Iowa Problem-Solving Project module on guesses are exemplary activities for this short unit. Similar modules on making tables and using resources are especially appropriate for introductory activities focusing on these respective skills. Once a skill has been introduced and practiced in isolation, it is to be used and reviewed during problem-solving sessions. Teachers are encouraged to remind students of the skills or to use student solutions to show ways in which these skills are brought to bear on a problem.

In addition to learning specific problem-solving strategies, students are presented with problems in applications that take more than one period or day to solve and require the use of several strategies. Projects in statistics exemplify settings that may take several days to consider, organize, and carry out. In numerous settings the attempt is made to break the learned expectation that all mathematics is assigned one day and completed the next day.

In the second and third years, students work on problems in pairs and small groups. It is considered important that they learn how to communicate about mathematical situations. In several applied areas, such as statistics, geometry, and measurement, student projects are designed that will employ group work in planning and carrying out the plan. Important in some of these projects is the expectation of prolonged time commitment in carrying out the task. Many of the previously presented problem-solving skills such as finding relevant data are needed.

One part of the problem-solving strand focuses on the construction of mathematical sentences for word problems. Although this is not the only form in which problems are presented, the ability to solve word problems is considered a valuable tool. An emphasis on language as a way of describing mathematical relationships is stressed in this approach. Some time is devoted to the literal translation of specific mathematical vocabulary, but this is balanced with a caution for dependency on direct translation. Several specific ideas are represented in Barnett, Sowder, and Vos (1980).

## THE SYLLABUS

A year-by-year outline of the three-year Applied Mathematics Program for non-college-bound students follows.

---

### Course Content: Year One

**Arithmetic**
1. Recognize many different uses of numbers.
   a. Distinguish among numbers used as counts, measures, locations in reference frameworks, scales, codes, names.
   b. Recognize the need for counting numbers, rational numbers, negative numbers, and other sets of numbers.
   c. Use numbers as locators.
   d. Interpret formulas as ways of expressing numbers.
2. Associate arithmetic operations with physical world phenomena.
   a. Associate addition with putting together and shifting.

---

    b. Associate subtraction with taking apart, shifting, and comparison.

    c. Associate multiplication with a number of $N$-tuples, size change, area and volume, acting through, and rate factor.

    d. Associate division with rate comparisons, ratio comparisons, and recovering factors from products.

3. Express numbers in equivalent and approximate forms.

    a. Order whole numbers and decimals.

    b. Recognize many names for a given number, including equivalent fractions.

    c. Round numbers to an indicated place value.

    d. Rewrite numbers in different forms.

4. Use approximation to estimate the results of computations with whole numbers, fractions, and decimals.

    a. Estimate the results of a computation to one significant digit.

5. Use a calculator to compute with whole numbers, integers, and decimals, and use mental arithmetic or pencil-and-paper algorithms where appropriate.

    a. Read and interpret parentheses as grouping symbols.

    b. Apply conventions regarding order of operations.

    c. Solve formulas in which the unknown variable stands alone on one side of the equation.

    d. Use standard algorithms to add, subtract, and multiply two-digit numbers and divide a three-digit number by a one-digit number or multiple of ten.

    e. Use a calculator to compute with whole numbers and decimals.

6. Solve routine problems.

    a. Solve one-step word problems using a calculator where appropriate.

## Algebra

1. Use variables and the language of algebra.

    a. Use letters to name numbers.

    b. Use expressions including letters to describe a sequence of operations involving an unknown number.

    c. Interpret parentheses and other grouping symbols to denote order of operations.

    d. Use conventions regarding order of operations.

    e. Use 2 and 3 as exponents for numbers and variables and $b = \sqrt{x}$ as a solution for $b^2 = x$.

2. Find an unknown value using a formula.

    a. Substitute known values into a formula.

    b. Solve an equation for an unknown value that appears alone on one side of the equation.

3. Simplify elementary algebraic expressions.

    a. Solve proportions as equal ratios or equivalent fractions.

    b. Recognize the equivalence of $ac + ad$ and $a(c + d)$.

4. Solve linear and quadratic equations.

    a. Use guess-and-test procedures to solve linear equations in one variable.

    b. Recognize the equivalence of $a + x = b$ and $x = b - a$.

    c. Recognize the equivalence of $bx = a$ and $x = a/b$.

5. Associate equations with their graphs.
   a. Plot points in a Cartesian coordinate system.
6. Represent problem situations by open sentences.
   a. Write equations for one-step routine problems.

**Geometry**
1. Recognize and name common geometric figures.
   a. Recognize angles, triangles, squares, rectangles, parallelograms, rhombuses, trapezoids, circles, prisms, cylinders, and spheres, and use the terminology associated with each.
2. Identify properties of common geometric figures.
   a. Describe any figure listed in item 1a in such a way as to distinguish it from any other.
3. Determine measurement properties of common geometric figures.
   a. Use instruments appropriate for measuring angles, length, area, and capacity.
   b. Know and use the following angle measurement properties of triangles: the sum of the measures of the angles of a triangle is 180 degrees, the base angles of an isosceles triangle are congruent, the line of symmetry of an isosceles triangle bisects the vertex angle and is perpendicular to the base.
   c. Know and use the following segment measure properties of triangles: the Pythagorean theorem, 30-60-90 and 45-45-90 triangle relationships, the line of symmetry of an isosceles triangle bisects the base.
   d. Find perimeter and area of triangles and rectangles, and volume of right prisms.
4. Recognize relations among common geometric figures.
   a. Identify right angles, supplementary angles, vertical angles, alternate interior angles, and corresponding angles.
   b. Identify parallel and perpendicular segments, rays, and lines.
5. Apply properties of figures and relations among figures to determine unknown measures or properties.
   a. Use the measurement properties in item 3b and the measurement properties of those figures listed in 4a to determine the measure of angles.
6. Locate points and lines in one-, two-, or three-dimensional coordinate systems.
   a. In one- and two-dimensional coordinate systems, locate a point whose coordinates are given or give the coordinates of a specified point.

**Statistics and Probability**
1. Collect and organize data into tables, charts, and graphs.
   a. Identify procedures for collecting data for an experiment.
   b. Collect data through surveys, physical experiments, and other sources.
   c. Organize data into graphs, tables, and charts.
   d. Organize data using stem-and-leaf techniques.
   e. Present data to others in a clear form.
2. Read and interpret tables, charts, and graphs.
   a. Read tables, charts, and graphs.
3. Use central tendency measures and dispersion measures.
   a. Identify different uses of numbers in statistical reporting.

4. Understand simple probability statements.
   a. Use counting skills to determine probabilities as statements of relative frequency for independent events.
5. Use statistics in decision making.

---

### Course Content: Year Two

**Arithmetic**

1. Recognize many different uses of numbers.
   a. Interpret numbers used as scales.
   b. Use numbers to interpret a probability statement.
2. Associate arithmetic operations with physical world phenomena.
   (Review and reinforce previous objectives.)
3. Express numbers in equivalent and approximate forms.
   a. Order fractions and decimals.
   b. Express whole numbers and decimals in scientific notation.
   c. Express fractions as equivalent decimals and decimals as equivalent fractions.
   d. Express fractions and decimals as equivalent percents and percents as equivalent fractions or decimals.
   e. Use 2 and 3 as exponents and interpret square root and cube root as their inverses.
4. Use approximation to estimate the results of computations with whole numbers, fractions, and decimals.
   a. Estimate results of a computation to two significant digits.
5. Use a calculator to compute with whole numbers, integers, and decimals, and use mental arithmetic or pencil-and-paper algorithms where appropriate.
   a. Add, subtract, and multiply fractions having denominators of 2, 3, 4, 8, and 10.
6. Solve routine problems.
   a. Solve one-step problems involving fractions and decimals.
   b. Solve rate problems using diagrams illustrating the many-to-many correspondence.
   c. Solve multiple-step problems.

**Algebra**

1. Use variables and the language of algebra.
   (Review and reinforce previous objectives.)
2. Find an unknown value using a formula.
   (Review and reinforce previous objectives.)
3. Simplify elementary algebraic expressions.
   a. Add, subtract, multiply, and divide monomials.
   b. Recognize the equivalence of $\dfrac{a \cdot b}{a \cdot c}$ and $\dfrac{b}{c}$ when $a \neq 0$.
   c. Recognize the equivalence of $\dfrac{a}{b} + \dfrac{c}{d}$ and $\dfrac{ad + bc}{bd}$.

4. Solve linear and quadratic equations.
   a. Solve linear equations in one variable.
   b. Recognize the equivalence of $ab = 0$ and $a = 0$ or $b = 0$.
   c. Solve quadratic equations in one variable using the quadratic formula (introduced without proof but verified by examples).
   d. Solve $\dfrac{a}{b} = \dfrac{c}{d}$ for $a$, $b$, $c$, or $d$.
5. Associate equations with their graphs.
   a. Construct the graph of a linear equation in two variables.
   b. Determine the slope, $x$-intercept and $y$-intercept of a linear equation in $x$ and $y$.
6. Represent problem situations by open sentences.
   a. Write equations for multiple-step routine problems.
   b. Write equations for routine rate problems.

**Geometry**
1. Recognize and name common geometric figures.
   a. Recognize pyramids and cones and use the terminology associated with each.
2. Identify properties of common geometric figures.
   a. Identify squares as rectangles; rectangles and rhombuses as parallelograms.
   b. Know and use the common properties of rectangles and parallelograms.
3. Determine measurement properties of common geometric figures.
   a. Find approximate lengths and areas of irregular figures.
   b. Determine that $C/d$ is constant for all circles.
   c. Know and use area and circumference relationships for circles.
   d. Find area of parallelograms.
   e. Find volume of rectangular and triangular prisms and right circular cylinders.
4. Recognize relations among common geometric figures.
   a. Identify parallel and perpendicular planes.
   b. Identify congruent and similar triangles.
   c. Identify corresponding parts of congruent and similar triangles.
5. Apply properties of figures and relations among figures to determine unknown measures or properties.
   a. Determine measures of unknown sides and angles in similar or congruent triangles.
   b. Determine measures of central angles or inscribed angles when the arc is given, or of the arc when the central angle or the inscribed angle is given.
6. Locate points and lines in one-, two-, or three-dimensional coordinate systems.
   a. Determine the graph of a linear equation in two variables.
   b. Determine the equation of a line in a two-dimensional coordinate system.
   c. In a three-dimensional coordinate system, locate a point whose coordinates are given or give the coordinates of a specified point.

**Statistics**

1. Collect and organize data into tables, charts, and graphs.
   (Review and reinforce previous objectives.)
2. Read and interpret tables, charts, and graphs.
   a. Interpret tables, charts, and graphs.
3. Use central tendency measures and dispersion measures.
   a. Determine mean, median, and mode for a set of data.
   b. Construct box-and-whisker plots as a way of showing dispersion of data in a frequency distribution.
   c. Calculate and use standard deviation for a set of data.
4. Understand simple probability statements.
   a. Construct and use sample spaces and tree diagrams as counting techniques in determining probabilities.
5. Use statistics in decision making.
   a. Identify elementary misuses of statistics (such as misleading graphs and the use of an inappropriate measure of central tendency).
   b. Identify common frequency distributions (such as rectangular, skewed, J-shaped, bimodal, bell-shaped).
   c. Use statistical techniques and measures to solve appropriate routine and nonroutine problems.

## Course Content: Year Three

**Arithmetic**

1. Recognize many different uses of numbers.
   (Review and reinforce previous objectives.)
2. Associate arithmetic operations with physical world phenomena.
   (Review and reinforce previous objectives.)
3. Express numbers in equivalent and approximate forms.
   a. Approximate fractions by more common fractions.
4. Use approximation to estimate the results of computations with whole numbers, fractions, and decimals.
   (Review and reinforce previous objectives.)
5. Use a calculator to compute with whole numbers, integers, and decimals, and use mental arithmetic or pencil-and-paper algorithms where appropriate.
   a. Add, subtract, and multiply mixed numerals.
   b. Compute with numbers expressed in scientific notation.
6. Solve routine problems.
   (Review and reinforce previous objectives.)

**Algebra**

1. Use variables and the language of algebra.
   a. Use subscripted variables to represent numbers.
2. Find an unknown value using a formula.
   a. Solve a formula for an unknown value which does not appear alone on one side of the equation.
   b. Evaluate polynomials in $x$ for various values of $x$.

3. Simplify elementary algebraic expressions.
   (Review and reinforce previous objectives.)
4. Solve linear and quadratic equations.
   a. Solve systems of two equations in two variables by graphing.
   b. Solve systems of two equations in two variables by algebraic methods.
   c. Solve inequalities of the form $ax + b < c$.
   d. Solve equations involving sin, cos, and tan.
5. Associate equations with their graphs.
   a. Determine the appropriate graph for a linear inequality.
   b. Determine the equation of a straight-line graph.
   c. Sketch the graph of a quadratic equation in one variable by plotting points.
6. Represent problem situations by open sentences.
   a. Write inequality statements representing one-step, multiple-step, and rate problems.

**Geometry**

1. Recognize and name common geometric figures.
   (Review and reinforce previous objectives.)
2. Identify properties of common geometric figures.
   a. Know and use the properties of common three-dimensional figures.
3. Determine measurement properties of common geometric figures.
   a. Use trigonometric ratios to determine unknown sides or angles in right triangles.
   b. Find areas of trapezoids.
   c. Find surface area of rectangular and triangular prisms and right circular cylinders.
   d. Use the Pythagorean theorem to determine the measure of the diagonal of a right rectangular prism.
   e. Find volume of right circular cones, right pyraminds, and spheres.
4. Recognize relations among common geometric figures.
   a. Identify congruent and similar figures in two and three dimensions.
5. Apply properties of figures and relations among figures to determine unknown measures or properties.
   a. Determine measures of unknown sides and angles in similar or congruent figures.
6. Locate points and lines in one-, two-, or three-dimensional coordinate systems.
   a. Determine distances between points in a one-, two-, or three-dimensional coordinate system.

**Statistics**

1. Collect and organize data into tables, charts, and graphs.
   a. Construct scatter diagrams.
   b. Identify basic sampling procedures.
2. Read and interpret tables, charts, and graphs.
   a. Interpret scatter diagrams as naive measures of correlation.
3. Use central tendency measures and dispersion measures.
   (Review and reinforce previous objectives.)

4. Understand simple probability statements.
   a. Determine the probability of a combination of independent events.
5. Use statistics in decision making.
   a. Interpret correlation statements for correlation values between 1 and −1.
   b. Identify the distinction between correlation and causality.
   c. Construct null and alternative hypotheses for a hypothesis-testing experiment.
   d. State the possible consequences of rejection or acceptance of the null hypothesis in a hypothesis-testing experiment.
   e. Carry out the hypothesis-testing experiment in an applied setting.

The mathematical content identified in this chapter cannot be effectively taught to non-college-bound students by rote methods or by the kind of formal presentation that might be expected to be effective with college-bound students. Whenever possible, concepts should be represented using concrete materials or illustrations. The concepts should be developed actively and concretely, and examples should be provided. Teachers should be confident that students understand the concept before practice for speed and accuracy is assigned.

In general we favor an eclectic approach that includes some discovery learning, some small-group projects, some computer-based activities, and some reading of mathematics-related material (for example, *Flatland*) as well as the use of teacher-centered approaches.

## CONCLUSION

New curricula are necessary for the improvement of mathematics programs for the non-college-bound, but new curricula alone are not enough. The General Mathematics Project at the Institute for Research in Teaching, Michigan State University, has identified three "Indicants of Success," one of which is *modifying the mathematical content*.

Without attention to the other two indicants, *improving classroom communication* and *using the social organization to improve general mathematics instruction,* a change in content alone will probably be insufficient. This chapter has focused on the content of the curriculum, but interested readers are encouraged to investigate the promising results having to do with classroom communication and social organization that are being developed at Michigan State. (For further information, contact Perry E. Lanier, Coordinator, General Mathematics Project, Institute for Research on Teaching, College of Education, Erickson Hall, Michigan State University, East Lansing, MI 48824.) The research on effective instruction in mathematics conducted by Good, Grouws, and Ebmeier (1983) could also lead to improvements in mathematics programs for the non–college bound.

Integrated programs such as the one described here are not easy to develop and not easy to implement. Implementation is best achieved with the aid of student text materials that are organized under an integrated format. Although high school teachers customarily teach discrete courses (algebra, geometry, etc.), it is appropriate to observe that in K–8 mathematics programs such discrete courses are the exception rather than the rule. In K–8 programs, arithmetic, geometry, and statistics have been integrated into each course (or at least into the texts for each course). In high school, the second-year algebra course is frequently a collection of topics rather than a continuous development of a single topic. Although the integrated syllabus of New York State, outlined in chapter 17, has not been widely adopted elsewhere, it, and the similar programs described in chapters 16 and 19, do illustrate the possibility of achieving an integrated curriculum at the high school level.

The National Science Board Commission on Precollege Education in Mathematics, Science and Technology (1983, 43) has added its endorsement of an integrated curriculum to those of previous groups:

> The current sequence, which isolates geometry in a year-long course rather than integrating aspects of geometry over several years with other mathematics courses, must be seriously challenged. Some concepts of geometry are needed by all students. Other components can be streamlined, leaving room for important new topics.

The instructional resources identified in this chapter were, for the most part, intended to be self-contained texts for discrete courses. Until commercial textbooks have been developed that treat the topics identified in the Applied Mathematics Program in an integrated format, a program of discrete courses as advocated by Usiskin, containing the content identified here, is a reasonable alternative. The problem of integrating content should not be allowed to become a rationale for not giving students access to the mathematical content of the Applied Mathematics Program.

## REFERENCES

Barnett, Jeffery C., Larry Sowder, and Kenneth E. Vos. "Textbook Problems: Supplementing and Understanding Them." In *Problem Solving in School Mathematics,* 1980 Yearbook of the National Council of Teachers of Mathematics, edited by Stephen Krulik, 92–103. Reston, Va.: The Council, 1980.

Carpenter, Thomas P., Mary Kay Corbitt, Henry S. Kepner, Jr., Mary Montgomery Lindquist, and Robert E. Reys. *Results from the Second Mathematics Assessment of Educational Progress.* Reston, Va.: National Council of Teachers of Mathematics, 1981.

Chambers, Donald L. "New Directions for General Mathematics." In *The Agenda in Action,* 1983 Yearbook of the NCTM, edited by Gwen Shufelt, 200–211. Reston, Va.: The Council, 1983.

College Board. *Academic Preparation for College: What Students Need to Know and Be Able to Do.* New York: The Board, 1983.

Conference Board of the Mathematical Sciences. *The Mathematical Sciences Curriculum K–12: What Is Still Fundamental and What Is Not.* Washington, D.C.: CBMS, 1982.

Cox, Philip L. *Geometry in Easy Steps: An Informal Approach.* Newton, Mass.: Allyn & Bacon, 1983.

Good, Thomas L., Douglas A. Grouws, and Howard Ebmeier. *Active Mathematics Teaching.* New York: Longman, 1983.

Hoffer, Alan C. *Geometry: A Model of the Universe.* Reading, Mass.: Addison-Wesley Publishing Co., 1979.

Immerzeel, George, and Earl Ockenga. *Calculator Activities for the Classroom,* Books 1 and 2. Palo Alto, Calif.: Creative Publications, 1977.

Jacobs, Harold R. *Elementary Algebra.* San Francisco: W. H. Freeman and Co., 1979.

Jacobs, Russell. *Problem Solving with the Calculator.* Phoenix, Ariz.: Jacobs Publishing Co., 1977.

Kissane, Barry V. "Activities in Inferential Statistics." In *Teaching Statistics and Probability,* 1981 Yearbook of the NCTM, edited by Albert P. Shulte, 182–93. Reston, Va.: The Council, 1981.

Liebetrau, Albert M. "An Elementary Course in Nonparametric Statistics." In *Teaching Statistics and Probability,* 1981 Yearbook of the NCTM, edited by Albert P. Shulte. Reston, Va.: The Council, 1981.

Matsumoto, Annette N. "Correlation, Junior Varsity Style." In *Teaching Statistics and Probability,* 1981 Yearbook of the NCTM, edited by Albert P. Shulte, 126–34. Reston, Va.: The Council, 1981.

Mosteller, Frederick, William H. Kruskal, Richard F. Link, Richard S. Pieters, and Gerald R. Rising, eds. *Statistics by Example.* Reading, Mass.: Addison-Wesley Publishing Co., 1973.

National Assessment of Educational Progress. *The Third National Mathematics Assessment: Results, Trends, and Issues.* Denver: Education Commission of the States, 1983.

National Commission on Excellence in Education. *A Nation at Risk: The Imperative for Educational Reform.* Washington, D.C.: U.S. Department of Education, 1983.

National Council of Teachers of Mathematics. *An Agenda for Action: Recommendations for School Mathematics of the 1980s.* Reston, Va.: The Council, 1980.

———. *Experiences in Mathematical Ideas,* vol. 1. Washington, D.C.: The Council, 1970.

National Science Board Commission on Precollege Education in Mathematics, Science and Technology. *Educating Americans for the Twenty-first Century.* Washington, D.C.: NSB, 1983.

O'Daffer, Phares. "Geometry: What Shape for a Comprehensive, Balanced Curriculum?" In *Selected Issues in Mathematics Education,* edited by Mary Montgomery Lindquist. Berkeley, Calif.: McCutchan Publishing Corp., 1980.

Pereira-Mendoza, Lionel, and Jim Swift. "Why Teach Statistics and Probability—a Rationale." In *Teaching Statistics and Probability,* 1981 Yearbook of the NCTM, edited by Albert P. Shulte. Reston, Va.: The Council, 1981.

Rising, Gerald R., et al. *Unified Mathematics,* Books 1, 2, and 3. Boston: Houghton Mifflin Co., 1981.

Schools Council Project on Statistical Education. *Statistics in Your World,* 27 student booklets and teacher's notes. Slough, Buckinghamshire, England: W. Foulsham & Co., 1981.

Tanur, Judith M., Frederick Mosteller, William H. Kruskal, Richard F. Link, Richard S. Pieters, and Gerald R. Rising, eds. *Statistics: A Guide to the Unknown.* San Francisco: Holden-Day, 1972.

Usiskin, Zalman. "A Proposal for Reforming the Secondary School Mathematics Curriculum." Paper presented at the 61st Annual Meeting of the National Council of Teachers of Mathematics, April 1983, Detroit, Michigan.

———. "What Should *Not* Be in the Algebra and Geometry Curricula of Average College-bound Students?" *Mathematics Teacher* 73 (September 1980): 413–24.

Usiskin, Zalman, and Max Bell. *Applying Arithmetic.* Preliminary ed. Chicago: Department of Education, University of Chicago, 1984.

# 19

# Unified Mathematics in a New Jersey High School

## Peter A. Tenewitz

COLUMBIA High School serves the urban/suburban communities of South Orange and Maplewood in the northeastern metropolitan area of New Jersey. The school enrolls more than 2000 students, of which 75 percent or more pursue a college education. In 1973 the mathematics teachers of Columbia High School completely restructured and rewrote the curriculum. This project was the culmination of several years of research and pilot programs by the entire faculty. We have continued to evaluate and revise both the order of the units of study and the emphasis we place on selected topics. The program is flexible enough to allow any student who is so motivated, regardless of ability, to take as many as four years of meaningful mathematics. In addition to the year-long courses in sequential and unified mathematics, a number of one-semester courses appeal to personal needs and interests. The grading philosophy allows all conscientious students to be successful at their own ability level. The program today is well structured, has realistic standards for each level, and requires that students perform to the extent of their ability. Each individual's progress is maintained through teachers working in teams. A full-time mathematics laboratory and resource area is an essential ingredient in supporting this program.

The curriculum at Columbia is integrated with matrices, transformations, and functional concepts unifying algebra and geometry while calculators and computer programs provide important numerical experiences and tools for realistic problem solving. Because the four-year course of study is composed of sequential units, teachers do not have to make a decision during the school year about final course coverage. Each ability group works at its best pace, and the number of units these groups successfully learn varies from year to year. The high school transcript describes both the extent and the rigor in the sequential program for each student.

### CURRICULUM INTEGRATION AND NEW AREAS OF STUDY

With the increased availability of microcomputers and inexpensive calculators, there has been a marked change in approach to, and subject content of, courses at the secondary level. Linear algebra, matrices, probability and statistics, and programming languages have influenced the pedagogical development of algebra, geometry, and trigonometry. The practical aspects of these subjects can be seen almost immediately when applied to business and governmental operations through the use of computer technology. Elective courses in calculus and in finite mathematics highlight further mathematical applications in the physical sciences and in the biological and social sciences, respectively.

Calculator and computer skills are introduced in the ninth and tenth grades and employed for four years in both assigned and optional projects. Each classroom has a set of hand-held calculators that are used for applications in such units as introduction to irrational numbers, logarithms, solutions of right and oblique triangles, matrices, statistics, area and volume, coordinate and vector geometry, and solutions of quadratic equations. A unit on BASIC programming and computer literacy is taught in the ninth grade. Applications that require programming an algorithm are assigned for computer solution. Programs are written for such units as solving polynomial and transcendental equations, graphing trigonometric functions, determining limits, amortizing mortgages, computing compound interest, and making inflationary forecasts.

A unified approach to mathematics necessitated a modern approach to geometry. The traditional synthetic Euclidean geometry did not seem satisfactory. However, a development through coordinates, vectors, and transformations was consistent with recent curriculum recommendations. The School Mathematics Project (SMP) and the Secondary School Mathematics Curriculum Improvement Study (SSMCIS) of the late 1960s were helpful guides to our efforts. These programs, however, were five- or six-year programs developed for the upper 15–20 percent of secondary school students. Our curriculum was to be a cohesive four-year program of study for *all* students. The introduction of formal geometry through transformations and the early introduction of matrices and their representation of transformations produces a true blend of algebra and geometry.

The traditional organization of mathematics, which separates the study of arithmetic, algebra, and geometry, was discontinued. Our curriculum was restructured so that all areas of arithmetic, algebra, and geometry reinforced each other, based on the fundamental ideas of sets and mappings and complemented by calculator and computer programming results.

## SEQUENTIAL MATHEMATICS

A natural extension of modernizing and unifying the mathematics curriculum is to build a four-year program of related sequential units rather than the traditional full-year courses. Our program allows considerable flexibility in course coverage, permitting any team or group to set its own pace based on students' abilities and motivation. The teacher evaluates progress continually and can finish the year at any point in the curriculum. Thus it is possible, in as little as one year, for one group of students to cover twice as many sequential units in much more depth and rigor than a less capable group might accomplish. A topic outline at the end of this chapter shows the sequence of units that make up the four-year course of study.

At the end of each school year there must be a clear communication of both the subject material covered and the rigor with which it was covered so that the following year students with similar backgrounds can easily be scheduled together. This information is expressed in a three-digit numeral recorded on the transcript: the first two digits indicate the last unit of study completed (with units numbered from 10 to 95), and the third digit indicates the ability level or rigor involved. A third digit of 1 indicates minimal coverage emphasizing basic skills. A third digit of 3 indicates normal coverage for college-capable students, and a 4 indicates much rigor and emphasis on difficult abstractions and concepts. As examples, consider the following:

> MATH 623 indicates completion through unit 62 in an average college preparatory class.
>
> MATH 894 indicates completion through unit 89 in a top college preparatory class.
>
> MATH 321 indicates completion through unit 32 at a level not sufficient for success in college mathematics.

The sequential-unit curriculum is the basic program for all students not classified remedial. The curriculum guide differentiates for ability levels. Each ability level has a textbook appropriate for its use, and the many departmental workbooks are similarly differentiated. The classes range from low ability groups to advanced college preparatory classes. At no time is a student locked into a particular class. Teachers work in teams with a team coordinator for each ability level. They meet often, both formally and informally, to discuss all aspects of the curriculum, but their most important decisions are to move students to higher or lower class levels. Faculty members are at all times conscious of student placement and are always ready to reschedule a student for his or her best learning environment.

This reassignment is possible at any time of the year, in any grade, because we schedule four or five different ability levels during the same period. When students move into faster-paced classes, they often need tutoring to bridge the gap in units covered. Assigning students to the mathematics laboratory provides this help. A student is not allowed to elect a lower-level class than what was recommended. Class size is flexible and indeed, in this kind of team teaching, changes throughout the year.

In addition to the obvious advantages to students, team teaching (1) necessitates discussion groups on curriculum, (2) upgrades teaching techniques by observation and comparison, (3) uses faculty strengths efficiently, and (4) provides in-service training for teachers new to the system.

## INDIVIDUALIZATION

The concept of individualization is one of the main features of this curriculum. Pilot programs have shown us that students with average motivation will learn best in a group situation, whereas highly motivated students, regardless of ability, can learn equally well through independent study.

Our marking philosophy reflects this individualization. Basic to this philosophy is the belief that any student who wishes to take mathematics and who shows reasonable effort should be given that opportunity. Teachers, in their turn, place students according to their ability, and marks are reported relative to the ability level of the students and the instruction given in class. This means that a student in an honors class may receive a D or F, but a student in a modified class, because of great effort, may receive an A or B. When students are receiving marks that seem inconsistent with their ability, we reconsider their placement.

As noted previously, the course description reports what type of class the student participated in and what degree of rigor was involved. In addition, the weighting of grades for class rank allows the student to achieve a grade that is relative to the difficulty of the course. These two factors (course description and class rank) allow a teacher to evaluate a student's work in closer keeping to what can be expected of the student in class. Thus, even slower students who are interested may take three or four years of mathematics, and an honest and accurate description of their progress is reported.

## THE MATHEMATICS LABORATORY

The mathematics laboratory is another important feature in the teaching of mathematics at Columbia High School. Not only is it an extension of classroom teaching, but it is the location for many diverse types of activities. One area has resource books, pamphlets, and magazines; a game closet contains puzzles, models, and commercial laboratory games suitable for project work. A mathematics teacher is available to help students every period of the day beginning at 7:45 A.M. Students are encouraged by their teachers as well as by their counselors to use this help. Those who have been absent for an extended period of time may be assigned to the laboratory for individual help until the necessary sequential work has been made up. Those who are making a team change may be assigned to the lab for makeup work.

For students new to the school who have not studied all the previous sequential units covered by their classes, individualized programs are often determined and administered in the mathematics laboratory.

## OTHER MATHEMATICAL ELECTIVES

Columbia also offers a variety of electives ranging from quarter courses to year-long courses. These electives do not follow a sequence but give students an opportunity to take subjects of personal interest or need.

| Year Courses | Quarter Courses |
|---|---|
| General Mathematics I | Remedial courses in basic arithmetic |
| General Mathematics II |   skills |
| General Mathematics III | **One-Semester Computer Courses** |
| AP Calculus | Introduction to Computers |
| **One-Semester Courses** | BASIC II |
| Mathematics of Personal Finance | FORTRAN A |
| Probability and Statistics | FORTRAN B |
| Career-oriented Mathematics | APL I (COBOL) |
| Finite Mathematics | APL II (PL/1) |
| Mathematics Seminar | Math Lab Technology |

## THE COMPUTER PROGRAM

One-semester computer courses are designed so that a student's time is equally divided between classroom theory and laboratory practice (writing, running, and correcting programs). This year, thirty-eight sections of computer programming are open to all students. Many students elect them after recommendation by their mathematics teachers. Honors mathematics and physics students are particularly encouraged to take several courses.

It is our belief that any student graduating from a comprehensive high school should have some basic knowledge of both a programming language and the physical nature of a modern computer. Although BASIC is the language taught in the ninth-grade mathematics program, advanced courses in BASIC, FORTRAN, COBOL, PL/1, and Lab Technology are offered as semester courses.

Capable and interested students are trained each year to run the computer system. They also assist beginning students with their programs and work with the mathematics laboratory teacher in many of the other activities.

Talented students have written programs that are used regularly in classwork. Students are encouraged to use the computer for any aspect of their school life, and it is not unusual to have project work in science, English, social studies, or foreign language tied in with a computer program. The computer-related activities are many and varied, ranging from club-sponsored ones to those of individual students. The computer lab is open and staffed daily from 7:15 A.M. to 4:45 P.M.

## CONCLUSION

A variety of indicators confirm the success of the program at Columbia High School. We mention three of them here.

1. In the fall of 1983 the school's total enrollment was 2050, and there were 2247 enrollments in mathematics classes. In the second semester there were 2257 mathematics enrollments. Thus it is apparent that a number of students elect more than one mathematics course in a given semester. Only two years of mathematics are required for graduation.

2. Advanced Placement Calculus scores and CEEB Mathematics Level 1 and Level 2 achievement scores are consistently above the national mean.

3. Each year the school's Math Team participates in a variety of contests sponsored by national, state, local, and private organizations. Results have been excellent, with both individual and team honors won each year. In the summer of 1981 a Columbia High School student, Jeremy Primer, whose program of study had been extensively individualized, took a first place in the International Mathematical Olympiad with a perfect score. (This was the year that the United States team took first place.)

Although the success of a program must be measured by tangible statistics, an additional and most satisfying feature of the program at Columbia is the enthusiasm of the faculty and their ongoing discussion of teaching techniques, curriculum needs or revisions, student progress, motivation, and suitable testing.

## Columbia High School Unified Curriculum

### Topic Outline

**Average Ninth-Grade Coverage**

10. Numbers and Variables
11. Basic Properties of Real Numbers
12. Operations with Integers
13. Solving Equations
14. Solving Inequalities
16. Introduction to BASIC
    Programming
17. Functions, Relations, and Graphs
18. Systems of Linear Equations
20. Polynomials
21. Factoring
22. Rational Expressions
23. Irrational Numbers
24. Quadratic Equations and
    Inequalities

**Average Tenth-Grade Coverage**

26. Vectors
28. Matrices
30. Points, Lines, and Planes
31. Angles and Perpendicular Lines
33. Review of Coordinate Formulas
34. Calculators
36. Basic Transformations
38. Transformations and Matrices
40. Introduction to Proof
42. Reflection Symmetric Figures
43. Parallels
44. Congruent Triangles
45. Quadrilaterals

**Average Eleventh-Grade Coverage**

46. Coordinate and Vector Proofs
48. Similarity
49. Perimeter and Area
50. Review of Polynomials
52. Relations and Functions
54. Quadratic Functions
56. Complex Numbers
58. Conics
60. Systems of Equations
62. Circles

**Average Twelfth-Grade Coverage**

64. Geometric Inequalities
66. Space Geometry
68. Area and Volume
70. Introduction to Probability
71. Statistics
72. Exponents
74. Logarithms and Exponents
76. Sequences and Series
78. Math Induction
80. Trigonometry I
81. Trigonometry II

**Top Twelfth-Grade Coverage**

85. Set Notation
86. Functions as Mappings
87. Analytic Geometry
88. Limits and Continuity
89. The Derivative
91. Curve Sketching
92. Polynomial Equations
95. Integration

*Note:* Gaps in the numbering sequence of the units allow the flexibility of inserting new units or extending or relocating existing units.

# 20

# Integrating Computers into the Mathematics Curriculum

## Patricia Fraze

ANN ARBOR Huron High School is one of two three-year comprehensive public high schools in a mid-sized community (Ann Arbor, Mich.) that is home to a large number of research and technical firms and to a major university and medical school. Approximately 25 percent of our 1750 students are members of a minority group (18 percent black, 5 percent Asian American, 2 percent Hispanic). The high school staff has the equivalent of eighty-one classroom teachers and thirty other professionals.

Over 75 percent of the students currently enroll in mathematics, although only one year in grades 9–12 is presently required for graduation. The enrollment pattern for the second semester, 1982, is displayed in table 20.1.

TABLE 20.1
Second Semester Mathematics Enrollment

| Grade | 10 | | 11 | | 12 | |
|---|---|---|---|---|---|---|
| Sex | M | F | M | F | M | F |
| Percent | 100 | 96 | 85 | 82 | 55 | 40 |

The mathematics staff has thirteen teachers (two part time), of whom three are black and eight are women.

### BRIEF DESCRIPTION OF THE MATHEMATICS PROGRAM

The department offers twenty courses, most of which fall into one of four sequences: accelerated/advanced placement, regular, less rigorous (x classes), and basic/remedial. Typical sequences of courses are given in figure 20.1.

Flexibility is a major criterion for the establishment of any new course. It is also incorporated as much as possible into our system of course levels, which in turn aims at providing a course suitable for every student's background and interests. We encourage strong students at one level to take two mathe-

237

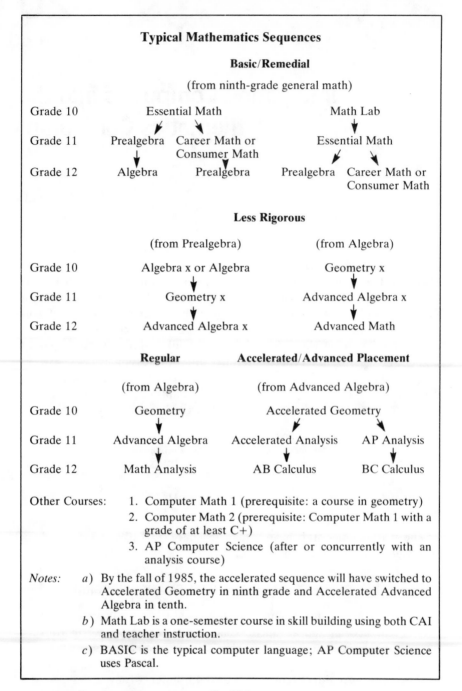

**Typical Mathematics Sequences**

**Basic/Remedial**

(from ninth-grade general math)

|  |  |  |
|---|---|---|
| Grade 10 | Essential Math | Math Lab |
| Grade 11 | Prealgebra   Career Math or Consumer Math | Essential Math |
| Grade 12 | Algebra   Prealgebra | Prealgebra   Career Math or Consumer Math |

**Less Rigorous**

(from Prealgebra)        (from Algebra)

| | | |
|---|---|---|
| Grade 10 | Algebra x or Algebra | Geometry x |
| Grade 11 | Geometry x | Advanced Algebra x |
| Grade 12 | Advanced Algebra x | Advanced Math |

**Regular**        **Accelerated/Advanced Placement**

(from Algebra)        (from Advanced Algebra)

| | | | |
|---|---|---|---|
| Grade 10 | Geometry | Accelerated Geometry | |
| Grade 11 | Advanced Algebra | Accelerated Analysis | AP Analysis |
| Grade 12 | Math Analysis | AB Calculus | BC Calculus |

Other Courses:   1. Computer Math 1 (prerequisite: a course in geometry)
2. Computer Math 2 (prerequisite: Computer Math 1 with a grade of at least C+)
3. AP Computer Science (after or concurrently with an analysis course)

*Notes:*   *a*) By the fall of 1985, the accelerated sequence will have switched to Accelerated Geometry in ninth grade and Accelerated Advanced Algebra in tenth.

*b*) Math Lab is a one-semester course in skill building using both CAI and teacher instruction.

*c*) BASIC is the typical computer language; AP Computer Science uses Pascal.

Fig. 20.1

matics courses, if necessary, in order to advance to another level. Generally, students who drop down a level may move back up with determined effort or perhaps by taking a summer school course. In addition, students are usually able to switch levels of a course between quarters. Students who have completed elementary algebra and geometry have the option of enrolling in a computer mathematics course in place of, or in addition to, another course.

## COMPUTER INTEGRATION

### Evolution

The 1983–84 school year initiated the fourth and final stage of a gradually expanding computer-enhanced mathematics program that began in 1969. We started with a handful of time-sharing terminals for students enrolled in Computer Math or in Accelerated/AP Analysis. The addition of two groups of six to eight microcomputers three and four years ago allowed us to integrate computers into Advanced Algebra, Math Lab, Calculus, Math Analysis, Essential Math, and Career Math. The establishment of a second lab of sixteen microcomputers in September 1983 allowed us to extend student computer use to Prealgebra, Algebra, and Geometry and to offer the new AP Computer Science course.

### The Program

> Our aim is frequent and meaningful computer usage that progresses in accordance with the student's sequential study of mathematics.

Our primary objective is that every mathematics student in each of our four levels of courses use the computer in a variety of ways (computer-assisted instruction, interacting with software, writing or running programs) that relate directly to the mathematics concepts she or he is studying. Our aim is frequent and meaningful computer usage that progresses in accordance with the student's sequential study of mathematics.

Career Math, Essential Math, Algebra, Geometry, and Advanced Algebra students use teacher-produced computer supplements coordinated with the curriculum.

In algebra and geometry courses, 1983–84 was a year in which teachers experimented with computer integration. Algebra students spent from several days to two weeks on introductory programming in the computer lab and an equivalent amount of time in the classroom working related exercises. Geometry teachers tried to give their students some hands-on computer experience as they worked their way through a new geometry text. The computer supplements for both courses require students to determine the output of programs, modify programs, write elementary programs related to the course, and interpret and manipulate the output from programs they run.

The program is most effective in advanced algebra and analysis classes, where we have had more years of experience with integration. These courses are rich in computer applications. During most units, computer programs are discussed in class or assigned as homework or projects. (See fig. 20.2 for examples.)

---

### Examples of Advanced Algebra Computer Programs

1. Linear Sentences
   a) Solving linear equations and inequalities
   b) Solving absolute value equations and inequalities
   c) Finding an equation of a line, given a point and slope or two points
2. Linear Systems: Solving with Cramer's rule
3. Quadratic Sentences
   a) Solving any quadratic equation or inequality
   b) Given coefficients of $y = ax^2 + bx + c$, finding the vertex, the axis of symmetry, and the maximum or minimum value
4. Exponents and Logarithms: Producing tables for compound interest/growth, for depreciation/decay, for annuities, for present/future values
5. Sequences and Series: Finding $N$ arithmetic or geometric means between two given numbers
6. Trigonometry: Solving triangles
7. Polynomial Equations: Estimating roots
8. Probability and Statistics
   a) Simulating dice/coin tosses
   b) Analyzing data (mean, variance, standard deviation)

### Examples of Analysis Computer Programs

1. Graphing functions
2. Analyzing a cubic polynomial function (maximum, minimum, inflection points, slope)
3. Finding real zeros of polynomials by Newton's method
4. Computing the area under a curve to desired accuracy
5. Producing tables from infinite series to desired accuracy
6. Using DeMoivre's theorem to find the powers or roots of complex numbers

---

Fig. 20.2

In addition, computers are used in classroom demonstrations to introduce or reinforce mathematical concepts such as the following:
- The relationship between the graph of a function and its inverse
- The arithmetic of functions (graphs of $f + g$, $fg$, $f/g$)
- The effects of $a$, $h$, and $k$ on the graph of $y - k = af(x - h)$
- The effects of $a$, $b$, and $c$ on the graphs of ellipses

$$\frac{x^2}{a^2} + \frac{y^2}{b^2} = 1 \qquad (a^2 = b^2 + c^2)$$

and hyperbolas

$$\frac{x^2}{a^2} - \frac{y^2}{b^2} = 1 \qquad (c^2 = a^2 + b^2)$$

- The convergence of a sequence or series
- The effects of $a$ and $b$ on $y = af(bx)$, where $f(x)$ is a circular function

It is our aim to have each student who completes Advanced Math or an analysis course understand and use the BASIC commands (PRINT, LET, IF . . . THEN, FOR/NEXT, GOTO, and READ/DATA) and fundamental subroutines.

### Key Components

In the development of this program and in the in-service training of our teachers, we have had dedicated teacher leadership since 1969. In recent years, our mathematics coordinator, principal, director of secondary education, associate superintendent for curriculum and instruction, and school board have strongly supported an expanding high school computer program with funds for hardware, software, and the production of instructional materials by staff during the summer.

All instructional computer materials have been written by Huron's mathematics teachers. Our teachers have also invested many additional hours preparing computer assignments, grading computer projects, and keeping the lab open for students.

Finally, since 1978, the district has had a Computer Education Committee to assist in coordinating the purchase of equipment and the use of computers in our schools for grades K–12. Both comprehensive high schools in the city have a teacher designated as building computer coordinator and have given this person released time for overseeing equipment and working on staff development.

## A LOOK TO THE FUTURE

Our district is currently discussing a high school improvement proposal that is likely to take effect in 1985: that the graduation requirement in mathematics be increased to two years in grades 9–12. The program of every student would include logic, problem solving, probability and statistics, basic concepts of algebra and geometry, and computer competency. This proposal would have little effect on students who currently study mathematics through advanced algebra. However, a whole restructuring of courses and the development of new curricula and materials will be needed for other students, especially for those who take non-college-preparatory classes.

# 21

# High School Mathematics Enrollments: The 100 Percent Goal

## Jacqueline Henningsen

RECOMMENDATION 6 in NCTM's *Agenda for Action,* proposes that

> more mathematics study be required for all students and a flexible curriculum
> with a greater range of options be designed to accommodate the diverse needs of
> the student population. (NCTM 1980, 1)

In terms of implementation, this is a significant but difficult recommendation. Although it seems reasonable to expect that it will receive support from the membership of NCTM on an intellectual level, it will not be easily accepted. The basic problem is that a decision by a school district to implement this proposal will be a decision not based on an acceptance of the logical truth of these statements but instead weighed in terms of declining school enrollments and budget tightening. It is likely to be a very political affair, with even teachers of mathematics lining up on opposite sides. Difficult questions must be explored before a mathematics department decides to try to implement this recommendation:

1. How can such a proposal be implemented during a time of budget cuts?
2. How can it be maintained when there is declining enrollment?
3. How can the appearance of an attempt to merely save jobs be avoided?
4. Which group of students will be served first?
5. Should other mathematics courses in the curriculum be given equal weight to those taught in the college preparatory track?
6. Can a student who doesn't do well in freshman algebra or geometry later succeed in college preparatory mathematics?
7. Will high-ability students continue to be served by a traditional college prep program?
8. Is the *best* option for a student doing poorly in advanced algebra to drop out of mathematics?

Thanks are given to Al Gloor, department chairman, and the other mathematics department members at Westside High School who provided suggestions and current information.

9. Are there other courses that need to be added to the curriculum to prepare students for technological change?

10. Is there a core of mathematics that should be taught to *all* students?

Some will find it easy to say, "Of course, all students deserve more mathematical opportunity." Others will shake their heads and say, "Why don't we put our time and effort into working with those who will benefit most?" If we as an organization hope to develop active support for the sixth proposal in the *Agenda for Action,* we must provide concrete examples of what to expect from "a flexible curriculum with a greater range of options."

This chapter will not try to answer all these questions; instead, it will explain how one public high school developed a program that without any state or local requirements in mathematics, enrolls over 95 percent of its student body of approximately 1500 in mathematics classes. The faculty at this school debated all the previously listed questions and many more. They then developed a program based on their answers.

Westside High School in Omaha, Nebraska, is a suburban school with modular scheduling and a tradition for excellence in college preparatory education. In the last decade, however, it has developed a more diverse student population with a wider range of needs and abilities. Several years ago the members of the mathematics faculty realized that the existing program was not meeting the needs of a number of students, and they began questioning their traditional beliefs about what a high school mathematics curriculum should include. *The eventual conclusion reached by the staff was to try to provide mathematical education to the total school population at a level appropriate to the abilities and needs of as many subgroups as possible.* This is the main feature that makes Westside's program worth discussing in the context of the *Agenda for Action* proposal. Previous unsatisfactory experiences with completely individualized learning focused curriculum changes at Westside toward the identification of programs with the following structure:

1. The course sequence of first-year algebra, geometry, advanced algebra, precalculus, and advanced senior mathematics will provide the backbone of any program developed. This is called the core program.

2. From this backbone the following two types of courses developed:

*a*) Half-step exploratory courses. These courses are designed to allow a student having difficulty at a core level to take time to regain self-confidence, to mature, and to explore areas of mathematics that are interesting, useful, and frequently overlooked in a regular program. These courses are available between each of the core courses. Students may either elect to take them at registration time or "drop" into them during the year if difficulty in the related core course develops.

*b*) Extra noncore courses. Semester-length courses in computer science and probability/statistics are frequently chosen by students to be taken either alone or in conjunction with other mathematics courses. Calculus is also considered a noncore course because high-ability students first enroll in an advanced senior mathematics course that contains topics such as group and set theory, matrix algebra, and theory of limits and then may choose to take calculus concurrently.

## THE CURRICULUM

Prior to 1972, two unique "half-step" courses were already in place that provided for the needs of students who seemed to fall between the traditional courses in the curriculum. (See fig. 21.1 for a flowchart of the curriculum.) The first, called algebra-trig, was a course designed for students who felt they needed trigonometry but had not done well in the previous algebra course. This course consists of a semester of algebra review with materials prepared by staff members, followed by a semester of trigonometry. The second half-step course was called basic geometry. It involves a discovery approach and hands-on manipulative experiences. It was designed for students who were not ready for formal proof in a regular course. Two major components of study in basic geometry are (1) measurement applied to line segments, angles, surfaces, and volumes; and (2) properties of triangles, parallel lines, similar figures, polygons, circles, and spheres. Basic geometry was originally viewed as a terminal course for students who had taken algebra 1 but has since become a half-step toward

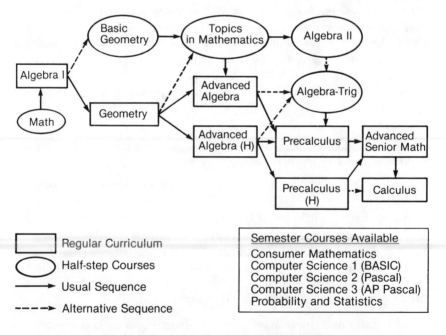

Fig. 21.1. Curriculum flowchart—full-year courses

other courses. Entry into both of these courses is controlled by grades in previous courses and by teacher recommendation.

In the early and mid-1970s, interest in the school centered on the development of minimum competency programs. Westside developed a model program in the area of competencies that is still in effect. Those students with marked deficiencies were assigned class times with a mathematics specialist separate from the regular program. A comfortable atmosphere for learning, caring and competent teachers, and interesting activities (such as computerized drill work) encouraged many of these students to enroll voluntarily in further classes after they completed their competency work. An instructor and an aide are now assigned part-time to this program. These individuals have a special room with a daily open-door policy for students needing mathematics review.

In the mid-1970s a program was also developed for students who wanted or needed mathematics beyond algebra 1 and geometry but who had not felt comfortable in their previous mathematics class. This interesting program, called Topics in Mathematics, set about the task of developing (1) an appreciation of the extent to which mathematics is involved in our lives, (2) a willingness to try to solve problems in mathematics, and (3) the skills to make these attempts possible. In order to accomplish these goals, a wide variety of interesting mathematical areas are explored. Hand-held calculators are made available to all students, and they are aided in using them to start anew on areas that have previously been troublesome. Each year this course is molded and developed by the interests of the teachers who teach it. Many students find they can understand and enjoy mathematics through this program. A typical course outline is shown in figure 21.2.

---

Another factor that led to increasing enrollments in mathematics was the identification of the under-enrollment of females in advanced mathematics classes.

---

Although some faculty members were interested in the development of new options for students, others were equally interested in improving the content and delivery of the core courses. Team leaders were chosen for the geometry, second-year algebra, and precalculus programs. Teachers in each of these areas then worked together to share and develop materials and procedures. Techniques appropriate to the type of course, the personalities of the teachers, and the school structure were investigated. In geometry, lab days were installed, during which individual conferences were held; common lessons and joint exams were prepared; and experiments with new methods such as proofs by flowcharting were tried.

In the second-year algebra program, the algebra team members worked with many different approaches, such as team teaching, large- and small-

---

**TOPICS IN MATHEMATICS**

1. Reasoning—inductive and deductive
2. Sequences—arithmetic, geometric, binary, power, Fibonacci
3. Functions—graphing linear and quadratic, interpreting data from graphs
4. Calculator—solving expressions, estimating, evaluating formulas, finding the unit price of goods, determining the better buy
5. Direct variation/inverse variation—problem solving
6. Rate tables—electric bills, gas bills, lumen count
7. Percent—review and problem solving
8. Tessellations
9. Fundamental counting
10. Probability
11. Trigonometry—sine-cosine-tangent functions, right triangle trigonometry, problem solving
12. Computer—computer literacy, basic computer programming
13. Statistics—tallying, frequency distributions, central measures, rank
14. Geometric solids—construction and study of regular polyhedrons, cylinders, cones, prisms, pyramids
15. Word problems—selecting the best answer, problem solving
16. Area/perimeter
17. Review of algebra 1—operations with integers, order of operations, solving equations, multiplying polynomials, graphing, slope, y-intercept, factoring quadratic expressions

---

Fig. 21.2. Course outline of Topics in Mathematics

group formats, and various ways of encouraging interaction among students. Basically, two different college-bound groups were identified by the algebra team. One group had moderate or low interest in pursuing scientific and technical studies, whereas the other had high interest in this area. Two courses with the same basic structure but with more review for the former group and more enrichment and rigor for the latter group were developed. The first of these courses is presently called advanced algebra; the latter, advanced algebra (H). In addition, many juniors from the Topics in Mathematics course chose to take advanced algebra their senior year, but for a number of them, stress caused by competition with students who had not had previous difficulty in algebra, along with past deficiencies in algebra 1, left them unable to apply their newly gained abilities and skills with confidence. The faculty then developed another program for interested students, called algebra 2. In this course emphasis was placed on clear and careful development of algebraic concepts without pressure to complete a specific body of material. Progress through the course followed the path of a regular advanced algebra course, but problem areas were carefully covered from several different approaches, and extensive drill was provided where background weaknesses were discovered. Methods of studying and learning were taught and then emphasized. Students and their parents were clearly informed that this course was not intended as a replacement for advanced algebra but instead was intended to strengthen skills and help in preparing students for any further mathematics they wished to take. Seniors who planned to start college mathematics courses after algebra 2 were generally counseled to register for a college algebra course as their first selection. Many graduates successfully followed this recommendation.

Another factor that led to increasing enrollments in mathematics was the identification of the underenrollment of females in advanced mathematics classes. Information emphasizing the importance of girls continuing in mathematics and science was provided to counselors and parents through many different approaches, including the use of an informative slide presentation prepared by a staff member on extended contract. This presentation was shown to all junior high school mathematics classes in the district. The ratio of male to female enrollments has now equalized at all levels up to calculus.

In addition to the special half-step courses, Westside High School has a regular offering, including probability and statistics, consumer mathematics, computer science 1, 2, and 3, algebra 1, advanced algebra, geometry, two levels of precalculus, calculus, and advanced senior mathematics. Course enrollments for 1984–85 are given in figure 21.3. It is important to realize that the staff has agreed to the need for classes with small enrollments in some areas and has accepted larger class sizes in other areas to compensate.

## IMPORTANT POINTS

The ability to provide courses to meet the needs of so many students has been possible for a number of reasons:

1. The school administration, an informed community, and an enlightened guidance department have provided support and encouragement. Members of the mathematics department gave special attention to the "education" of each group. A district-funded program that allows extended work during the summer on different targeted areas plus state and federal project grants allows the staff time to work on improvements.

2. The staff recognizes the differing maturation levels of students and is willing to provide for students where they *are,* not where they "should" be.

3. A school-wide restructuring of the meaning of a credit has been designed to include the concepts of the amount of in-class work and out-of-class time as a determining factor in class loads. Through faculty participation all classes have been assigned a weighting factor that is used for registration (see fig. 21.4).

4. A structure has been developed that allows students to "drop out" of one level of mathematics and "drop in" to another at several points during the year.

## Westside 1984–85 Course Enrollments

| Course | Enrollment Full Year | Sem 1/Sem 2 | Credit* | Open to Grades** |
|---|---|---|---|---|
| Advanced Algebra | 317 | | 5 | 10-11-12 |
| Advanced Algebra (H) | 50 | | 5 | 10-11-12 |
| Advanced Senior Math | 64 | | 5 | 12 |
| Algebra 1 | 89 | | 5 | 10-11-12 |
| Algebra 2 | 60 | | 4 | 12 |
| Basic Geometry | 31 | | 3 | 10-11-12 |
| Calculus/Analytic Geometry | 20 | | 6 | 12 |
| Computer Science 1 (BASIC) | | 152/121 | 4 | 11-12 |
| Computer Science 2 (Pascal) | | 27/77 | 2 | 11-12 |
| Computer Science 3 (AP Pascal) | | /35 | 2 | 11-12 |
| Consumer Mathematics | | 0/ | 3 | 11-12 |
| Geometry | 341 | | 4*** | 10-11-12 |
| Algebra/Trig | 104 | | 5 | 11-12 |
| Math | 15 | | 3 | 11-12 |
| Precalculus | 166 | | 5 | 11-12 |
| Precalculus (H) | 22 | | 5 | 11-12 |
| Probability and Statistics | | 21/ | 4 | 11-12 |
| Topics in Mathematics | 47 | | 4*** | |

Total first-semester mathematics enrollments = 1495
Total first-semester school enrollment = 1432
(For comparison, the corresponding 1974–75 course enrollment and school enrollment figures were 1746 and 2425 respectively.)

\* Credits are determined only by in-class time.
** These are general guidelines and exceptions are made.
*** Four class meetings a week plus a lab.

Fig. 21.3

5. Open study areas allow frequent out-of-class contact between students and teachers and also allow students to work on their mathematics in support groups. Each department has an instructional media center. Students may go to the center of their choice during unscheduled periods, and a teacher is always available to answer questions. Students are encouraged to work together on homework assignments and projects.

6. The department chairman is knowledgeable and the teachers are dedicated, enthusiastic, and creative.

7. Support staff has provided secretarial assistance to staff members. (Support staff are counted as a certain portion of a department's staffing allocation, so professional staff must agree to "trade" larger class sizes for secretarial help.)

8. Communication is open with junior high school staff members who have flexibility and professionalsim in their programs.

## GENERAL INFORMATION

**Definitions:**

CREDIT HOURS: The term "semester hour" of credit shall mean the credit given for classroom instruction of not less than 40 minutes (60 minutes if laboratory activities are involved) each week for one semester. Since the amount of time that our courses meet differs depending upon the mode of instruction used, the credit hours per course vary.

GROUP: The Group is determined by the difficulty or intensity of the course. For example, Group 5 courses are deemed to be of the highest intensity; Group 3 of average intensity with the majority of our courses in this Group; Group 1 are those courses of the lowest intensity. All courses are assigned a Group Designator for class rank and registration purposes. Additionally, from the Group Designator, the amount of outside classroom preparation time (homework) can also be estimated:

Group 5—Courses in this category will require the average student in that course to spend at least twice as much time in outside preparation as the student spends in class.

Group 4—Courses in this category will require the average student in that course to spend between 4/3 and 2 times as much time in outside preparation as the student spends in class.

Group 3—Courses in this category will require the average student in that course to spend between 2/3 and 4/3 as much time in outside preparation as the student spends in class.

Group 2—Courses in this category will require the average student in that course to spend between 1/3 and 2/3 as much time in outside preparation as the student spends in class.

Group 1—Courses in this category will require the average student in that course to spend less than 1/3 as much time in outside preparation as the student spends in class.

REGISTRATION POINTS: The Registration Points (R/P) are used to help determine if the student is enrolled in the appropriate course load. This number is obtained by adding the Group and Credit numbers for that particular course.

Fig. 21.4. Registration information from *Westside High School: Parent-Student Handbook for Educational Planning,* 1983–84

## LOOKING AHEAD

A new challenge faces the Westside program. Like many school systems, a declining student population makes it more and more difficult to schedule a large variety of courses. The staff and administration had already begun to deal with this problem several years ago by developing long-range plans. "Phasing," in which a student is assigned to a teacher but not to a specific class group, has provided some relief recently because of modular scheduling at Westside, but it probably would not be as effective in a traditionally scheduled school. A new computer center that serves not only the mathematics department but the needs of the entire faculty is the most recent focus of attention. Computer literacy for all students is a district goal and thus receives support from all areas.

Many variables, compromises, and a great deal of hard work by the staff go into providing flexible course offerings, but solutions to the problems can be found if a school system is dedicated to offering a curriculum in mathematics that can be adjusted to meet the needs of all students. One hundred percent enrollment in meaningful mathematics is not an unrealistic goal for Westside, but it means continually targeting a small problem population of students and determining how to meet their needs without losing the quality of the existing program.

Other schools that plan to implement the sixth recommendation of the *Agenda for Action* will probably find that a strong commitment by the department chairman is the first crucial factor. Next, the level of interest and support from other faculty members will have to be assessed. Some staff members will be excited to experiment with new courses; others will prefer to put their energy into improving existing courses. Both groups are necessary to build a program of high quality. An enthusiastic department can then plan ways to gain administrative and community support for their program. The flexibility to adjust year by year to both student and staff needs and abilities is essential.

## CONCLUSION

The sixth proposal of the *Agenda for Action* is a powerful statement of commitment to meeting the needs of students living in a mathematical/technological world. Those who believe in the importance of this concept can help implement it by creative restructuring, despite budget constraints.

### REFERENCE

National Council of Teachers of Mathematics. *An Agenda for Action: Recommendations for School Mathematics of the 1980s.* Reston, Va.: The Council, 1980.

## DATE DUE

| OCT 1 5 '86 | | | |
|---|---|---|---|
| | | | |
| | | | |
| | | | |
| | | | |
| | | | |
| | | | |
| | | | |
| | | | |
| | | | |
| | | | |
| | | | |
| | | | |
| | | | |
| | | | |
| | | | |
| | | | |
| | | | |

PRINTED IN U.S.A.